THE NEW NATURALIST
A SURVEY OF BRITISH NATURAL HISTORY

A NATURAL HISTORY OF MAN
IN BRITAIN

THE NEW NATURALIST

A NATURAL HISTORY OF
MAN IN BRITAIN

*Conceived as a study of changing relations
between Men and Environments*

by

H. J. FLEURE
F. R. S.

WITH 38 COLOUR PHOTOGRAPHS BY
ROBERT ATKINSON, JOHN MARKHAM AND OTHERS
38 PHOTOGRAPHS IN BLACK AND WHITE
AND 76 LINE DRAWINGS BY ALISON BIRCH

LONDON 1959

READERS UNION · COLLINS

This edition has been made specially available to members of Readers Union. It was first published by William Collins and was printed and bound by them at the Clear-Type Press, Glasgow. It is set in 11 pt. Baskerville type leaded

Full details of R.U. may be obtained from Readers Union Ltd. at 38 William IV Street, Charing Cross, London, W.C.2., and at Letchworth Garden City, Herts

" BRITAIN, best of islands, lieth in the Western Ocean betwixt Gaul and Ireland, and containeth 800 miles in length and 200 in breadth. Whatsoever is fitting for the use of mortal men the island doth afford in unfailing plenty. For she aboundeth in metals of every kind ; fields hath she, stretching far and wide, and hillsides meet for tillage of the best, whereon, by reason of the fruitfulness of the soil, the divers crops in their seasons do yield their harvests. Forests also hath she filled with every manner of wild deer, in the glades whereof groweth grass that the cattle may find therein meet change of pasture, and flowers of many colours that do proffer their honey unto the bees that flit ever busily about them. Meadows hath she, set in pleasant places, green at the foot of misty mountains, wherein be sparkling well-springs clear and bright, flowing forth with a gentle whispering ripple in shining streams that sing sweet lullaby unto them that lie upon their banks. Watered is she, moreover, by lakes and rivers wherein is much fish, and, besides the narrow sea of the Southern coast whereby men make voyage unto Gaul, by three noble rivers, Thames, to wit, Severn and Humber, the which she stretcheth forth as it were three arms whereby she taketh in the traffic from oversea brought hither from every land in her fleets. . . ."

extract from HISTORIES OF THE KINGS OF BRITAIN
by Geoffrey of Monmouth (died c. 1152), translated
by Dr. Sebastian Evans

". . . . This fortress built by nature for herself
Against infection and the hand of war,
This happy breed of men, this little world,
This precious stone set in the silver sea. . . ."

from Shakespeare, RICHARD II, Act 11, Scene 1

But now the gentle dew-fall sends abroad
The fruit-like perfume of the golden furze:
The light has left the summit of the hill,
Though still a sunny gleam lies beautiful,
Aslant the ivied beacon. Now farewell,
Farewell, awhile, O soft and silent spot !
On the green sheep-track, up the heathy hill,
Homeward I wend my way ; and lo! recalled
From bodings that have well-nigh wearied me,
I find myself upon the brow, and pause
Startled! And after lonely sojourning
In such a quiet and surrounded nook,
This burst of prospect, here the shadowy main,
Dim-tinted, there the mighty majesty
Of that huge amphitheatre of rich
And elmy fields, seems like society——
Conversing with the mind, and giving it
A livelier impulse and a dance of thought!
And now, beloved Stowey! I behold
Thy church-tower, and, methinks, the four huge elms
Clustering, which mark the mansion of my friend;
And close behind them, hidden from my view,
Is my own lowly cottage. . . .

FEARS IN SOLITUDE, *by S. T. Coleridge; written in April 1798 during the Alarm of an Invasion.*

CONTENTS

CONTENTS

COLOUR PLATES

*It should be noted that throughout this book Plate numbers in arabic figures
refer to Colour Plates, while roman numerals are used
for Black and White Plates*

PLATES IN BLACK AND WHITE

ACKNOWLEDGMENTS

FOR PERMISSION to reproduce the figures appearing in the text acknowledgment is made to the following sources :—

University of Bristol Spelaeological Society—Fig. 6; Society of Antiquaries of London—Figs. 11, 12 and 53 ; Prehistoric Society—Fig. 13 from *Proceedings of the Prehistoric Society 1938,* Vol. IV, p. 242 ; Royal Archaeological Institute of Great Britain and Ireland ° *Archaeological Journal,* Vol. XCVI—Fig. 15, Vol. CII—Figs. 24 and 25, Vol. CIV—Figs. 26, 30 and 31 ; Ministry of Works : *Guide to Stonehenge (1947)*—Fig. 16, *Stonehenge, Today and Yesterday* by F. Stevens—Fig. 17, with the sanction of the Controller of H.M. Stationery Office ; *Acta Archaeologica,* Vol. 16, 1945—Fig. 20 ; the Trustees of the British Museum : *A Guide to Antiquities of the Early Iron Age (1925)*—Figs. 21, 22, and 45 ; Royal Commission on Ancient and Historical Monuments and Constructions of Scotland in the Outer Hebrides, Skye and the Small Isles (9th Report) with the sanction of the Controller of H.M. Stationery Office—Fig. 23 ; Clarendon Press : Fig. 27 based on Fig. 103 from *Prehistoric and Roman Wales* by R. E. M. Wheeler, Fig. 29, based on Map II from *Roman Britain and the English Settlements* by R. G. Collingwood and J. N. L. Myres, Fig. 33, based on Pl. 26b from *A History of the Anglo-Saxons,* Vol. I by R. H. Hodgkin ; Cambrian Archaeological Association—Fig. 28, based on Pl. VII in *A Hundred Years of Welsh Archaeology,* Fig. 35, based on Pl. I, Fig. 1, Vol. XCIV *Archaeologica Cambrensis* ; National Museum of Wales and the Press Board of the University of Wales—Figs. 34 and 36, *Personality of Britain* (3rd edn.) by Sir Cyril Fox ; B. T. Batsford, Ltd. : Figs. 37, 38 and 70, based on drawings from *Everyday Life in Anglo-Saxon, Viking and Norman Times* by M. & C. H. B. Quennell, Fig. 73 based on a drawing from *A History of Everyday Things in England* by M. & C. H. B. Quennell ; Royal Anthropological Institute : Figs. 56 and 57, *Man— A Record of Anthropological Science,* Vol XLIV ; *House Tradition in the*

xiii

Outer Hebrides—the Black House and the Beehive Hut by Werner Kissling, Dr. Jur (Königsberg) ; The Honourable Society of Cymmrodorion— Figs. 58, 60 and 62, based on photographs in *The Welsh House* by I. C. Peate.

EDITORS' PREFACE

IN THE synthesis of British ecology that the *New Naturalist* series is trying to make, it seemed to us that an essential and vital element was man himself in his relationship, through the ages, with the very varied natural environment afforded by the British Isles. We believe that the study of the natural history of man in Britain can contribute to the view that he must be regarded as one with nature. We believe that the search for a true relationship of man and his environment can alone save our beautiful islands from wrongful changes, from the degradation and destruction which may result equally from unplanned development as from wrongly conceived physical planning.

Surely no man is so well fitted to undertake a review of this vast and complex field as Professor Fleure. A Channel Islander by birth, he is able to view the British scene with some slight detachment; his long association with the University of Wales at Aberystwyth and his later connection with the University of Manchester have given him distinctive viewpoints; whilst no man by academic training and subsequent studies could more adequately have prepared himself for such a task. Trained as a natural scientist, it was in these fields that he held his first University appointment. When he was promoted to the Chair of Geography and Anthropology in the University of Wales he succeeded in maintaining an even balance between what became his two main interests. In due course he served as President of both Section E (Geography) and Section H (Anthropology) of the British Association for the Advancement of Science. His election to Fellowship of the Royal Society as an anthropologist is perhaps matched by the highest awards which have reached him from Geographical Societies on both sides of the Atlantic. It is now more than thirty years since he published his *Human Geography in Western Europe*, and more than twenty years since he, with the late H. J. Peake, began that remarkable series of volumes, the *Corridors of Time*, from 1927 onwards. His long connection with the Geographical Association as its Honorary Secretary and Honorary Editor will be known to many readers.

It is accordingly with great pleasure that we introduce *New Naturalist* readers to this *Natural History of Man in Britain*, a book which we feel sure will bring the reader no nearer to deciding whether Professor Fleure is an historian, anthropologist, geographer or naturalist, so perfectly does he combine the varied approaches. To his study of the human animal, and his relations with himself and the other lives around him, Professor Fleure brings just that spirit of patient enquiry and tolerant humanity that has inspired all the best of our country's long line of naturalists. It is the fruit of a lifetime's gathering.

THE EDITORS

AUTHOR'S PREFACE

THE IDEA of a book with this title came from the Editors of the *New Naturalist* series of books, and the writer is very grateful to the Editors for their active and sustained interest in the book as it grew. The author has tried to trace main lines of evolution in matters in which deliberate choice between alternatives has been somewhat less important than response to environment. No hard and fast line can be drawn so what is included or excluded is the result of decisions that are submitted to the tolerant judgment of the reader.

Dr. Julian Huxley has made very many valuable suggestions, Dr. Dudley Stamp, Mr. James Fisher and Mr. J. Gilmour have also helped the writer considerably, and he would wish further to express his special gratitude to Miss Joan Ivimy, as well as to the artist, Miss Alison Birch, who has drawn the text figures. His friends, Doctors Elwyn and Margaret Davies, have kindly contributed to overcome some difficulties and Mr. F. Smith of Messrs. Collins has given valuable help.

Mr. Robert Atkinson and Mr. John Markham added greatly to such interest as the book may have by their initiative and enthusiasm in taking nearly all the photographs. Others who kindly contributed towards the colour illustrations are Mr. P. L. Emery, Mr. Eric Hosking, Mr. Cyril Newberry and Mr. S. C. Porter. Sir Charles and Lady Darwin most kindly allowed reproduction of the photograph of Charles Darwin (Plate X).

Two special notes need to be added here. The inferences published here for the first time in Chapter 9 are results of work in progress since 1905. Some 14 years ago the Leverhulme Trust, through Lord Haden Guest, made a generous grant to aid this work. It is hoped that a fuller and more closely argued account of these researches will appear independently before long; the delays of publication have been due largely to an effort to avoid certain grave errors into which statisticians dealing with these matters have been led.

B

The aim of this book, a picturing of British life, is to stimulate interest in our evolution and in its portrayal in our Museums. The museums of local culture as well as the Folk Culture department of the National Museum of Wales at Cardiff and at St. Fagan's Castle point to the need for a great effort to collect and preserve vanishing types of objects, especially in rural life. The strengthening of our museums of local culture, the collecting and storing of material in danger of being lost, and perhaps the making of an ENGLISH MUSEUM and a MUSEUM OF SCOTTISH LIFE are aims to be cherished.

H. J. FLEURE

LONDON,
January, 1950

CHAPTER I

A GENERAL INTRODUCTION

T HE INTRODUCTORY quotation from the translation of Geoffrey of Monmouth's work is eloquent of the characteristics of the various parts of Britain but it does not go so far as to picture for us the differences between the various parts of our island. That island is almost unique in its possession of a very rich series of geological records from the pre-Cambrian to the post-Pleistocene, from mountains, admittedly not very high, to lands below sea-level, from acid-soiled moorlands to rich loams of lasting value once they were cleared for cultivation. The broad general gradation from older, harder, less fertile, to younger, softer, easier lands is from north-west to south-east, and we shall introduce our discussion by trying to follow this gradation in giving brief sketches of our chief regions as homes of men.

An outstanding feature of the story of man in Britain is that, in the course of the historic centuries, a considerable measure of unity has been achieved without a great deal of forcible repression of diversity. Unity in diversity, both in considerable measure, is a feature of Britain. How that diversity should be described in a brief sketch is a question to which many diverse answers could be given. Politically and in a sense historically we might speak of Scotland, England, Wales. Archæologically Fox has emphasised " Lowland " and " Highland " Britain, a division which has much value. But it is too broad, in that Highland Britain includes both the Atlantic coastlands and the great moorland areas of the north and west, while Lowland Britain includes the south-east of England and also the Midlands north-west and west of the Jurassic scarp. Belloc with some justification argued that the Jurassic scarp is the most important dividing line in England ; it includes the Cotswolds, Edgehill, the Northampton heights and Lincoln Edge, south of the Humber. The line Mersey, South-Pennines, Humber is another dividing mark with strong claims on various grounds. Climatically the division into Atlantic coasts, Southern and Northern Moorlands (the latter north of the Highland line in Scotland), South-eastern and North-eastern lowlands has some value and some limitations. Relief and structure mark as units the Scottish Highlands and Hebrides, Midland Scotland, the Southern Scottish Uplands and the Cheviots, Northern England, Wales, the Midlands, South-east England with a special sub-division for East Anglia and one for Kent and, finally, the South-west. Islands, notably Shetland and Orkney and Man, need to be added as distinct elements.

As this book attempts to look at the Natural History of Man in Britain it must concern itself with folk-life. One acknowledges freely that many features have been introduced, even imposed, by conquerors and infiltrating leaders of various kinds, and, where the will-power of a leader or leader-group is heavily involved, we may allow the conventional acceptance of the connotation of "natural" to exclude such matters as being more appropriate to political retrospect. Where they have left a permanent regional impress on the life of the people, i.e., when the people have assimilated a good deal of what was introduced or imposed by leaders, the present review must obviously take these things into account. There will be, as usual in human considerations, a marginal zone in which the writer's limitations, aptitudes and experience will inevitably affect treatment. That this may perhaps give added vitality must be pleaded in defence of human fallibility which should also ask for leniency when, inevitably, treating subjects within the fields of other specialists.

Among the divisions of Britain based on physical features, climate, archæology and history, that of the Atlantic coasts of Britain from Scilly and Cornwall to Orkney and Shetland seems clear on nearly all grounds. In this division, moorlands of hard ancient or igneous rock typically back river valleys, the lower ends of which have been drowned by the rise of sea-level as the Pleistocene icesheets melted. These coastal valleys may have a heavy rainfall, in heavy showers rather than long-continued drizzle, and stormy winds and waves ; but they are rarely very cold in winter or very warm in summer and their vegetation shows the result in the wide distribution of such introduced southern plants as fuchsia and the dwarf palm. In the south-west of England and parts of South Wales early spring gives opportunities for growing vegetables for market.

Gold grains in the streams, tin-sand in Cornwall, copper grains in Cornwall and Ireland, hard crystalline rocks that could be ground to make edged stone-tools, all helped to draw the attention of voyagers of ancient times (after 2500 B.C.) to Atlantic Britain, which is rich in prehistoric stone monuments known to specialists as passage-graves and gallery-graves. These monuments show the special attraction of peninsulas for early mariners and their need for trans-peninsular land-routes to avoid the tide-races and various other dangers to small craft at the terminal headlands with their projecting rocks and islets. The impress of maritime activities then given to Atlantic Britain has persisted, with various revivals, ever since. Bronze Age traffic along and across the Irish Sea was followed, perhaps after a break, by movements of the Iron Age, involving the building of promontory, hilltop and hillbrow fortresses, some of which may even have originated in Roman times, but as the work of non-Roman groups. This last inference has been made notably in the case of the finest of these, the fortress town of Tre'r Ceiri on one of the summits of Yr Eifl, S.W. Caernarvonshire. The settlements at and near Glastonbury are generally allowed to be somewhat earlier in origin. In post-Roman times the Celtic saints moved along the coasts of Atlantic Britain north to Iona, south to Cornwall and on to the Channel Islands and Brittany. Later came Norse and Danish rovers, Anglo-Irish aristocrats and medieval pilgrims.

In all these early stages of the life of our Atlantic shorelands the south coast of Wales was of far greater importance than the opposite (southern) coast of the Bristol Channel, and the north coast of Wales was also not of great value. The last was hampered by its lack of shelter east of Llandudno, the second was in competition with the S. Wales coast which had Milford Haven, Swansea Bay and a number of other refuges, and was moreover on the way from Ireland and the valuable peninsula of North Pembrokeshire to the Cotswolds, the Mendips and Salisbury Plain. Norsemen, Anglo-Normans and Flemish immigrants all used sunny South Pembrokeshire and made of it "Little England beyond Wales." When Anglo-Norman power spread in Ireland, the port of Chester, and so the North Wales coast route, gained importance, to lose some of it as the Dec silted up and shipping came to need deeper water. In the seventeenth and eighteenth centuries ocean trade began to bring life to many small ports and some took up shipbuilding, especially in the early nineteenth century. The steamship, increasingly built of iron plates, caused these little ports to decline or become merely holiday resorts. They had neither the depth of water nor the accommodation and communications nor the businesses that could have made it worth while for big boats to call. Traffic was increasingly concentrated at great ports ; ships no longer needed alternative landings to suit difference of wind and tide.

Plymouth, with Devonport and Stonehouse, has expanded an historic link with the Navy and also became a port of call for some mailboats. Bristol, once England's second city, grew with the help of its outport at Avonmouth but was nevertheless outdistanced by Merseyside and Clydeside. Newport, Cardiff and Swansea have grown as coal exporters, a business now in eclipse (1948), and as importers of copper, tin, lead and iron ores. The Liverpool group, Merseyside, has, collectively, practically attained to a million of population. The ancient cathedral and university city of Glasgow has been metamorphosed into an industrial centre of one and a half million; its ancient function as the seat of the archbishop in charge of the west coast of Scotland is forgotten.

Shipbuilding and the processing of imports such as grains, oils, fibres, sugar and tobacco, are typical activities near the great ports, and trade has brought Asiatic and African elements into the population alongside of a ceaseless Irish immigration in the last 100 years. Old-time local fishing with small boats, a nursery for seamanship in the days of the clippers, has been superseded by fleets of steam trawlers, some based on Fleetwood and Milford Haven, some coming from much further away. A few successors of the old seamen's tradition become captains and engineers.

Atlantic Britain north of Kintyre has taken little part in post-medieval maritime developments, its mountainous coasts and boisterous seas having been impediments ; but Shetland and Orkney have been of more importance in maritime life, the latter especially because of the large natural harbour of Scapa Flow.

In spite of the liability of Atlantic Britain to oceanic storms and heavy showers, the more southerly part of this region, especially Pembrokeshire and Cornwall, enjoys more sunshine than many inland areas. It of course also profits in this respect from the absence of urban smoke which so seriously affects South Lancashire and Clydeside. In the twentieth century the mild temperatures, and the sunshine of early spring, have made Cornwall and the Scillies almost rival the Channel Islands in the early produce trade. This, with the tourist business, has been some compensation to the Cornish people for the decline of tin and copper mining.

The Highlands of Scotland, a great area of highly metamorphosed and hardened ancient rocks with igneous penetrations, are bounded on the south by what is called the Highland Line or the Highland Wall, a conspicuous feature at many spots between Stonehaven and Helensburgh. To the north we are among great mountain shoulders with deep glens, the sides and floors of which have in many cases been shaped by Pleistocene glaciers, no doubt working along already existing valleys (plate 2, p. 19). Wet moors, rough slopes, rocky outcrops, long lakes, paucity of roads, climate unfriendly to most crops except to some extent oats, have all combined to keep the population small and to permit the continuance until the mid-eighteenth century of mutually hostile clans with perennial blood feuds and raids. It was therefore a region with few villages and fewer towns, but rather with hamlets, sometimes under the shadow of a fortification or a church. The late eighteenth century saw some opening up of the country, the establishment of burghs here and there in the lower eastern areas, and some increase of order. The old chieftains no longer needed fighting men, and many clansmen left the glens and settled on wet coastal flats as fishermen and cultivators of potatoes. When, after 1840, the grasslands of North America and the Dominions began to be opened up for cultivation, a growing stream of emigration from the Scottish Highlands set in. What are called deer forests, owned or seasonally rented by wealthy people from the south, have contributed to the depopulation of the Highlands. Special understanding of the local soil opportunities must govern any attempts at cultivation, and farmers must rely considerably on stock. The long-haired Highland cattle can withstand the difficulties of the moorlands, and the sheep often show traces of ancient breeds (see *Natural History in the Highlands and Islands* by F. Fraser Darling).

On the west the mountains often slope down to the drowned valleys, and opposite the mainland are mountainous or rocky islands such as Jura, Mull and Skye and the Hebrides, in some respects a continuation of the Highlands structurally and physically diversified by Tertiary volcanic outbursts. Archæology on the whole supports the idea of the Hebrides as in some senses an insular extension of moorland Britain, as the prehistoric stone-circle of Callernish suggests. Stone circles standing free are characteristic monuments of prehistory on our moorlands, but not in Atlantic South Britain save on Preselau (also spelt Preseli, etc.), Pembrokeshire, where the moorland and Atlantic cultures of antiquity met and influenced one another, with results that will demand attention later in this book and that are among the most remarkable features of the story of early Britain.

On the north-east, the open country of Caithness brought maritime traders of prehistoric times who also built Maes Howe, a remarkable monument in Orkney, and, in the days of the spread of the Vikings, Orkney and Shetland and Caithness and the drowned valleys of East Sutherland were used by the wanderers. The fertile and relatively low and open land of Buchan in N.E. Aberdeenshire attracted circle-building prehistoric people (makers of Beaker Pots to be discussed later) as well as later invaders and immigrants ; it has had a larger development of farming and fishing, and, at the gate of entry from the south near the mouth of Don and Dee, stands the granite city, historic Aberdeen.

The Midlands of Scotland are bounded north and south by great fault-lines running N.E.—S.W. That on the north goes from near Stonehaven to near Helensburgh, and is sharply cut by many rivers. That on the south goes from near Dunbar to near Girvan, and it also is cut by streams in many places but the cuts are not as sharp as those in the north. Between these two faults, which respectively define the southern edge of the Highlands and the northern edge of the Southern Uplands, lies the Midland Area, known to geomorphologists as a rift valley, comparable to the great series of rift valleys of S.W. Asia, the Red Sea and E. Africa. It is floored by Old Red Sandstone and Carbon-iferous rocks with abundant igneous intrusions, and these geological diversities divide the area into zones of diverse human import.

Strathmore is mainly Old Red Sandstone and its historic interest is attested by the fact that it gives sites to Montrose, Brechin, Forfar, Coupar, with Dunkeld at the Tay exit from the Highlands and Scone and Perth, Dunblane and Stirling, at southern exits from this zone, which is bounded on the south by the igneous lines of the Ochil and the Sidlaw Hills. The Tay makes its way out to its Firth between the Sidlaws on the north and the Ochils on the south and the coast north of the Tay has Dundee and Arbroath. The number of these towns linked with medieval authority, ecclesiastical and civil, indicates the relatively early development of this zone, partly to protect the Low-lands from Highland raiders. The soil is in places good, and, with sites of southward aspect, has been used for growing soft fruit. The numerous old towns and the good soil have as a consequence a much greater density of population than occurs north of the Highland line save in Buchan. Naturally the neighbourhoods of Perth, Dundee and Aberdeen have much higher densities still.

South of the Ochils we are on Carboniferous rocks with the coal and iron industries that have accumulated the great population of the Edinburgh-Glasgow area, and seem likely to accumulate still more if further coal resources are utilised around the Firth of Forth. In the Middle Ages, St. Andrews played the part on the east coast that was described for Glasgow on the west, until, towards the full Renaissance Edinburgh and Aberdeen outgrew the old archiepiscopal and university city. Already before coal and iron there was a good deal of population here, as in parts of Strathmore, but the good soil in the Lothians and the rise of Edinburgh to become a national capital in contact with France and the Low Countries have provided a basis on which industry was able to build its agglomerates. Few cities can rival Edinburgh and London in the chains of evidence they display, sometimes with splendour and sometimes with squalor, of many stages of a long evolution. In the southern part of the Midland zone lines of igneous rock and a narrow belt of Old Red Sandstone appear and match the corresponding belts of the northern part of the zones. But, in the south, they are narrow and for the most part only moderately useful for agriculture, and they have been tending to lose population to industry nearby. There is here, in the southern border of the Midland zone, hardly the development of historic centres characteristic of the borders of Strathmore, but this is partly because of the proximity of Glasgow and Edinburgh. South of the Midland zones, above the Fault Line, comes the moorland and hill country known as the Southern Uplands. Often bleak, it has considerable stretches near, or over, the 2,000-foot contour, but it lacks the grandeur of the Highlands and its highest shoulder is on Broad Law at 2,754 feet. Streams have dissected it on both flanks and the Clyde headwaters are near those of Annan and of Tweed. It is primarily a sheep country with memories of border warfare, and a surviving woollen (tweeds) industry of moderate scale. A few wild spots are found here and there but most of the river valleys are rather to be described as picturesque.

The south-western flank (Galloway) has many prehistoric stone monuments and remains left by early maritime traders, its harbour at

Whithorn has memories of the Celtic saints, and, altogether, the district is somewhat of a land apart, away from border wars, interested in the crossing to Antrim (now Stranraer to Larne). Most of this region is tending to lose rather than gain population. It has much less memory of clan organization than the Highlands, and more of the idea of retainers gathered around the castle or mansion. Near the English border, it has tended to emphasize its Scottish loyalties in religious matters, and neither the Roman Catholic nor the Episcopal Church is conspicuously strong here.

The old walled town of Berwick-on-Tweed dominating the mouth of that river is a county and borough by itself ; it looks out westwards from its hill across the river to the outposts of the Cheviots. The Cheviots are almost separated from the Southern Uplands by Teviot-dale and Liddisdale. From Old Red Sandstone in the north they rise to an igneous mass culminating in " The Cheviot " (2,676 ft.), the mass having the Till curving around its eastern face to join the Tweed. It is a sheep country and has been a broad barrier between Scotland and England. To the south-west is the lowland way across the head of the Solway Firth from Carlisle to Ecclefechan and so on to Beatock, Carstairs and Midland Scotland. To the north-east is the coastal plateau giving an easier route north via Berwick to the Lothians, with Edinburgh Castle dominating the entry from the south-east into the Scottish Midlands, a fact which has greatly contributed to that city's becoming the national capital. South Scotland preserves a number of Celtic names, among which one may instance Pen, for a summit, and Ecclefechan (little church). The Celtic tradition illustrated by these names is Brythonic (i.e., related to the Celtic of Wales, Cornwall and Brittany) and not Gaelic (the Celtic of the Western Highlands and Western Ireland and, formerly, of the Isle of Man).

England north of the Mersey, South-Pennine, Humber line is a collection of regions which possesses a character of its own. Its outstanding uplands are the faulted arch of the Pennines, with the steep fault-slopes mainly on the west, and the dome-like mass of the Lake District of Cumbria, consisting of early Palæozoic rock in the north and the Borrowdale volcanic series farther south. The Cumbrian hills rise to Scawfell Pike (3,210 ft.), the highest point in England, and from near this point valleys, many containing the oft-described lakes, radiate out roughly like the spokes of a wheel. It has been a stock-farming country and has been largely transformed into a holiday resort and a place of retirement, in which process the influence of Wordsworth has played a large part. Its seaward flank has coal and hæmatite iron ore and therefore industry and ports. Its landward flank has a pass below Shap Fell separating the Cumbrian Mass from the backbone-like Pennines.

The Pennines in places have large outcrops of Carboniferous Limestone, with sharp edges and great bare patches on the porous rock when it is not covered with glacial deposits. Elsewhere there are large areas of Millstone Grit, very hard and often buried under boulder-clay which give large surfaces of wet moor. Rivers on both flanks of the Pennine backbone have worked back deep into the hills and thus give a number of passes, used in several instances by railways linking the industrial lowlands east and west.

The faulted western sides are known as Edges. The impressively long, straight edge east of the Eden valley rises sharply to Cross Fell (2,830 ft.). The Edges towards south-east Lancashire, are steep and face west and south-west catching much rain. This gave water-power, used as cotton-spinning became mechanised in a humid atmosphere at Bolton, Oldham, etc., but, before that time, made the sheep and wool industries gravitate to the less steep Yorkshire side. The dales of the east flank of the Pennines once had forest, and, when this was reduced, came to be used for sheep and cattle, encouraged by the Cistercians of the twelfth century. The west flank remained relatively poor.

The great Roman road (note the place names Ardwick-le-street, Chester-le-street, etc.) leading to the Roman Wall, that follows the igneous ledge of the Whinsill in parts along the gap Newcastle-Carlisle, goes northward via York. Indeed, in the east, the gradients right away to the Midlands of Scotland are far easier than on the west, where the passes at Shap and Beatock summit have to be surmounted. The names of York, Durham, Newcastle and Berwick-on-Tweed tell of the greater importance of the east side in the Middle Ages in spite of various devastations. York could receive small ships of old and was the second city of Britain until Bristol outdistanced it in the Middle Ages.

In still earlier times the relative openness of the east Yorkshire regions, i.e., the North York moors and the fertile wolds, drew immigrants in the Iron Age, and as far back as that of the people who made Beaker pots, about 1800 B.C. These early peoples pressed westwards, probably across the Ouse, from the Wolds to the Peak District and through Stainmore Gap to Penrith. They thus made contact with the west and, in the Peak area, with outposts of the early maritime cultures spoken of above in dealing with Atlantic Britain. Generally speaking, early woodlands covered a lesser proportion of the North of England than they did of the North and West Midlands ; and the North of England was at times, such as the Early English period, linked rather with south-east Scotland than with lands farther south. The persistence of a separate, if subordinate, archbishopric of York owes a good deal to these woodland barriers to the south, among which Sherwood has become a centre of legend. Elmet, mainly between Wharfe and Aire, has left Celtic memories. The early English immigrants no doubt used the Humber but found much swamp near the lower course of the Yorkshire Ouse; and forested Elmet, beyond the swamp, to the west, was not conquered until the days of Edwin of Deira whose victories occurred about 625 A.D.

The enormous growth of industry and population in the Mersey basin in Lancashire has given that region, in modern times, larger cities than Yorkshire now has. The new Liverpool has immensely outdistanced the much older but still very large eastern port of Kingston-upon-Hull, itself in a measure a successor of Beverley. The trinity of Manchester-Salford-Stretford, even without its sprawling extensions, has about as many people as Leeds and Sheffield combined, and with those extensions it probably houses nearly two million people. Before that immense growth of South Lancashire's population, and the reclamation and utilization of the Mosses on the north side of the Mersey, there was a belt of wet country from the Mersey northwards nearly to Wigan. A crossing at Warrington and one at Manchester-Salford have long been in use, but Lancashire from Wigan northwards was of old much isolated from the southern parts of England. At the religious crisis of the sixteenth century many families here continued to adhere to the Roman Church, and that tradition has persisted to modern times, especially in and near the Fylde. On the Yorkshire side there were also adherents to the Roman Church, as the Pilgrimage of Grace attests, but the newer elements in the aristocracy on this side, more in touch with the Court and with the ecclesiastical centre of York, brought their people more markedly into the Anglican Church. That aristocracy, in general, profited from the seizure of what had been monastic lands.

It is highly characteristic that the titles Duke of Lancaster, Duke of York, Earl of Chester, Duke of Gloucester should have been absorbed by the Royal Family. These were in effect areas behind the Scottish and Welsh borders and these titles in non-royal hands might have meant rivalries like those between France and Burgundy. The writ of the Bishop of Durham in mediæval days reached right across the country to the north of Wear and Ribble and this power was strengthened by its claim to sanctity as well as by its splendid castle-and-cathedral city of Durham. An ecclesiastical lord was on the whole less of a threat to the king than one who was purely political and military as well as being one who was likely to found a family.

The Atlantic coasts of Wales have behind them a large area of moorland and mountain from which deep valleys, some once glaciated and U-shaped in section, a few of marked post-glacial cutting, radiate out to sea. Wales thus has a high moorland core instead of a Midland trough such as Scotland possesses. Scotland has the historical foci in that trough and, in the end, its great capital city of Edinburgh. Wales has never had a fully recognised capital. But Celtic languages have disappeared from Scotland save for a Gaelic remnant in the western Highlands and the Hebrides ; whereas the seaward valleys of Wales, protected by the moorland core, have kept their language and indeed in the last half-century, redeveloped it with the help of the new University of Wales. On the other hand, Scots Law, with Edinburgh as its centre, and the Church of Scotland have maintained themselves and evolved in modern times. Wales, without a capital, has lost its legal tradition and no one of the churches in Wales can claim the national prestige that the Church of Scotland enjoys throughout its country.

Northwest Wales, west of the Vale of Clwyd and north of the Welsh valley of the Severn, is largely mountain and moorland and is dominated by the Snowdon range (Eryri). That range has two main parts—Carnedd Dafydd and Carnedd Llewellyn are the northerly portion and Snowdon, Glydr Fawr and their outliers are the more southerly component. They are separated by a long trough which, judging from its land forms, was used by an ice-sheet from the region of Llyn Idwal and Tryfaen. It is characteristic of the region that land slopes up the mountain shoulders from the western coastal plateau, but that on the side turned away from the ocean (i.e. on the east and north-east) there are great cirques, hollowed out almost to armchair forms and still remarkably fresh. It is significant that the ice-sheet mentioned as coming along the trough from the cirque of Llyn Idwal to add to the ice in the cirques overrode some of the higher land as it went eastwards and, where this occurred, there are no cirques but much of the surface has been scraped bare. The whole region is one of poor soils and sparse population apart from the maritime fringe where Edward I built his castle-towns (bastides):[1] Conway, Beaumaris, Caernarvon, Criccieth, Harlech. Aberystwyth is another bastide farther south.

The moorland and its valleys are characterised by stock-farms, many sheep at the present time, but more cattle before the eighteenth century. The countryside has many traces of the ancient custom of taking the animals to summer pasture (hafod) on the high moorland and bringing them down to the coastal lowlands for the winter.

South of the moorlands of the north of Wales the Severn basin on the east and the Dyfi basin on the west almost interlock, and there is a low pass at Llanbrynmair (Church of St. Mary at Hill). To the south the moorland expands again and we find Plynlymon and its southward neighbours, the Epynt, Radnor Forest, the Black Mountains of Brecknock, the Brecon Beacons, the Black Mountains of Carmarthen and Preselau. But these are divided by much more open valleys than are the members of the moorland group in North Wales, and the area above the 2,000-foot contour is much smaller. Stock-farming is a general feature. Here cattle play a larger part than they do in the north, and as a consequence milk production looms large and also provides recruits for the milk trade of London and other cities. But sheep and wool are also important, especially on the northern flank of Preselau.

There is no doubt that the lower lands separating these moorlands were heavily wooded of old, save in places too much exposed to gales of salt sea-wind. Men used the moorlands and their brows before they were equipped to cut the dense woodland effectively. We find on the Welsh moorlands, as a characteristic type of prehistoric stone monument, the free-standing stone circle, a type reaching right out to the Preselau hills, where the builders came into touch with the culture of the western maritime folk of the third millennium B.C.

---

[1] Bastides were planned castle-towns inhabited, in the case of Wales, by Anglo-Norman colonists as burgesses. Not until long afterwards were Welshmen allowed to live or to own property in the bastide town. The parallel streets and wall can be seen in Caernarvon (Fig. 42, p. 173).

The isolation of the Welsh moorlands and valleys, though sufficient to maintain the old language in use, was not sufficient to prevent conquest by Edward I ; and the subsequent stories of Wales and the Scottish Highlands have diverged widely as a result. In spite of stress on kinship Wales shows few traces of anything comparable to the old clan organization of the Scottish Highlands.

The eastern valleys down from the Welsh moorlands have been exposed to much English influence, and have themselves exported men and women to the Anglo-Welsh border and, especially in modern times, to the English cities. That export from Wales shows characteristic features: builders and contractors in Merseyside may often hail from the quarrying areas of Anglesey, London milkmen have notable links with cattle areas in Wales, especially mid-Cardiganshire and Carmarthenshire, London drapers include more than a few who come from the sheep and wool country of South Cardiganshire and North Pembrokeshire.

A very special part of the Welsh moorland not hitherto mentioned is the coalfield of Glamorgan and Monmouth, a highland of grit with coal-seams and with a drainage scheme of southward-flowing rivers in deep narrow valleys that were most beautiful until mining began. Here is little space for urban centres and it seems that the name " ribbon development " was first applied to the long rows of houses in these narrow valleys, houses often built just below a great dripping rock slope, and in a valley too narrow to get much sun through the winter. Yet this unfavourable environment has somehow drawn to itself a self-conscious community of miners of remarkable intellectual and moral power, diluted with flotsam and jetsam from many distant areas. " The valleys," as they are called, offer a challenge to modern idealism in many directions. One of the factors of the " quality " of this population has been its long-continued, but now discarded, habit of combining winter work in the mines with summer work on farms in mid-Wales, thereby maintaining a contact with the rural tradition so strong in Wales. Another factor has been the maintenance of mutual help in face of ceaseless risk from rock-falls, inflammable gas, silicosis, unemployment, and ill-health due to lack of sunlight and bad housing.

From the humanist as well as from the structural and physical points of view one should divide England south of the Mersey and Humber into various regions: (a) The Midlands north-west and west of the Jurassic scarp of the Cotswolds, Edgehill, Northampton Heights and Lincoln Edge; (b) the Jurassic scarps and the Chiltern, etc., scarp of the Chalk; (c) East Anglia ; (d) The old wooded areas in and around the London Basin, chiefly Essex, Hertford, parts of Bedford, Middlesex and Surrey; (e) Kent ; (f) The Chalk Counties and the Hampshire Basin, i.e., Sussex, Hants., Berks., Wilts., Dorset., and (g) the South-west.

The Midlands are largely floored by New Red Sandstone (Trias); older rocks reach the surface here and there. Among these the coal measures are of special economic importance while the Archæan rocks give the hard upland of Charnwood Forest. The Longmynd on the Welsh border is another Archæan knob and it has various Palæozoic outcrops forming hills and edges round about it. Between the New Red Sandstone and the Jurassic scarps is a belt of Lias Clay. Much of the surface is covered with boulder-clay deposits of the Ice Ages, but these are not as stony as some nearer the high centres of glaciation. Before clearance the Midlands were largely covered with large oak, ash and elm. It is now claimed that the beech also entered Britain at an early post-glacial date ; it occurs in the Midlands but is most important farther south. The dense woodland of large trees implies a small population in early times. Hill-brows, notable in Cheshire and on the Breidden and the Malvern Hills, have great Iron Age fortifications roughly dateable to the last two centuries B.C. The Midlands were in the Civil Zone of Roman Britain and Roman roads such as the Watling Street, with important branches to Chester and to Uriconium, and also the Fosse Way S.W. to N.E., indicate some opening up of the country. Roman withdrawal left this area sparsely populated and weak. Under the early English, it became a type area of the open field system with a three-year rotation to be discussed in a later chapter. Whether that three-year rotation replaced an earlier two-year rotation, such as long persisted on the lands of the Jurassic scarp and its south-eastern flanks, is a question to which no satisfactory answer can be given. All one can say is that towards the west there are large areas which, until the development of modern agriculture, were under the three-field system with no trace of the two-field at all.

As forest clearing proceeded many special schemes of land-tenure and land-use were devised to meet very varied circumstances. Sherwood and Arden long remained rich in great trees.

Cleared land here typically gave good grass for cattle, and cattle have long been brought to the rich pastures of Northamptonshire for

Shetland
Islands

Orkney
Islands

Hebrides

B R I T A I N

HIGHLANDS

Sutlaw Hills

Ochil
Hills

SCOTTISH
MIDLANDS

Pentland
Hills

SOUTHERN
UPLANDS

Cheviot Hills

Insill

THE PENNINES

Eden

Lake
District

Yorkshire
Moors

Isle
of Man

Vale of York

Wolds

A T L A N T I C

Anglesey

Peak
District

Lincoln Edge

Fen-
land

EAST
ANGLIA

CAMBRIAN Mts

ENGLISH
MIDLANDS

Northampton
Heights

Edgehill

Cotswolds

Chilterns

London Basin

Forest
of Dean

Mendips

North Downs

Exmoor

Salisbury
Plain

South Downs

Bodmin Moor

Blackdown
Hills

Hampshire Basin

Dartmoor

Isle
of Wight

THE SOUTH-WEST

FIG. 1

Sketch map showing chief areas of moorland in Britain and regional divisions. The chief scarps of S.E. Britain are indicated by black lines

C

fattening. Drover Roads and " Welsh Lanes " occur here and there
west of these pastures. The " Welsh Lanes " got their name from the
drovers bringing cattle from Wales to Northamptonshire. Cheeses,
notably " Stilton " (named from an inn at which it was sold to stage-
coach passengers) and " Cheshire " are well-known products, and the
cattle skins formed the basis of the leather industries of Northampton
and Higham Ferrers. The lords of manors were powerful in this area
in the Middle Ages and manor and township often coincided. The
area was largely Royalist in the seventeenth century under its
aristocrats, and later on industry grew especially in areas such as that
of Birmingham outside the incorporated towns.

These became centres of religious dissent after the enactment of
the oppressive laws known as the Act of Uniformity, the Conventicle
Act, the Five Mile Act, etc. Among these centres Birmingham and
Stoke, as also further north Manchester, Leeds and Sheffield, have
become large cities owing much to nuclei of thoughtful and enterprising men, who tended for some generations to gather around the
churches of Presbyterian-Unitarian allegiance, and around the groups
of the Society of Friends. The coalfields in and near the borders of
this area have given an immense development of modern industry and
an associated leftward trend in social, political and religious matters.

The lands of, and between, the Jurassic and Chalk scarps have a
very different story. The abundance of finds of early times, mapped
40 years ago by Crawford so far as beaker pottery was concerned,
show that there was a good deal of fairly open country, perhaps with
bush, but at any rate not very densely wooded, save for hanger woods
of beech on some chalk or limestone scarps from which water trickled
out. Bush or grass, to be changed by man into arable or sheep-pasture
according to the amount of soil, covered large areas and, as farming
with rotation in land use developed, it seems to have been mainly
a two-field system, with a three-field arrangement here and there.
Possible reasons for this will be discussed in a later chapter.

Along the ridges are traces of prehistoric tracks ; and earthworks
occur on hillbrows. Along the hillsides are many remnants of trackways, such as the Icknield Way, which seem to be linked with pre-
Roman Iron Age developments, as indeed Geoffrey of Monmouth's
histories suggest. Dorchester-on-Thames, near the entry from the
lower Thames into the country between the Chalk and the Oolite
scarps, was the seat of an early diocese which stretched right up to

Lincoln. Later the bishopric was removed to the latter city, and only in the sixteenth century was the bishopric of Oxford created. The belt of the scarps and the land between them was thus evidently recognised as a unit in Early English times. Its stone houses contrast with the timber-frame (black and white, or oak and brick) houses of the oak-forested Midlands to the west and north-west. Its sheep of the Cotswolds and Lincolnshire are the basis of the former's woollen industries and of the latter's one-time export of wool which led to the medieval growth of the port of Lincoln, becoming a bishop's see. The top of the Chilterns is largely covered with boulder-clay and has much woodland, as seen in such places as Whipsnade and Ashridge.

Oxford and Cambridge are of special interest here. Each has had an historic fair, St. Giles at Oxford and Stourbridge at Cambridge, each under the shadow, one might say, of an early Norman or pre-Norman motte-and-bailey fortification. Each is at a practicable junction of regions, one between the Middle and the South of England and the other between the scarps-belt and East Anglia. It is highly characteristic of British tradition that the historic universities have grown at these two centres, and not, as in the case of the Sorbonne at Paris, in the immediate vicinity of the royal court.

East Anglia is full of finds of most stages of prehistoric times ; it clearly had long ago a good deal of open country or light bush covering, with heaths, among which Brandon is specially well known. It has flint mines (Ch. III) belonging especially to the late Neolithic phase, but continuing in use from time to time, for example for the making of gun-flints for use in hot damp countries, such as Abyssinia during the wars of a few years ago, in which matches are inefficient. In the later part of the pre-Roman Iron Age, East Anglia and Colchester (the city of " Old King Cole " which in 1950 celebrated the 19th centenary of its foundation) in Essex were occupied by conquerors with good and large ploughs and a system of wheat-growing ; quite probably a rotation in land use was established. We may perhaps interpret some present conditions in East Anglia by suggesting that the old system lasted on, with modifications, through Roman, Early English, Danish and Norman phases of government. The large open fields of the two-field system of the scarp-lands or of the three-field system of the West Midlands are not usual here. The Early English came up the rivers and were attracted by the water-meadows for their cattle. It seems probable that a good deal of the older population fused itself into the newer in the course of time ; the English occupation of the region was hardly a deliberate military effort. We accordingly find enclosed fields, as well as a complication of small manorial tenures not coincident with townships. Sheep and wool helped the fortunes of Norwich until coal began to draw industry ; and Norwich as a port gathered the bishop's see of East Anglia to itself in Norman times. It is character-istic of Norwich as of some other cities that, with the loss of its primary industry, it has branched out into several new ones. Mustard, choco-late, tobacco, boots and shoes and others are mostly associated with the idea of packing in tins, cartons, etc., and with the deft fingers of women woolworkers of old. Flemish weavers and Protestant refugees, as well as Dutch drainage engineers, have all come to East Anglia ; and from Holland came the idea in the seventeenth and early eighteenth centuries of cultivation of root-crops in the fields. Lord Townshend (Turnip Townshend) was a Norfolk landowner of the early eighteenth century.

The spread of root-crops completely undermined the old two-field and three-field systems of Britain and brought an agrarian revolution, as we shall see in more detail in a later chapter. The Dutch drainage engneers created agricultural land in the fens north of Cambridge, and in the " Marsh " south of the Wash, some of the newly-formed fields being very large. Farmers sometimes have land both " in the Marsh " and in what is called " High Norfolk "; and the Norfolk four-course rotation has become famous in many lands and has been elaborated into much more complex schemes still. Cultivation is often highly skilled, with special crops and methods, and Havelock Ellis has drawn attention to the amount of ability contributed to British life by East Anglia in past and present. He also mentions the borderland towards Wales and this suggests some important reflections.

Repeated admixture of traditions has occurred in both areas. The long succession of immigrants into East Anglia has been mentioned; the number of Welsh names in the towns and villages of the western-most Midlands is known to everyone. The Welsh border folk often feel that they have one foot on the Welsh and one on the English side of the border : they can as it were step either way and look at the other side objectively and yet with knowledge and often with understanding. A somewhat analogous objectivity could grow in East Anglia with its many elements, apparently meeting and fusing without too high social barriers. As in the cases of Birmingham, Manchester, Liverpool and

PLATE I

Robert Atkinson

SHAKESPEARE CLIFF and DOWN, DOVER. The chalk cliff named from the
scene in 'King Lear'. November

PLATE 2

John Markham

BRAERIACH and CARN EILRIG, Cairngorms. May

Leeds, so in those of Norwich in East Anglia and Shrewsbury on the Welsh border, old Dissenting groups, becoming Unitarian, formed nuclei of cultural effort for some generations. With objectivity and cultural nuclei, we naturally get the emergence of ability and initiative in an atmosphere of freedom of conscience.

The wooded areas of the London Basin and its fringes can have had only small populations in early prehistoric times, though the Thames gave a way in, and its gravels gave sites for occupation. The steward-ship of the Chiltern Hundreds, now only a sinecure, by its persistence suggests the long-continued wildness of this woodland area with timber-frame houses and great barns developing as order grew stronger. As would be expected, some two-field and three-field schemes were established here ; and one at Hitchin has had a long persistence ; there have also been special local field-arrangements connected with local clearings, and there was a hunter's refuge at Welwyn. Verula-mium, a sort of Roman metropolis, probably had an important Belgic centre as its predecessor, and Mackinder once suggested that London may have developed as the port of that centre. This area has, in any case, become metropolitan England, with an unfinished discussion as to the continuity of London from Norman back to Roman and possibly pre-Roman times. We may get knowledge on these points from the examination of bombed sites. Of the continuity of greatness of our capital city from the Norman Conquest there is no doubt at all. It is practically unique among great cities for its succession of notable buildings put up during almost each half-century from the Norman Conquest to the World Wars of our own day. Its immense modern growth, heralded by stately squares and too often culminating in miserable tenements, its attraction for light industry spreading octopus-like tentacles into what should be garden land, its waste of endless hours and unmeasured power in moving millions to and from work, its impersonality that is yet of the very essence of its collective being, all give it a character that no other city is likely to develop.

Of Kent's wealth in early associations from prehistoric to Roman times, it will be necessary to speak here and there in the sequel. Cæsar says its then people were the most civilized in Britain, little as he knew of the rest save from prejudiced hearsay. Kent already grew wheat and had sizeable ploughs and a system of land inheritance and land division that managed to survive the early English invasions and the Norman Conquest. Enclosed fields, scattered farmhouses as well as picturesque hamlets, villages and towns are old-established features. Maritime traffic of the third or very early second millennium B.C., from across the North Sea, seems to have preferred the Medway entry and thus to have reached the old roads which ran, one along the top and another along the south flank of the North Downs, furnishing a link with Winchester and the Solent, as well as with Salisbury Plain and the west. The old road along the flank in the main became in the Middle Ages part of the Pilgrims' Way to Becket's Tomb (see plate 29, p. 306). The road may have extended to Canterbury even before this.

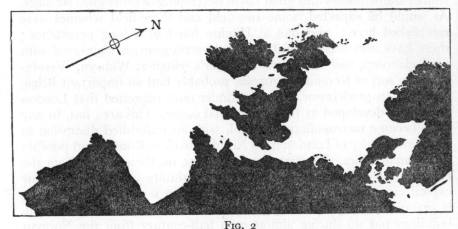

FIG. 2

Diagram map showing the intermediate position of the British Isles between N.W. and S.W. Europe

Little ships, perhaps from the late Bronze or early Iron Age onwards, increasingly ventured across the dangers of the Dover Straits. They needed alternative landings to cope with the vagaries of wind and tide. The focus behind these landings was Canterbury, Roman and Early English, growing in the Middle Ages, and later with Huguenot refugees. The landings were organised as the Cinque Ports with headquarters at Dover, now specially consecrated to the memory of the Dover Patrol to which Britain owes so much. It is significant that French atlases use their own spellings for Cantorberi, Douvres and Londres, and also Edimbourg. Just as it was noted above that our historic universities are at Oxford and Cambridge, not near the royal court, so our metropolitan church, from which the senior archbishop takes his title, is that of Canterbury, even if the archbishop is functionally more closely linked to Lambeth and the House of Lords. It is moreover characteristically British that, in the crypt of the metropolitan cathedral of the Anglican Church, a Huguenot service has been regularly held, by special permission, for centuries. It approximates to an Anglican service in the French language, and is now purely a picturesque survival, such as British tradition loves. The train ferries, the Kent coalfield and the Channel tunnel project may greatly alter Kent.

The Chalk Counties of the South and the Hampshire Basin, with the one-time thickly forested Weald, form a region of varied associations. Weald was a name used in Old English for forest land. Later its meaning became confused and the derived form Wold came to be used for open (high) country. Cissbury, Chanctonbury and other sites of the South Downs, and, far more, the expanse of Salisbury Plain and the Dorset Downs are full of remains (Chapter 3) of British life from the dawn of the Bronze Age, often called the Neolithic Period, to the pre-Roman Iron Age. Salisbury Plain, with Stonehenge, Avebury and many other ancient monuments, is our prehistoric metropolitan area ; it has communications along the Jurassic scarps to Lincoln, along the " Great Ridgeway " towards Oxford and the Chilterns, along the North Downs and the South Downs, along the Mendips to the Bristol Channel and along the Blackdown Hills to the far south-west. The Solent, the ribbon of water that divides the Isle of Wight from the mainland, gives a double entry to both vessels and tides, though the fairway is rather narrow for mammoth liners when the wind is strong enough to push their great hulls a little out of their course. Southampton Water profits by the double tide, first up the West Solent, then up the East Solent, so that it is never quite low water here ; and its shelter is of the best, though fog may be a hindrance. There is here less need for alternative landings and the old city of Southampton is dominant, with Winchester inland near the foot of the Downs. Winchester, at the foot of the chalk scarp, was important in Roman times and became a royal seat under the Saxon Gewissae. Its importance on the whole diminished in Norman times.

The rise of London after the Norman Conquest, a part of the widespread urban development in Western Europe (especially France), from about 1050 to 1200 or so, finally ended the old role of Salisbury

Plain. The Weald was important industrially for centuries more because of its iron ores and the abundance of wood for the smelters to burn. Hammer-ponds (places where hammers were worked by water power) are picturesque survivals of the industry. The whole region is full of little towns in which the medieval and Elizabethan atmosphere lingers on, and many a medieval church here has its windows and doors framed in freestone brought by sea from Caen. Alongside of this we have residences of both active and retired professional and business men, as well as coastal pleasure resorts. It is a region almost without manufacturing industry.

In the south-west from the Blackdown Hills to Land's End we are dealing largely with what at the beginning of this chapter was described as Atlantic Britain. Yet that aspect of British life hardly touches effectively the interior of Devonshire, whatever historic memories of the sea are called up by the names of Bideford, Plymouth, Totnes and Dartmouth on its periphery. On Dartmoor stand prehistoric circles and avenues of stone that tell of the efforts to establish contacts between ancient peoples of east Britain and those of the Atlantic west. Celtic speech lingered in Cornwall into the eighteenth century but apparently died long before this in Devon. Exeter grew, like Lincoln and Norwich, as a port and diocesan centre after the Norman Conquest ; this growth was part of the general urban movement, but specially related to the sheep-and-wool trade. But large towns are few, and the rich soils and mild climate make fruit-growing a success, though rainy cyclones are a perpetual cause of damp in old, and sometimes in new, houses. Somerset, at the base of the south-western peninsula, has its long traditions gathered around the caves of the Mendips and the lake dwellings near Glastonbury ; the Mendips too have evidence of prehistoric as well as medieval times ; and the villages near the Mendips, like those of the Cotswolds and of Suffolk and Norfolk, are famed for their great churches of the fifteenth century built on the profits of the sheep-and-wool business.

It is a feature of this region that the urban development before and after 1800 led to the building of crescents and terraces rather than of quite detached houses. Improvements of roads and vehicles, and also of social security, made social life in southern towns easier and led landed families either to have town houses, or to pass part of the " season " at Bath or some other social centre to marry off their daughters. The north was at that time occupied with its industrial expansion. Bristol, Bath and Exeter have a special character of their own as a consequence.

Industrial developments, apart from Bristol, have so far remained a minor matter, and ports, again apart from Bristol, have not had major modern development except in the special case of Plymouth mentioned earlier in this chapter.

The attempt has now been made to review briefly the mainland of Britain in its major regions with their opportunities and problems for man varying through the last 4,500 years or so. They all grade into one another and none has been isolated enough to persist in working out its fate separately. Intermingling has given us a tendency to objectivity and compromise among ourselves that are leading features of British thought.

Most of the topics briefly mentioned in the general review that has been attempted in this chapter are treated more in detail later, and some references to specialist works are therefore deferred to the appendices to those chapters. A few more general works should be mentioned here. Mackinder's *Britain and the British Seas* has long been a vital study of our islands. Sir Cyril Fox has given us an archæological study of *The Personality of Britain* full of suggestive maps. Professor G. M. Trevelyan's *English Social History* has high value, and Marjorie and C. H. B. Quennell's *History of Everyday Things in England* covers much that otherwise would have to be hunted in multifarious ways. Graham's *Social Life in Scotland in the Eighteenth Century* is most valuable. Ireland lies outside the scope of the present book, but readers who wish to consider matters relating to the green isle will find an attractive introduction in *The Way that I Went*, a remarkable study in the form of an autobiography by the famous Irish naturalist and scholar, Dr. Lloyd Praeger. Another type of introduction will be found, with many illustrative drawings by the author, in *Irish Heritage* by Professor Estyn Evans.

The writer of this book has made a review on lines somewhat parallel with those in this chapter, but with a greater emphasis on ancient heritages. It is printed as the (Sir J. G.) Frazer Memorial Lecture for 1947 by the Clarendon Press.

REFERENCES in the bibliography which particularly concern this chapter are Atkinson (1949), Bowen (1941), Darby (1936), Ellis (1904),

Evans (1942), Fleure (1947), Fox (1947), Geological Survey, Graham (1937), Land Utilisation Survey, Mackinder (1906), Medieval Towns Series, North, Campbell and Scott (1949), Pearsall (1950), Praeger (1947), Quennell and Quennell (1918-26), Smith (1949), Stamp and Beaver (1941), and Trevelyan (1946).

CHAPTER 2

IN THE BEGINNING

As WE may be practically certain that man did not originate in Britain, a study of his natural history in Britain should say something about how he reached our island and when.

The discoveries of Boucher de Perthes on the Somme, verified by Sir John Evans in 1859, the year of *The Origin of Species*, finally established the existence of Old Stone Age Man as the contemporary of extinct animals and led to modern chronologies. The age of man on earth has been extended from Archbishop Usher's 6,000 years to a period of the order of 100 times that length. Moreover, Africa has yielded many forms that in one way or another approach mankind, so the old search for the " Missing Link " is almost superseded ; and, what is more, there is greater possibility behind Darwin's suggestion of man's origin in Africa—or shall one say the possibility that some of the most significant stages of evolution of modern mankind occurred in Africa, perhaps North Africa and adjacent parts of Asia. Some students of the problem still think of Central Asia as an alternative birthplace of our species, but this probably is related to a very early stage of human evolution. We need no longer be haunted by the myth of a single couple of parents for mankind. We are dealing with a being that early acquired unique powers of adapting his mode of life to widely diverse surroundings and who wandered far and wide, with consequent divergences of evolution both because of the diversities of environmental influences on growth and on natural selection, and because of accumulation of diverse variations in more or less isolated groups. A variety of hominid forms need not be considered as biologically distinct, mutually infertile species.

Among general human characteristics, so widespread as to be very

25

old-established, one may mention a few. Most human beings prefer a temperature of 62°—75° Fahrenheit, but many enjoy colder intervals, finding them bracing, especially to the nervous system. This suggests that a region which had temperatures of this kind had a good deal to do with the evolution of man. In the Pleistocene Ice Ages, when apparently man was evolving towards his present physical condition, such temperatures were probably characteristic of some areas now desert in N.W. Africa ; and along the wadis of the Western Sahara have been found many implements (coups-de-poing) of early man. This is of course only a suggestion far from being proved as yet.

As a species we are remarkably poor in body-hair and must have lost it very early in the special evolution of mankind. Our animal relatives have hairy bodies ; and, among mankind, some Europeans, the Ainu of North Japan, a few groups in the Philippines, and the Australian aborigines have most body-hair. The majority of Africans and many Asiatics have lost almost all save the head hair.

Humanity typically has brown pigment granules in hair, eye and skin ; though, in fair-haired blue-eyed North-west Europeans, the melanin, as this pigment is called, is very much reduced. It is possible, even probable, that early man had a good deal of this pigment. It is a product of metabolism which, so far as the skin is concerned, is shed as the skin wears away, but it is of great value for stopping excess of ultra-violet rays, whether direct from the sun, or pouring through a blue sky, or reflected to some extent from a snow surface.

The erect posture, with the head balanced on the vertebral column and the hands free from the duty to help support the body, is another universal feature, probably not quite fully attained in some hominids (Near-Men) of the Pleistocene Age. This posture and balancing of the head still has to be learnt in the first two years of life, and the reduction of the relative size of the jaws has been an essential accompaniment of the change of posture and balance. Our animal relatives have relatively heavier jaws, and jaws and head there are held in place by strong neck-muscles. Their reduction in mankind has given the larynx and mouth a new freedom which may well have promoted the ability, so characteristic of man, of producing varied sounds. Language is a universal feature of mankind, going beyond expression of feelings and having sounds denoting things and ideas.

Some of the hominids nearest to man were still very heavy-boned

PLATE 3

House of Man who Married a Fairy, a mountain farmhouse near Snowdon. July

John Markham

PLATE 4

S. J. Hayes

S. J. Hayes

MODERN WELSH CORACLES, River Towy. Wickerwork (well developed in
the Early Iron Age) forms a frame for stretched oxhide

in head, face and jaws, and it is probable that vestiges of this boniness remain here and there among us ; and this characteristic reappears in some cases of abnormality of a part of the pituitary endocrine gland at the base of the skull. The reduction of this boniness has been a marked feature of the early story of man. It is justifiable to connect the changes just mentioned with man's spread, after he abandoned a tree-life, from woodland or bush margins out on to open grasslands ; and such existed in parts of Pleistocene times in regions now desert in north-west Africa. On these sparse grasslands the long-inherited forward look, the increasingly free hands, the quick run might all help success in the food quest very effectively.

The human hand is another of our general characteristics, and its working is closely linked with the eye and with the large brain. All men use implements, at least of wood and stone ; and this is to be correlated with the character of the hand.

All men use fire or flame, and this is no doubt a very ancient acquisition ; it has often been suggested that at first men could maintain a fire but could not light one, i.e., they were dependent on prior fires, ultimately on natural fire. There is the famed story of Prometheus, stealing fire from heaven and bringing it to earth in a hollow reed. Some rituals suggest that firemaking was a process of skill in ancient times and that the maintenance of fire, by women in many cases (note the Vestal Virgins), was a ceremonial affair. The use of fire not only to scare wild beasts, but also to give warmth and to make food easier to eat for people with jaws reduced from animal strength, suggests the immensely important part fire has played in the growth of civilization, and especially in helping man to spread northwards to Britain and colder lands.

Human babies are more tender than those of apes for lack of hair on the body, have heads too heavy to hold up at first and need months to learn to walk, so maternal devotion has found enlarged scope, and tempers power over the infant with love's restraints. In such ways maternal devotion has become one of the most important factors of progress. Durable social life has made communication by sound a means of categorical statement as well as of communication of the emotions, and thus has contributed enormously to the growth of reasoning. Much of this can be looked upon as an outcome of a process of foetalization, involving the maintenance throughout life of character-istics which, in animal ancestors, were transient phases of pre-natal or early post-natal growth. This foetalization is associated with the enlargement of the brain and the advantage accruing from longer training. Recently stone tools have been found in South Africa which seem to have an association with the type known as *Australopithecus*, a small-brained creature with obvious relationship to man. Perhaps use of tools preceded major growth of brain in mankind.

As all modern peoples live in groups that exceed what may be called the minimal family (one man, one woman and their children), as all evidence from the past suggests group life, and as group life is widespread among Primates, we may suppose it to be a primal human feature. If so, we must picture individuality as arising in the group, as, one might say, the fine flower of group life. We are thus freed from the cramping concept in Rousseau's *Contrat Social*, which assumed a primal noble savage parting with his freedom to secure the benefits of society. It is better to picture the struggle of individuality against the normalising tendencies of the group which fears disruption, but which, without the struggle for individuality, tends to fossilize its scheme of life and so to work towards a crisis it may not be able to survive.

With these thoughts in mind we may turn to Britain and picture repeated (some estimates make eleven) advances and retreats of Pleistocene Ice Sheets.[1] Whatever may be argued about earlier relations of Britain to the continent, so long as vast masses of water were locked up as land ice, the sea-level was lower by several hundred feet and Britain was a peninsula of the icy continent. Britain has yielded some of the earliest bony remains of humanity in Europe. How long ago this was remains to some extent uncertain. Baron de Geer in Sweden counted the annual deposits (Varves) of mud from glacier edges laid down during summer melts and estimated that the first major Ice Age (Würm) began to pass away about 18000 B.C. Milankovitch, working on astronomical data, suggested 22100 B.C. Carbon, atomic weight 12, has an isotope, atomic weight 14, and this isotope is gradually reduced in non-living carbonaceous matter. Analysis has made possible rough estimates of age of remains containing carbon and the dating suggested so far by this method is probably about 14000 B.C.

Of possible implements we have Benjamin Harrison's Eoliths of uncertain but early date from the Ightham area in Kent, and Reid Moir's identifications of implements from the very early Pleistocene near Cromer and elsewhere in East Anglia. All these have been

---

[1] Penck and Brückner (1908) suggested four main advances: Gunz, Mindel, Riss and Wurm.

disputed, as is natural when one considers the transition from natural flints to flints possibly chipped in use by man and so to flints chipped deliberately by man to suit his purposes. At Clacton, in Essex, rough flakes of undisputed human workmanship have been found in deposits associated with cold phases, and rough flakes are characteristic of continental deposits which have yielded indications of hominid beings with heavy bones, large jaws and not quite upright gait. In Britain we have had one find supposed by Elliot Smith to be that of a hominid, the female skull from under Lloyd's in the City of London.

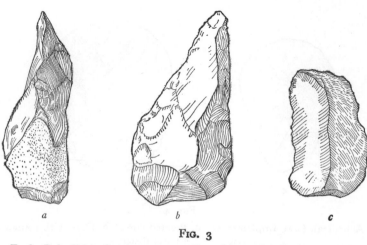

a   b   c

FIG. 3

Early Paleolithic Implements: *a*. Rough core implement. *b*. Somewhat finer core implement. *c*. Rough flake. (1/3 natural size)

In mild interglacial periods it seems that there spread northwards to Britain people who chipped flint,[1] usually to shape a lump or core into an implement which had either a point, or a continuously curved edge, though other forms do occur. The similarity of form is notable for the region from northern England to the Cape of Good Hope. The technique of making the core implements (Fr. *coups de poing*) gives evidences of high skill in carrying out a plan. They are evidently the work of beings near to *Homo sapiens* and probably actually within the *sapiens* group ; and in Britain a part of a skull has been found with

---

[1] Flint is named as the chief material but chert was sometimes used, also, especially in Africa, quartzites, rhyolites and obsidian.

core implements at Swanscombe, Kent.[1] It is only the back of the skull but the probability is that it belonged to a being which could be included in the more strictly defined group of *Homo sapiens* rather than to a hominid. So far as it goes, it somewhat strengthens the idea that the finely chipped core implements are the work of a very ancient variety of *Homo sapiens*, and, until further evidence accumulates, we may use the hypothesis that heavy-boned hominids spread from the icy continent in colder phases and beings more like ourselves came from the south (Africa, Spain, France, Britain) in milder phases of climate. The makers of core tools in Kenya, according to Leakey, seem to have been

a   *b*

FIG. 4

Acheulean Core Implements: *a.* Pointed core.   *b.* Core with rounded edge.   (1/3 natural size)

men who could hunt big beasts, probably by making pitfalls. That they also collected anything edible, plants or small animals, is not open to doubt. In fact both those who used mainly flakes and those who

[1] It has been found that buried bone gradually absorbs fluorine from the soil. The rate of absorption varies from site to site, but it has sometimes been found possible to ascertain, from buried bones of different ages, the rate of absorption on a particular site. This can be used to suggest a broad dating for skulls. By means of this testing for fluorine it has been shown that the Galley Hill skull is at any rate post-Palaeolithic. The evidence of the test demonstrates that the Piltdown skull and jaw are of one and the same date, a date that is probably not long before the Wurm Ice Age. The Swanscombe skull appears to be much older, as the presence near it of hand axes of Lower Palaeolithic Age suggested. This is important as suggesting that a being near *Homo sapiens*, to which group the Swanscombe skull approaches in spite of its thickness of bone, was in existence in the Lower Palaeolithic and was responsible for the fine hand axes. The facts about the fluorine test were communicated by Dr. Kenneth P. Oakley to the British Association for the Advancement of Science 1949, and are published in the Bulletin of the British Museum of Natural History.

PLATE I

AVEBURY, Wiltshire. Aerial view showing the circular bank and some stones of the original circles

Aerofilms, Ltd.

PLATE II

used mainly core-tools were hunter-collectors, but we must not assume that all cores are the work of one type and all flakes the work of another, the two ideas mingled. The improvement of core-tools, through finer chipping along the edges, became a very general feature in the course of time (Fig. 4), but evolution of the technique was still very slow.

Undisputed core-tools have not been found north of about latitude $53\frac{1}{2}°$-$54°$ in Britain, and they are not known from the Welsh highlands. The inference may be that the north and Wales may have retained ice for very long periods, or that early men, of whom there were only small numbers, did not drift so far. Hunter-collectors such as the Australian aborigines and some forest pygmies of Asia and Africa live for the most part in small groups ranging over a wide area, so that, in terms of density of population, the figure is 1 person to ten square miles rather than ten persons per square mile. Small isolated groups lead one to infer that close inbreeding occurred. This must have brought intensification of physical characteristics received probably through numerous cases of an identical person ancestral to both father and mother. Thus mutually isolated groups could come to differ markedly.

Penck and Brückner (1908, *Die Alpen in der Eiszeit*), suggested four main periods (p. 28) with subdivisions. Recent thought has led to a widespread belief that the interval between their second and third periods was very long and quite warm. In the intervals of milder climate, ice-sheets of the glacial phases melted and raised the level of the sea. So, in a region like Britain, the rivers' courses were shortened and their rate of flow slackened. They carried quantities of gravel and mud from the boulder clays of the previous glacial phase, and thus laid down quantities of gravel on their flood plains. During the oncoming and waning of glacial phases quantities of this gravel and mud, often in a semi-frozen state, slipped down the river banks, which were being cut down, because water was locked up in ice-sheets and the sea-level was being or had been lowered. This slipping down of gravel and mud is called solifluction. The cutting down of the valleys left portions of the previous flood-plain floored by gravels on either side of the river and these are called river terraces. Five successive solifluctions have been traced in some river valleys and they are related to four successive river terraces, which have yielded implements. The earlier two terraces show no mixing of core and flake tools, but that occurs in the third terrace,

D

which is thought to belong to an interglacial phase early in the series of Wurm Ice Ages.

After this mingling of traditions, which seems to have occurred in western Europe and Britain (then still a part of the continent), core tools become less important but perhaps survived in Spain and North Africa ; flake tools are shaped much more skilfully to triangular points and other special forms. Then followed a great revolution. Flakes, henceforth more common than cores for a long time, came to be very variously shaped for different purposes and many were no doubt hafted on wooden shafts. Scraping, boring, piercing, cutting, were all envisaged, and it is very probable that the idea of "spare parts" spread. A sharp point fixed on the end of a wooden shaft could be thrown some distance, especially with some spear-throwing device such as the Australian aborigines have. All this implies a greatly increased power of action at a distance, in hunting. In France and parts of northern Spain, from the late phases of the Pleistocene, cave-paintings, modellings and engravings on ivory and bone tell of the desire for children, of what seem like tents and may represent summer dwellings, of close observation of animals in the hunt and of the use of a disguise of an animal's skin and head. Rock paintings, chiefly in eastern and southern Spain (and Africa), some of which may be later in date, are full of representations of action and have a less naturalistic convention than most French ones, but we have so little palæolithic art in Britain that we must not expand this subject here.

The headless skeleton from Paviland Cave, Gower, is one of the best known of our British finds from the Upper Palæolithic (see W. J. Sollas, Journ. Roy. Anthropol. Institute 1913). It is stained with ochre, as are several of those deliberately buried in French caves, and it had a stone specially laid at the head and one at the feet. The ochre stain illustrates a practice which in later times became both widespread and persistent ; the red colouring simulates blood which, in the folk mind, " is the life " ; and this staining, as well as the burial of implements and ornaments with the dead, implies a belief in either rebirth or immortality, probably the former. The notion of re-birth is a very common one in many regions, and may be related to the observation of likenesses between living and dead, as well as to the fact that, in humanity, mating is not so generally followed by pregnancy and a birth as it is among many kinds of animals man has had opportunity to observe. The notion of the supplementing of mating by the entry

of an ancestral spirit (often of the husband's ancestors) into the prospective mother, and that of the need to acquire a store of vital essence
for re-birth, sometimes from aliens by such practices as head-hunting,
are important for any understanding of social ritual. Ideas of this
kind seem to have played a considerable part in later prehistoric times
in Britain, as we shall see. During the upper Palæolithic era a milder
phase of climate was interpolated between two colder ones. The
earlier of these cold phases witnessed the spread to Britain of flake-users
allied to the people of the French Aurignacian culture of cave-dwellers.
During the milder phase people of the French Solutrean culture

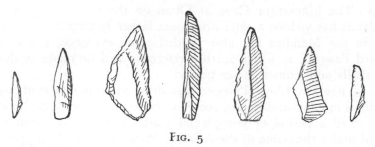

FIG. 5

Pigmy flints of the end of the Old Stone Age. (Natural size)

lived in open country in S.E. England. During the later of the cold
phases the Aurignacian culture developed into what is called (in
France) Magdalenian, with rather less skill in flaking stone but more
in making bone implements. In the cold phases these people lived in
caves (see plate 6, p. 51) and the group at Cresswell, Derbyshire, pains-
takingly investigated by A. L. Armstrong, has become the classic upper
Palæolithic site for Britain. A few indications of carving and of colouring on stones are all that we have in Britain to represent the wonderful
art of the French caves of the Aurignacian and Magdalenian periods.

It is probable that the population of Britain in the later part of
the Old Stone Age did not exceed a few hundreds, and that it increased
only very slowly, to a few thousands, during the long aftermath of the
Old Stone Age, lasting on in Britain until the third millennium B.C.

The bitter weather that so seriously affected Britain in February
and March, 1947, probably gives us hints of the blizzards and accumulation of snow and ice when oceanic depressions of air pressure tried to
enter Britain as the glaciers diminished. A period of damp cold, probably

with long persistence of ice in N. Wales, Cumbria and the Scottish highlands, kept tundra vegetation dominant until, as the cold diminished, coniferous forest spread. This was an environment not very friendly to either man or beast, and hunting and gathering would yield poor results. On moorlands and their brows above the forest lived hunters using " pygmy " flints called Tardenoisian, from La-Fère-en-Tardenois in France where an early collection of them was made. In addition, the seashore and some caves in limestone were used. In Britain we have finds of Tardenoisian implements made long ago by Dr. Colley March on the moorlands near Rochdale and others found especially in the Pennines, while some have been collected in Wales. The Macarthur Cave at Oban on the coast of the Scottish Highlands has yielded a skull and some larger implements. Aveline's Hole in the Mendips has also yielded some evidence, collected by Edward Fawcett, to which further reference will be made in dealing with skulls and human types below.

Long ago Dr. Lloyd Praeger first drew attention to evidences of variations in climate since the Ice Ages ended. In particular he found evidence of a period of post-glacial warmth which has been much studied under the name of the Atlantic Phase, commonly supposed to have attained its greatest developments about the fifth millennium B.C. in our region.

This appears not to have led to any great multiplication of human groups in Britain. Our country was undoubtedly an island at the time and even stood less out of the sea than it does now, so migration of land-mammals, and of men without boats, from the continent would not be effective. And food plants in Britain were few and poor. The great change to deliberate food production on any considerable scale had to wait for further development of human transport.

This long period of continuation of ancient ways in hunting and gathering has been called the Mesolithic or, sometimes, the Epipalæolithic Age. During its course, along with flakes, fairly large tools, made by chipping flint cores, came into general use. They were sometimes provided with a transverse edge, like that of a chisel. They may have been used for cutting tree branches, perhaps also for digging up edible roots. Fishing was undoubtedly important and a prong of a fish-spear has been collected from submerged peat (moorlog). Thatcham, in Berkshire, has yielded a notable number of flint implements of comparatively large size, many of them with a transverse edge.

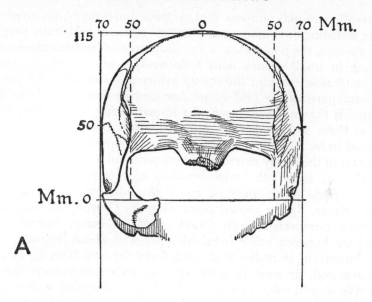

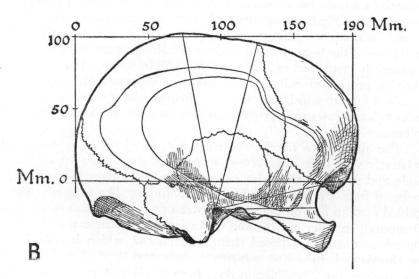

Fig. 6

Skull of Late Palæolithic Age from Aveline's Hole; front and side views

Generally, we may suppose that, as deer and wild cattle increased with the warming of climate, and plant roots, bulbs and fruits became more numerous, the population of Britain increased to some thousands, still living in small groups with little equipment.

We must now consider the scanty evidence concerning the people of the later parts of the Old Stone Age and its aftermath. The first point here is that no single case of a human being, other than *Homo sapiens*, of these or later periods is known from any part of Europe ; and it used to be thought that hominids had disappeared in face of the competition of the newly emerged *Homo sapiens*, man in the full modern sense. More recently, other considerations have come to light. In the first place, *Homo sapiens* may be much older in origin, as has been suggested above. In the second place, Dorothy Garrod, McCown and Keith have interpreted skulls found at Mt. Carmel, Palestine, as intermediate between other hominid types and *Homo sapiens*.

It is important to realise that adult form depends both on genetic inheritance and, at least in some degree, on circumstances during growth. We should think of a young hominid undergoing a change of growth in which the coarsening of the bones is less and the skull becomes a modified enlargement of what was previously an infantile form. In this particular case the jaw muscles at the side of the skull and some of the bones related to these remained strong for a while, and apparently restrained expansion of the skull in width. The brain-case, then in process of enlargement upwards, expanded in length backwards, a feature which seems to have helped, along with the reduction of mouth and jaws, to improve the balancing of the skull on the vertebral column.

The skulls of a number of early specimens of *Homo sapiens* are relatively very long and narrow, several still have fairly strong brows, wide and powerful cheek bones and large teeth, though all these are reduced from the sizes found in the hominids. The majority have a gabled median line on the skull, between the attachments of the great (temporal) muscles moving the lower jaw ; and these muscles make their way down in a broad (temporal) hollow, which is conspicuous on the skull, behind and somewhat above the level of the orbits. A few, such as the Cro-Magnon skull from the Dordogne, France, show a much shorter face and the skull is not as markedly gabled along the median line, its relative height is less and its width greater than in the majority. It is therefore unfortunate that several writers have

used the term Cro-Magnon Race to cover all the people of West
Europe of the late Palæolithic Age. It is the other type just described
that is more general in the late Palæolithic burials and that we are
concerned with.

Leslie Armstrong has recently found (1947-8) a female skull of
undoubted upper Palæolithic age near Cresswell and it shows the
features above mentioned, but, being female, has bony ridges less
developed. Armstrong's discovery makes it probable that the very
similar male skull from Langwith, near the above, but not securely
dated, is also upper Palæolithic. A skull from Baker's Hole resembles
the others and is also Palæolithic. The Cheddar skull is again similar
but has less marked brows. Skulls from Cissbury and Dartford are,
again, like the above, but undated. A skull from Halling is again
very high, but not quite so narrow ; it has been dated to an intermediate milder phase during the last great glaciation.

The skulls from MacArthur Cave, Oban, and Aveline's Hole in the
Mendips are probably somewhat later (early Mesolithic), they again
are very long, narrow and high, and show most of the characters
above mentioned.

The evidence, admittedly not as strong as one could wish, at
least shows that the high, gabled, narrow head of considerable length,
with temporal hollows well marked and cheek-bones strong and wide,
was of considerable importance in the later part of the Old Stone Age
and probably in its aftermath, in Britain as in Europe. But it was not
the only type.

What gives a special interest to the main type just discussed is that
it has analogies of a fairly clear character with some modern peoples.
The Australian aborigines in very large proportion show most of these
characters, they occur among jungle tribes in India, they are known
from South African natives in certain areas of backwardness and
poverty, they are evident in North Africa, Sardinia, North Portugal,
the Dordogne in France, the Plynlymon and Denbigh moorlands in
Wales, and, in stray individuals, here and there in the general British
population. Measurement has shown that one might expect to find less
than three in a sample of a hundred in many parts of Wales, but that
the proportion rose considerably on the Welsh moorlands named.
If one notes, among the places mentioned, Wales, North Portugal,
South Africa, Australia, one realises that this constitutes a mainly
peripheral distribution of a discontinuous nature. This is an indication

that we are dealing with some old features, still lingering on the remote fringes ; but it is quite likely that survivals will be found in many other spots, though nothing can be discovered to match the case of almost the whole aboriginal population of Australia, and that, at any rate, can hardly be interpreted otherwise than as a survival.

The notion of continuity of physical characteristics over thousands of years is far easier to understand on Mendelian lines than it was in pre-Mendelian days. But we should beware of supposing that such continuity is either complete or general. Genes from different types co-exist in most individuals and express themselves in varied combinations. That the particular group of characters discussed above fairly often occurs as a whole is an interesting phenomenon, not an illustration of a general law of fixity of type.

Inbreeding, such as must have occurred in the small isolated human groups of very early times could lead to repeated unions of heritages carried by the same genes from the same ancestors, and these genes could spread widely through a local group. It is at least probable that intensification of characteristics under these circumstances could result in their marked persistence among the people of a region which did not receive floods of immigrants, but was, on the other hand, likely to export population.

REFERENCES : see end ch. 4, p. 99.

CHAPTER 3

EARLY IMMIGRATIONS AND HUSBANDRY

WHILE Britain was passing through the Mesolithic phase of culture and the Atlantic phase of climate, mankind elsewhere was evolving from the hunting-and-gathering stage to that of deliberate food-production. The aridity of North Africa had increased and so made hunting less successful ; and people had gathered near the great rivers, Nile and Euphrates and Tigris and other streams. Near the flood-plains of this region the ancestors of some of our cereals were found wild and were tended and in due course cultivated. It is probable that the first home of peasant-life based on grain production was somewhere between Cilicia and the Caspian Sea. The flood-plains, once they had been cleared and to some extent drained, were valuable for cultivation so long as the annual floods (in spring on the Euphrates and Tigris, in summer on the Nile) supplied fresh silt to keep up fertility. Barley, emmer wheat and probably millet were cultivated and settled life with food stores and consequent ideas of property and of social regulation of work was developed. This may be provisionally dated to about or rather before 5,000 B.C. The chipping of cores of flints to make tools had become rare in late Palæolithic times. It was resumed in the Fayum (Egypt) and probably elsewhere, and the tools, when used for digging, were subject to friction which smoothed their surfaces. In some such way the art of stone rubbing and polishing was developed. It brought into use many hard types of rock which had not lent themselves to chipping, and so helped men to spread in areas where such rocks as flint, etc., were not found. Settled villages and institutional organization led on to the development of larger aggregates, some of which eventually became cities ; and metallurgy began to supplement the making of rubbed-stone implements. The mixing of black tin sand (cassiterite) with copper was found to give an improved result (bronze), and even a little iron (probably meteoric) was used. Grains of gold were collected from streams and some silver also came into use, sometimes mixed with gold to form what is now called electrum. The settled life gave opportunities for increase of equipment in the form of pottery, woodwork, millstones and woven materials, and led to craft specialization and to commercial exchange.

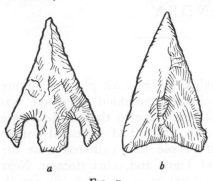

a   *b*

FIG. 7

Flint arrowheads with and without a median tang. (Natural size)

Stone for grinding into axes, copper and tin sand, flint for fine chipping to make barbed arrowheads, gold and silver, probably precious stones and pearls were sought, beads were made from various stones, and intercourse and ideas thus spread outwards from S.W. Asia and the Nile.

Improvement of implements led to modifications of the hoe, including its transformation into a spade, a man's implement, whereas the hoe was a hand-tool largely, but by no means exclusively, used by women. Domestic animals were added to cultivation as part of man's equipment and led to the evolution of the plough. Cultivation almost certainly preceded domestication of animals in most regions, and pastoral nomadism is usually a specialised mode of life followed by men who have cut loose from cultivation. The cattle became really useful for work when castration (gelding) of the surplus males was introduced. The castrated beasts tended to put on fat, a valuable food-adjunct in cool climates, as war-time Europe knows too poignantly, and a commodity which helped men to spread, especially as the grasses north of latitude 40°N. or so are usually richer in vitamins than those between or near the tropics ; cattle are thus able to feed better and grow stronger, with, on the whole, fewer insect pests as another advantage.

It is desirable to guard against the tendencies of several sociological writers to make the evolutionary sequence from the hunter-collectors include a supposed nomad pastoral stage preceding that of cultivation.

It is probable that all this scheme of a life of food-production, commerce and craftwork was for a long time mainly confined to its original homes, especially as the population of those days had to depend on locally produced food. Transplantation, at one move, of such an interwoven complex of ideas and practices was difficult, especially its spread away from flood-plains with their ever-renewed fertility. But, by the beginning of the third millennium B.C., organizations and institutions had become sufficiently self-conscious, and records had become sufficiently good, for the general scheme to spread. There is evidence of its spread to the Indus basin, the Aegean and China at least, as well as, in some degree, to the Western Mediterranean and Europe generally, by sea as well as by land. The spread of the idea of food-production to Europe and Britain is thus a local expression of a more widespread phenomenon. It was due partly to contagion of ideas from the old centres, and partly to the hunt of the peoples of those old centres for copper, tin-sand, gold grains and other materials for use and ornament (amber was a famous and treasured material). It involved some developments of boats for coastwise maritime voyages, a development concerning which our knowledge is still scanty.

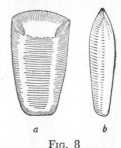

a   b

Fig. 8

Polished Neolithic adze; front and side views. (1/3 natural size)

It is possible that, even without contagion of ideas from S.W. Asia and the Nile, men were learning to shape stone tools by grinding after preliminary chipping. An edge transverse to the tool's main axis made it an axe with which bushes and branches could be lopped. At any rate, neolithic tools, as those which are shaped by grinding are called, give in many regions the first indubitable indications of an advance from the old life. Cissbury, in Sussex, on a site occupied also in later Iron Age and Romano-British times, has yielded abundant evidence of the making of stone axes by first chipping and then grinding ; and sites among the basalts of Antrim also abound in evidence of this craft.

Grimes' Graves, at Brandon, in Norfolk is another site at which flint was extensively quarried, presumably from the third millennium, B.C., for the making of implements ; this was done in pits in the chalk, galleries leading off from them where layers of flints were available. Leslie Armstrong's minute and careful examination of the floor of one

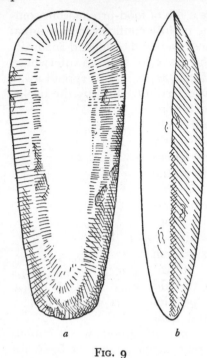

a   b

FIG. 9

Polished Neolithic axe; front and side views.   (1/3 natural size)

pit which was very poor in flint revealed a most interesting ritual centre. Laid on a slab were objects including deerhorn picks, hammerstones, phalli, etc., apparently dedicated to the Mother Goddess, whose figurine, a small one, is, like so many others from the late Palæolithic onwards, shaped to suggest the pregnant condition. Did the miners abandon this particular pit at a certain depth and ask the goddess for better luck next time? The use of flint at Brandon went on after the introduction of metal, for strike-a-lights and later for gun-flints. If one of the Brandon workers made "Old Stone Age Flints" for sale to unwary collectors, we cannot use this to claim lineal descent of the industry from that far-off time. It is however quite probable that flint chipping has been more or less continuous here from the days of the Mother Goddess and the neolithic tools. Often, only the preliminary chipping was done at the flint centre and the final grinding and polishing was left to others. The beginner may thus be confused in his impressions as between chipped cores of the Old Stone Age or the Mesolithic period and those neolithic tools that have not yet been ground or polished, and sometimes were not intended to be so treated save along the cutting edge.

The introduction of grinding freed men from their widespread dependence on flint, chert and rhyolites, quartzites and obsidians. Many hard crystalline rocks could be ground far more satisfactorily than they could be chipped; and this made Atlantic Britain more attractive economically. It had previously been kept back by having little flint or chert, save small beach pebbles, chiefly from Antrim, that had been spread in the moraines of the Ice Ages as far south as the southern part of Cardigan Bay.

The story of the great change to general food-production in Britain has two beginnings. On the one hand, coastwise voyagers came from the Mediterranean, the Iberian peninsula and Brittany to our western peninsulas. On the other hand, people from the continental plain migrated somewhat later across the North Sea, probably across its southern part, and, first of all, occupied parts of eastern Britain. The stages of these two processes of immigration are of great interest archæologically; the reader who wishes to follow them in detail may refer to books and papers mentioned at the end of this chapter, which must confine itself to some general statements. There is some probability that the beginning of the western maritime movement antedated that of the eastern immigrations, some of which may have been lured on by what was happening in Cornwall, Pembrokeshire, Anglesey and Caernarvonshire, the Isle of Man, Galloway and the Clyde, and Ireland. But both zones witnessed a number of successive movements covering, altogether, several centuries, perhaps 2400-1600 B.C.

We unfortunately know little of the habitations of the western

FIG. 10

Figurine of Mother Goddess, found at bottom of a flint miner's pit at Grimes' Graves, Brandon, E. Anglia. (Height 4¼ inches)

maritime folk, but we have the most massive monuments connected with what we infer was their ritual ; and these monuments give evidence of different groups with diversity of ideas and customs. It may be helpful to think, by way of comparison, of the contrasts between Portuguese, French and British settlements of the seventeenth and eighteenth centuries on the coasts of India ; their respective churches and houses show appropriate differences due to diversities of heritage. One feature, however, is common to nearly all the monuments of Brittany and Atlantic Britain and Ireland of that time. They are built of great stone blocks, most often unhewn. Sometimes rock was found which allowed itself to be cut into rectangular blocks, and we accordingly find attempts at mortarless (ashlar) building ; but the common plan is to use huge pieces of stone in the rude state, sometimes pieces weighing many tons—eight-, ten-, even fifteen-ton blocks are common, and a few are much larger. The constructions using these great stones are called the western megaliths. We cannot do more than make hypotheses about the ideas which led men to build them.

They were mariners along what was then the far fringe of the world, and, like so many migrants of later times, they held to the traditions of the East Mediterranean civilizations which had given the impulse to their movements, and this whether the wanderers to Britain, for example, had come all the way from the Eastern Mediterranean or merely from the Iberian peninsula or Brittany, to which had drifted people from the Eastern Mediterranean.

As has already been suggested (Chapter 2), a feature of the ideas of many peoples past and present is the belief that, for the birth of a child, mating should be supplemented by the entry of an ancestral spirit into the prospective mother. We may think of these maritime folk as mainly young men taking to themselves women from among the folk they found in a more or less Mesolithic stage in countries to which they came. Professor Estyn Evans has shown that builders of megaliths and mesolithic folk lived side by side for a time in North Ireland, and similar conclusions have been reached in Denmark. The children of these marriages must grow up as near as possible to the paternal tradition ; and, from what happens among many peoples, we may infer that the wife joined the husband's group and looked to receive the spirits of her husband's folk into herself for re-birth. West-coast megaliths may indeed have been stores of human remains incorporating vital essence or spirits, in any case awaiting re-birth. Probably the vital essence or spirit was associated with the head or some other organ which was preserved in the store, and after a certain time, when re-birth might be supposed to have taken place, the remains would be of no account and might be destroyed to make room for new ones. A place for ceremonial, of a character one could but guess at, is a feature of many monuments and it habitually faces the main entry into the place of burial, or perhaps it should be described as the place for egress of the spirit.

In various parts of the world in which this type of belief is found there may be a separate place for those whose vital essence or spirit is not wanted, e.g., in parts of Chota Nagpur those who have been eaten by tigers or have died in certain other special ways are held to be undesirable or unlucky and are buried apart.

Another feature of ancient custom is the "judgment" on the dead as well as on the living, and the giving of a white stone to those who are "justified" or acquitted. One of our western megaliths, Cashtal yn Ard, Isle of Man, has a special section, right at the end farthest from the ceremonial forecourt which is in front of the burial chambers, and that special section has yielded a large number of white stones. Biblical students will recall the giving of the white stone mentioned in the Revelation of St. John, chapter 2, verse 16. It is quite probable that the mounds of graves ("Barrows") on the chalk were kept scoured and were therefore permanently white, and New Grange, near the Boyne, E. Ireland, was originally covered with white quartz. One may make a mental picture of the dead being judged before burial (probably burial of the head only in some cases) and of burning (in the case of Cashtal yn Ard, but of what parts of the body we cannot

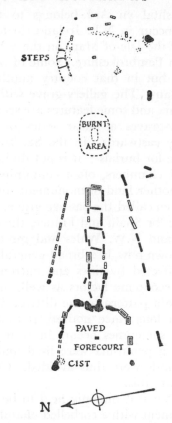

STEPS

BURNT AREA

PAVED FORECOURT

CIST

N

● Original stones unmoved
▭ New stones in identified holes
∴ White quartz pebbles

6 0   18   36 Feet

Fig. 11

Plan of the Gallery Grave, Cashtal yn Ard, Isle of Man

tell), and of a dancing floor or place of other ceremonies connected with hoped-for re-birth right at the other end of the monument. Monuments in Brittany have been the scenes of fertility rites surreptitiously practised within recent times. So has the Giant at Cerne Abbas.

Cashtal yn Ard belongs to the type known as gallery-graves. They occur in N.E. Ireland, in and near the Firth of Clyde, in the east of the Isle of Man, on the S.W. flank of the Pennines and in one case in Pembrokeshire. Some of their features occur in French monuments but in that country another variety, the passage-grave, was dominant. The gallery-grave with a forecourt is again important in Sardinia and some features are seen in Malta. In our British and Irish gallery-graves a linear series of cists stretches from the forecourt usually eastwards. In the Sardinian examples there is one long enclosure for burials ; it is not divided into cists. Cists are small stone-walled chambers, often containing human remains.

Another kind of monument found along the coasts of West Britain has been called the passage-grave. It and its many variants are characteristic for Spain and France, the Channel Islands, Cornwall, parts of S.W. and N.W. Wales and most of Ireland. Dr. Margaret Davies has shown how, in a broad general way, the choice of places of landing was affected by tides and currents, probably by stone supplies and other economic factors as well, and how these landing-places helped to give a pattern to the distribution of megaliths. One fact of distribution long since noticed is that the passage-grave type of monuments sometimes occurs in transpeninsular zones, as though routes across a peninsula were used and the dangers of navigation around headlands were thus avoided. Cornwall, S.W. and N.W. Wales all illustrate this.

What is commonly held to be the basic type of passage-grave is a monument with a corbelled chamber communicating with the exterior by a passage and probably typically covered originally by a mound covering both chamber and passage, the passage being necessarily long if the mound is large. There may be a ring of stones forming the margin of the mound and these may be either exposed or embedded in the mound.

The corbelled chamber occurs in Spain ; there is one fine example at L'Ile Longue, in Morbihan, Brittany ; New Grange on the Boyne, in Ireland, is one of the finest in existence and is a member of a small local group of very important tombs. Maes Howe, in Orkney, is another specially important case, and the cairns of Caithness also show this feature. The idea of corbelled roofing is thought to have originated in S.W. Asia, but it may have developed independently in various regions. The passage did not lend itself to corbelling, which is appropriate

PLATE III

Aerofilms, Ltd.

a. SILBURY HILL, Wiltshire. Mound raised in prehistoric times near Avebury; date and purpose unknown

John Markham

b. CEFNAMWLCH, Caernarvonshire. A simplified megalithic monument

PLATE IV

John Markham

CAPEL GARMON, Caernarvonshire. A passage grave

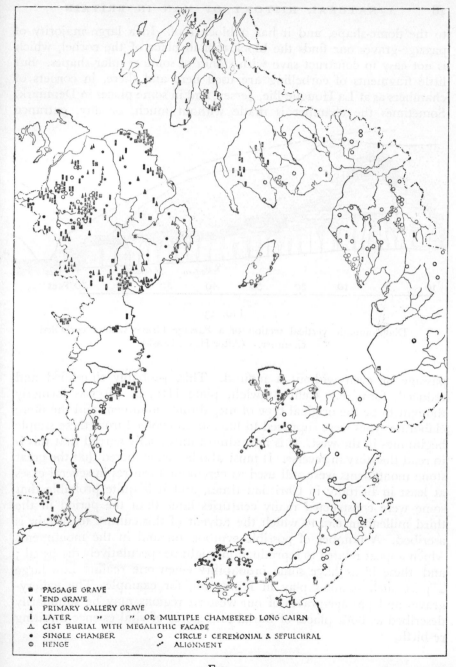

FIG. 12

Map showing distribution of megalithic monuments around the
Irish Sea. (After **Dr.** Margaret Davies)

to the dome-shape, and it has a block roof. In a large majority of passage-graves one finds the block roof in place of the corbel, which is not easy to construct save with stones of some regular shapes. But little fragments of corbelling are used here and there, in corners of chambers as at La Hougue Bie, Jersey, and in some places in Denmark. Sometimes the chamber is made without much, or any, entrance

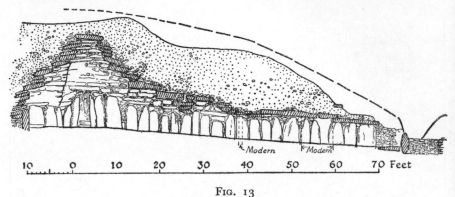

FIG. 13

Diagrammatic vertical section of a Passage Grave with a corbelled chamber.   (After H. G. Leask)

passage or even without a mound. This, probably simplified and reduced, form (e.g. Cefn Amwlch, plate IIIb, p. 46) was formerly thought to be the original type of megalithic monument and the more elaborate types were supposed to have been evolved from these simple beginnings in the west. It is now almost universally agreed that this is to read the story in reverse. It must also be remembered that the great stone monuments were still used as ceremonial centres in several cases at least in Brittany in Christian times, and it is quite probable that some were constructed many centuries later than the period in the third millenium B.C. to which the advent of this culture to Britain is ascribed. A number of possible symbols on and in the monuments which appear related to reproduction might be speculatively discussed ; and these ideas have some probability when one realises how large a part such symbols play in Hinduism, for example. The gallery-graves and passage-graves of our western regions may be summarily described as both places of burial and stores of vital essence awaiting re-birth.

Another group of graves is that found among the Cotswold Hills and in South Glamorganshire as well as to some extent in Wessex. This group partakes of the general nature of the passage-graves but has some features of its own. It is supposed by many to result from the work of settlers coming to the Bristol Channel from Brittany, which seems to have continued to spread its influence across the Channel in the early days of metal.

Before attempting to say more about megalithic monuments and their builders it is advisable to turn to the immigrants to the east, of those early days. Windmill Hill, near Avebury, Wilts., has become famous as one of the earliest settlement-sites. It has concentric banks and ditches, now at least quite slight. These are broken by numerous gaps which are original features. It is probable that the banks were bases of palisades. The ditches may have been shelter lines. It is related to other sites on the South Downs, some of which, like Maiden Castle, in Dorset, and the Trundle, near Goodwood, were reoccupied and altered, by the heaping up of great ramparts, many centuries later, in the pre-Roman Iron Age. There are also analogous sites in France, and Michelsberg, in the Rhineland, is a classic case. It is likely that the people who organised these settlements came across the south of the North Sea or the Straits of Dover or the east end of the English Channel. The Scottish sites which have related pottery show Iberian (and therefore maritime) links.

Another group of people of different origin and habit is that evidenced by pottery found near Peterborough ; they seem to have favoured low, wet areas and some have thought they came from the South Baltic region to South and Middle Scotland as well as to Eastern England. Others think the Peterborough pots largely a native adaptation of the type of pottery found at Windmill Hill. Suggestions have been made that the Peterborough people brought the horse with them because horse remains have been found with their pottery. This needs further investigation, but, in any case, the horse did not become important in Britain until much later. Horse remains occur in megaliths in Brittany and the Iberian peninsula, but we are not sure whether they were domesticated animals. It is probable that the wild horse did not reach Britain after the Ice Age. The cave-bear, cave-hyena, mammoth and other beasts of the Ice Ages had died out. The deer, the wolf, wild cattle, swine and possibly sheep were features of our fauna along with beavers and lemmings.

The Peterborough bowls are decorated with multiple repetitions of small indentations in lines. Another early ware of our western regions has been called bag-ware by Mr. Peake who has suggested that its model was a skin bag, probably a scrotal sac (the sac containing the two testes of the male). The scrotal sac is used as a pouch or bag in several regions, including parts of East Central Europe, at the present time. Still another series of immigrant-groups is sometimes referred to as the " Beaker People," and they seem to have played an important part in British development. The "Beaker" pot is, basically, a bell-shaped vessel, the sides of which are almost S-shaped in vertical section; it is of fine material and represents skill in pottery superior to that of the other more or less contemporary groups.

It is thought by many archæologists that beakers originated in the interior of Spain, where they are found with poor flint implements. That such skilled pot-making should originate amid poor equipment is a difficulty. It may be that some of the equipment was better

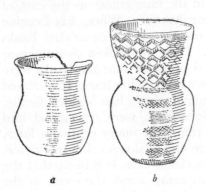

a   b

FIG. 14

a. Bell-beaker.   b. Long-necked Beaker. (Both 1/6 natural size)

but of perishable material. It may also be that the beaker pot was introduced into Spain from elsewhere, and its shape might easily be derived from that of some pieces of the painted pottery of S.E. Europe and S.W. Asia. Beakers, like all early western pots, are not painted; they are decorated by incised lines or indentations of one sort or another, arranged in angulated designs, often with horizontal zones. The problem of the place of origin of these beakers, however, need not detain us further here, as it has little relation to the great work of the people of the Beaker culture in Britain. The common type in Britain is not bell-shaped and has not the S-section mentioned above, but has a high almost cylindrical neck rising from a constriction above a bulbous body. There is no doubt that the people who made these latter pots had come through Holland from the Rhineland and perhaps Bohemia and Moravia. In Central Europe they had mixed with people who made stone battle-axes with a hole bored through, and decorated their

PLATE 5

Robert Atkinson

a. UNRECLAIMED FEN, near Wicken, Cambridgeshire. November

Robert Atkinson

b. RECLAIMED MARSH, near Terrington St. Clement, Norfolk. November

The low-lying land, south of the Wash, includes undrained freshwater
fen, and, near the sea-wall, drained salt-marsh

PLATE 6

Robert Atkinson

CAVE SHELTER, Oldbury, Kent, in which implements ascribed to the latter part of the Palaeolithic Age have been found

pots by impressing string on the surface (Corded Ware, Schnurkera-
mik). They had finely-worked barbed and tanged flint arrowheads,
and what are supposed to be bowmen's wrist-guards (rectangles of thin
stone). They spread west in Britain to get bronze implements which the
megalith builders were making in Ireland from Irish copper. Theirs
is the equipment of a warlike people and they specially occupied
places along the east coast of Britain and Scotland, the lower Tweed
and Buchan being specially important in the latter region. They
spread inland or westwards to Wiltshire, the southern Pennines and,
probably via Stainmore Pass, to the Carlisle area. That they were
seeking contact with the western maritime activities (p. 44) seems
clear from this general distribution and the many finds of solitary
beakers westwards beyond the places named, as well as quite a few
in Ireland. The finds of early bronze implements and weapons in
western Britain give some support to this idea, too.

We must here notice that some bell-shaped beakers do occur in
Britain ; a few may be copies of Dutch bell-beakers, but some appear
to be associated with the movements of megalith builders from south-
western Europe. Whatever its origins, the Spanish bell-beaker culture
had many links with the megalith builders of West Portugal ; and
the rich ornamentation of these pots spread thence with some groups
of megalith builders to Brittany and to the south of England, where
also fine Breton stone axes and other objects came in through the Christchurch district (Hants.) to Salisbury Plain. On the Plain here we
therefore have a mingling of several cultures : the Windmill Hill
group, Central European and Dutch beaker-makers, immigrants from
Brittany. Salisbury Plain becomes in this way a metropolitan area
of early South England, and one should note that on it meet lines that
permitted communications along the South and North Downs, along
the high edge of the Berkshire Downs and the west flank of the Chilterns
(the tops of the Chilterns were largely covered with material closely
related to boulder clay and with woodland), to the Cotswolds and on
along Jurassic scarps to the Lincoln Edge, westwards along the Mendips
and south-westwards on the Blackdown Hills to Dartmoor, Bodmin
Moor and West Cornwall. These lines of ancient communication were
for the most part not heavily wooded, so they could be cleared and used
by men without iron axes.

West Cornwall, the western end of the Mendips and the Severn
estuary and the way from the S.W. Pennines to the Mersey near

Warrington, as well as that via Stainmore Pass north-westwards to Cumberland, all gave the easterners chances of contact with the western maritime peoples. They seem to have been drawn by the lure of metal. Graves of Beaker people round about Bohemia often have copper daggers ; early Beaker graves in east Britain are without metal. Was this because of a tabu against putting a newly introduced material into graves, or was it because the Beaker people had not yet gained sufficient contact with the metal-workers of the west ?

The Netherlands have graves of this period that once had wood posts strengthening and surrounding mounds of earth. In Britain we have remains of wood circles at Arminghall, in Norfolk, at Woodhenge (Salisbury Plain region) and at Bleasdale, Lancashire. The last may be a good deal later in date. The idea of a palisaded circular rampart with a fosse around it is important among herding peoples if they have a seasonal round-up of their beasts, and probably the beaker people were warlike herders. Coming into contact with the stone construc-tions of the western maritime people, the beaker people seem to have exchanged wood posts for standing stones, and so we get the idea of a stone circle with a ditch and sometimes a rampart. Post-holes of supposedly timber-circles of very early Neolithic date in Oxfordshire suggests that the idea may not be one due to the Beaker peoples.

Even in its imperfect state, Avebury is our most impressive pre-historic monument (plate I, p. 30). An encircling bank, still complete save on the north-west where farming has encroached, rose more than 50 feet above the bottom of a ditch within it, a very unusual feature. Four gaps in bank and ditch gave access to an inner sacred area of over 28 acres. Here were three stone circles (two long known, one recently discovered) on a nearly N.-S. axis. The sacred area was bounded by standing stones, making the largest prehistoric stone circle known, with a diameter of over 365 yards. A curving avenue, about 50 feet wide in most of its length, may be traced to the " Sanctuary " on Overton Hill ; it was bounded by standing stones several of which have been excavated and re-erected through efforts of A. Keiller. Stuart Piggott has recently suggested that the " Sanctuary " with its complex system of post-holes was a timber-frame building that was several times reconstructed as well as enlarged. To its timber-frame were added circles of stones.

The stones of the avenue and great circles are called " Sarsens," a folk-name for foreigners (Saracen, Sarrasin, etc.). They are remains of

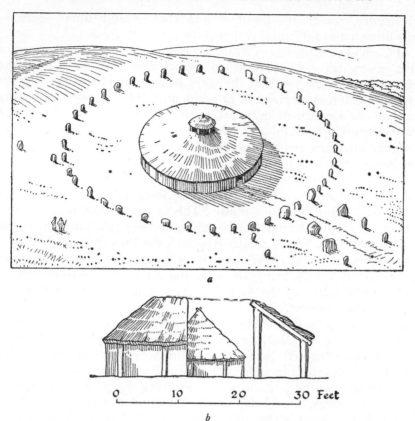

FIG. 15

Reconstruction; from the plan of the Sanctuary, suggested by Prof.
Stuart Piggott

a thin layer of early tertiary sandstone which once covered the chalk
of the Marlborough Downs. The sandstone was jointed, so early man
found large blocks almost ready for monumental use though he
dressed them further at both Avebury and Stonehenge. It is believed
that to erect these stones in position a pit for the base was dug, then
the top of the stone was roped to posts suitably placed and the ropes
were pulled to lift the stone until it was in position to slide into the
pit prepared for its base. There are burials near some of the stones
of the Avenue. The avenue stones were apparently alternately tall

and slender, sometimes pointed, and shorter and squat, possibly symbolising male and female respectively.

At Cashtal yn Ard, Isle of Man, a standing stone, north of the entry to the gallery grave, has a rounded conical projection on its top; the slightly shorter stone south of the entry is flat-topped and the top has a groove which may or may not be accidental. These stones, and many others on our western monuments, again suggest sex symbolism. The area between Carn Meini and Moel Trigarn, two of the Preseli Hills, Pembrokeshire, has yielded four of the five types of foreign stones of Stonehenge, and it is from this area that 82 great stones were taken in the second millennium B.C. to Stonehenge (see p. 57). The fifth kind of foreign stone is that of which the so-called Altar Stone, from Cosheston, Milford Haven is made. This suggests, what is on general grounds most probable, that the foreign stones were taken to Stonehenge by sea along the S. Wales coast. Reaching the Bristol Avon they were no doubt rafted up this river and its tributary the Frome. A short drag overland would bring them to the river Wylye, down which they could be rafted to the Wiltshire Avon and so they would reach the Stonehenge Avenue.

As to reasons for the moving of these stones, we can but speculate. They were almost certainly sacred before they were moved, and they may have been valued by some combination of easterners (beaker people) and westerners (people of the passage graves or gallery graves). The easterners, as the late incomers, marrying the girls of the natives and the westerners, are likely, in the course of generations, to have been much influenced by the cults of the west. These cults included rites based on the idea of re-birth following entry of an ancestral spirit into the prospective mother, or at least this is highly probable. The easterners' stone circles and the tradition they have left, on the other hand, suggest astrological relations and cults; and their burial mounds are primarily individual, not communal graves. Was there some effort to make a conglomerate ritual? We need but recall the many efforts of the early Celtic Christian Church to use old-time sanctities and to adapt the megaliths to its purposes. The Roman Church in many regions has developed analogous policies. The Indo-Aryans with cults of sky and wind, fire and so on, coming into an India in which the Begetting Power and the Mother Goddess were of great importance, adopted these in various degrees; and Siva and Kali are still among the great personifications of deity in India at the present day.

It is of some interest that the ways into the sacred area at Avebury have attracted later intrusions of farmers with the result that a village now occupies a part of the circle towards the north-west. But the medieval church of Avebury stands conspicuously outside the sacred circle. Was it that Avebury, like Stonehenge, retained too strong a hold on the folk-mind to be Christianised? We note that, analogously, the famous Alignments of the Carnac district in Brittany have not been Christianised in any way.

It has been shown that in Java the megalithic culture had "regions of the dead " marked off, as the Carnac alignments seem to bound a region of the dead in Brittany. It is possible that at some period the Avebury, perhaps the Stonehenge, region had some ritual status of this kind and that a part of Preseli (Prescelly, Pembrokeshire) was another such area.

Farther north, we have the great circle at Arbor Low, Derbyshire (plate 8, p. 59), in an area famous for its beaker graves, and adjoining an area with gallery-graves (The Bridestones at a fine view-point east of Congleton is a notable example). The stones of Arbor Low are now all prostrate and it seems more probable that they were thrown down by the followers of a rival cult than that they were originally arranged in this way. Long Meg and her Maidens near Penrith, and the Stone Circle at Keswick are related monuments in Cumbria on the way to north-east Ulster. These facts give a special interest to the large stone circle, with a fosse, called the Giant's Ring near Belfast. This circle has a monument of the passage-grave type at its centre, which suggests a combination of two cults.

Some Hebridean cairns have an outer circle of standing stones in addition to a circle outlining the mound and called a Peristalith; and the impressive circle with avenue and alignments at Callernish in the Long Island (Lewis) is a development of these ideas, which are also expressed in Orkney (Stenness). Stone circles occur on and near alluvial gravels of the Ness, Nairn and Spey rivers, and it is probable that the easterners (beaker graves are numerous in Buchan, Aberdeen-shire) spread west in North Scotland. To what extent it may have been a coastwise maritime spread, perhaps using Orkney on the way, we cannot at present decide. The cross-country ways in Highland Scotland would seem to have been too difficult; and this is true of early E.-W. communications across Scotland in a general way, even of that across from the Firth of Forth to the Firth of Clyde.

Whereas the west Baltic and to some extent Ireland, south Britain and Finistère (Brittany) have yielded beads of Baltic amber from graves of this period, Scotland has a notable and native substitute. The beads are spoken of as jet, in this case a lignite from the Carboniferous strata. In one grave, jet beads were found so arranged as to suggest that they had been threaded in many rows forming a broad crescent.

It should be mentioned here that Caithness has yielded beaker-sherds from Dunreay, and that it was, or had been, a great centre of chambered cairns, with a good deal of corbelling (p. 46), while Maes Howe, in Orkney, is one of the finest examples of a corbelled tomb that we have. There are many cairns in Uist. It is difficult to avoid the idea that Beaker people and westerners effected some sort of combinations here and there in North Britain and probably North Ireland. The Beaker people seem to have adopted the idea of stone for the circle and a central grave, and perhaps superseded the idea of collective burial, replacing it by the single-grave idea.

For South Britain we have some interesting hints from folk-lore and tradition. Geoffrey of Monmouth, in the twelfth century, set down the tradition that the " foreign stones " of Stonehenge came from Ireland. H. H. Thomas, tracing their origin in 1923, showed geologically that, though they actually came from W. Pembrokeshire, at any rate, they came along the prehistoric trade route of Irish trade. Pembrokeshire folk-lore tells of sea traders with gold balls at St. David's Head and we know that gold of Irish origin has been found in Britain, W. France, N.W. Spain, Luxembourg, N.W. Germany and Denmark; and Irish origin has been claimed for gold objects from Palestine and from Hissarlik II (Hissarlik VI,[1] the later city on the same site, is the Troy the Greeks destroyed about 1184 B.C.). The supply of gold from the streams of Wicklow, Ireland, derived from veins in the granite of the Leinster Mountains, diminished after its exploitation in the Bronze Age, when it was used to make the magnificent gold ornaments of which the National Museum in Dublin and the British Museum in London have a few surviving examples.

An admirable book, *Stonehenge*, with many new facts and arguments has been written by R. J. C. Atkinson (1957) and readers should refer to it for details. The great monument includes constructions of various periods, probably 1900-1400 B.C. Carbonaceous fragments from

[1] Some workers make this Hissarlik VII.

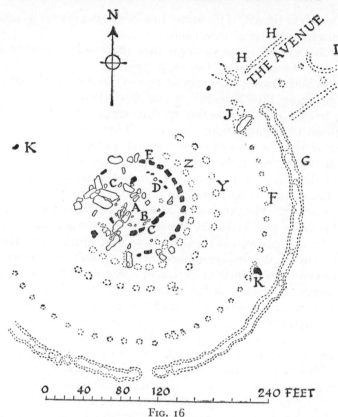

FIG. 16

Plan of Stonehenge before the new researches of 1953 onwards.
A. " Altar " Stone from Cosheston, Pembrokeshire. B. Horseshoe of Preseli
stones. C. Horseshoe of Sarsen Trilithons. D. Circle of Preseli stones.
E. Circle of Sarsen Trilithons. F. Circle of Aubrey holes. G. Ditch and
Valla. H. Avenue. I. Heel Stone and ditch around it. J. Gateway Stone
(so-called Slaughter Stone). Y and Z. Circles of post holes. KK gives a
N.W.-S.E. line. Standing stones are shown in black, prostrate ones are
in outline.

various spots have been analysed and dates have been inferred from
the proportion of radio-active carbon remaining (see p. 28).

The first phase of construction was probably not far from 1850 B.C.
It included the circular ditch and bank enclosing the monument, and,
within the bank, a circle of holes, the Aubrey holes, which were
probably ritual pits of some sort, also a local rough stone (a Sarsen,
see p. 52) set up outside the north-eastern entrance and traditionally

called the Heel Stone. This stone has been speculatively linked with supposed astronomical observations.

It is thought by some students that there was a timber structure at the centre of the circle (cf. fig. 15, p. 53).

The second phase (dated about 1700-1500 B.C.) involved the great feat of bringing the "foreign" stones from Pembrokeshire. People making beaker pots of superior quality spread from Central Europe via Holland to Britain about 1750 B.C. They were traders and had a tradition of ritual circles of timber posts; exchanges with Ireland via Pembrokeshire gave them contacts with the builders of megaliths. This and their obvious superior skill probably account for the transfer of 82 large stones to be placed in a double circle around the centre of the enclosure. The Avenue was probably laid out for dragging the stones up from the Wiltshire Avon by easy gradients and gradual curves. In this phase, also, a ditch was dug around the Heel Stone. The fashions of the beaker-makers seem to have declined within a couple of centuries of their arrival, and it is conjectured that they were mobile herder-traders with few women, and that they therefore often tended to marry indigenous girls unable to keep up the superiority of the pottery, which was a woman's craft until the potter's wheel was devised.

The important connection with Western France indicated by the megaliths was strengthened about 1500 B.C. as many Wiltshire finds testify. This is probably linked with the spectacular Third Phase of Stonehenge construction (1500-1400 B.C.). In phase IIIa the foreign stones were removed and the holes tightly refilled to give a clear level surface for the grand construction of Sarsen stones. The horseshoe was set up, with 10 uprights and five lintels, then the circle of 30 uprights and their 30 lintels was built around the horseshoe. The sandstone slab from Cosheston, Milford Haven, Pembrokeshire, was given a place of honour in the horseshoe and the other foreign stones were reset. Two stones were erected one on each side of the north-eastern entrance. One of the two has disappeared; the other, now prostrate, has been quite fancifully named the Slaughter Stone. Four, or, probably 5 station stones, as they are called, were placed just inside the bank; two survive in N.E. and S.W. positions respectively. It is interesting that the total number of these Sarsens of Phase IIIa is 82 (5+10+30+30+2+5), the number inferred for the original foreign stones.

In Phase IIIb a process of dressing the foreign stones was begun and a few were provided with tenons or mortices for setting up as

PLATE 7

STONEHENGE, Wiltshire. Note the tenon on the vertical stone in the foreground

PLATE 8

Arbor Low, Derbyshire. A prehistoric stone circle with stones thrown down. September

Cyril Newberry

trilithons. Two circles of holes (Y and Z) were dug around the great Sarsen circle, apparently to hold the remaining foreign stones, but a change of plans occurred. The Y and Z holes were not used, the foreign stones were arranged just within the Sarsen horseshoe and the Sarsen circle in Phase IIIc and some of the dressings which some of them had undergone were scrupulously chipped away. Were the constructors of Phase IIIb deemed impious?

Stonehenge was later on damaged perhaps deliberately, some think by the Roman Imperial power. If the Roman Empire damaged Stonehenge, it was probably still of ritual importance at least until the first century A.D. Geoffrey of Monmouth gives us the story, including the Irish-trade link, of the foreign stones as it had shaped itself by his time in folk-memory. It should be added that Cunnington (in 1801) found a boulder of Pembrokeshire spotted dolerite in Boles Barrow about three miles north of the Wylye stream and some 14 miles from Stonehenge. Probably it had been broken in dragging.

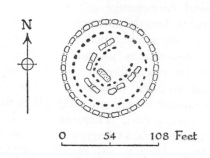

N

0   54   108 Feet

◼ Syenite and other foreign stone
   (from Pembrokeshire)
☐ Sarsen – local Wiltshire stone
▦ Fine grained micaceous sandstone
   (from Haverfordwest, Pembrokeshire)

FIG. 17

Imaginary reconstruction of Stonehenge,
central portion only

Since 1953 numbers of incised outlines and carvings have been discovered on the great Sarsens. It seems that all occur at a height above the ground suitable for handwork, so the carvings are likely to have been made after the stones were set in place. Among the carvings are numerous axeheads, also a hilted dagger said to be like one carved on a monument at Mycenae in Greece. This style of dagger in Mycenae is dated 1500 B.C. about, so the dagger carving at Stonehenge may well have been made some time during the third phase, and may indicate connections with or influences from Ægean culture. This idea is in harmony with general views of the Mediterranean influence on western megaliths, and is supported by many finds of E. Mediterranean beads in Wiltshire barrows. Other carvings at Stonehenge are being studied and one, sadly weathered, may be a representation of what has been called the Mother Goddess, or, in Dr. Crawford's book, the *Eye Goddess* (1957), whose cult he traces from Syria via the Mediterranean and the Atlantic coasts to Brittany and Britain. This reinforces the opinion that, at any rate, our megalith tombs of Brittany and Atlantic Britain have relations with a fertility ritual.

Around Stonehenge are numerous " long barrows," mounds of considerable length and moderate breadth, several of which have megalithic stone chambers. They have some relationship with the western monuments already mentioned but show other heritages instanced by resemblances to some long mounds which may possibly have had wooden chambers, unless these barrows with presumed wooden chambers are an adaptation from stone ones in cases when stone was not found. There are also, in the Stonehenge and Avebury districts, many round barrows or mounds such as are known in East Britain in association with burials in which beaker pots occur and other types of barrow are also found. All shows that Salisbury Plain was a centre of attraction and probably of mingling of diverse peoples during this period of development of what must have been a considerable civilization. Breton stone axes, and even Egyptian faience beads have been found in Wiltshire barrows, the latter dated not earlier than about the fifteenth century B.C., but no Irish gold has been collected on the plain, a remarkable fact when one realises the then metropolitan character of the region and the obvious organizing power of the builders of Stonehenge.

Another interesting mystery concerns beads and related objects in the graves of the period. The Portuguese graves have yielded about 1,100 beads of a pale greenish stone called callais, and the group of graves in the sacred enclosed territory in the south of the Morbihan, Brittany (see p. 55) has given about 800. Over 100 have been collected from Mediterranean France and a number are known from South Spain, also twenty-seven are known from Kadi Keui, near Constantinople. A few have been found in tombs near the Marne. This distribution is peculiar enough, but it is still more striking that not one has been found in the department of Finistère, which is just west of the Morbihan with its 800. Also none are known from the Channel Islands, the British Isles or the Baltic group of megaliths. In all these, including Finistère, one finds beads of amber or jet or both,

but no amber of this period has been found in Morbihan. Yet both
Finistère and Morbihan have megalithic monuments in abundance,
though the greater ones are in the latter. Was the British commerce
of the time connected more with Finistère ?

Related to, and yet distinct from, the Salisbury Plain monuments
is another group of long barrows in the Cotswolds; some of these are
much like monuments in north-west Wales. In the latter region Craig
Lwyd, Penmaenmawr, yielded stone valuable for implements. Implements of this stone spread, probably mainly by sea, to South Wales
and along the South Welsh coast to the Cotswolds. The megaliths and
general archæological interest of the South Welsh coastal region give
evidence of more activity than seems to have occurred along the
opposite, i.e., the southern, shore of the Bristol Channel, apart from
west Cornwall. The evidence points to the eastern part of the South
Welsh coast as marking a branch route leading to Salisbury Plain and
the Cotswolds while what we may venture to call the main route
crossed the Bristol Channel from the north of Cornwall to points on
the Welsh coast.

A great Breton feature is the numerous series of long lines of free
standing stones which seem to mark the boundary of the sacred region
of megalithic tombs west of the gulf of Morbihan. Stone alignments
were also made in Britain. There are several on Dartmoor ; one in
Cornwall, a few small ones in Wales, one at Shap in Westmorland and
one in Northumberland (both these are approaches to monuments),
as also a few standing stones that may once have been parts of alignments. We may provisionally suggest that alignments in Britain have
a relationship with those in Brittany, but should not make too much of
this, as men accustomed to megaliths might easily develop the idea of
series in straight lines. A tendency to E.-W. orientation is noticeable and
it is in relation with sunrise and sunset. Aristotle said that the aligned
stones of an Iberian warrior's tomb gave the number of enemies he
had slain, and the same idea has been found in modern Ethiopia.
Solitary standing stones, sometimes of great size and height, occur in a
good many places in west and north England and Wales, as well as in
Brittany. They may belong to the series of cultures that gave the megalithic constructions and are certainly prehistoric, some having Bronze
Age burials at their bases. Their sanctity is shown by the fact that early
Christianity, especially in Brittany and Spain, adopted several with
appropriate additions such as a crucifix or a niche for Virgin and

Child. An association with fertility ritual is indicated by the shaping of the top of some as a rough representation of the male organ of generation, a representation that is remarkably careful in one Breton case. Possible symbolism of the female may also be inferred in some cases (p. 54).

Reference should be made to archæological works for detail, but even the short outline here given will suffice to show that people came by sea from the south to our western peninsulas, and that others crossed the narrow seas from the Low Countries and perhaps northern France. Seamen and landsmen met in Britain, several different groups being concerned on either side with differences of route and of culture and of date of arrival. Salisbury Plain gives us a remarkable complex of achievement of the groups of that time ; and, especially towards the west coasts of Britain, we have many indications of the contacts between easterners and westerners, the former probably valuing the hard stone and the metals the latter were exploiting. Incoming groups, often men in large majority, found and took to themselves women belonging either to previous incomers or to the older native population. As a result of this, crafts of women brought in by invaders tended to degenerate, and ideas of construction went the same way as execution came to depend on the sons and grandsons of these women. It is often a useful hypothesis that the older features of the cultures of this phase are the more elaborate ones, and that there is a cumulative loss of immigrant skill and schemes. It would be a mistake, however, to look upon this type of change as merely degeneration ; there is also the fact of the turning of attention to new interests and the development of new skills. In the days of radar, flare-signalling may get less attention, and in the days of the auto-mobile the old carpenter-wheelwright's craft and the village smithy may decline.

The development of interest in bronze, the increase of skill in gold work and other facts may account for reduced interest in some older features, and it is even possible that the acquisition of increased prestige through the transfer of Pembrokeshire stones to Stonehenge, together with the elaborate orientation of stones for astronomical observation at the latter, may have made Stonehenge loom larger in people's minds than the older Avebury. Readers of the Old Testament will recall the prestige of Shiloh when it acquired the sacred stones called the Tables of the Law.

PLATE 9

John Markham

TRE'R CEIRI. Iron Age B fortress, probably of Roman times, on the lesser of the two summits of Yr Eifl, West Caernarvonshire. A rough stone rampart skirts the hill brow, steep steps lead up to the entry

PLATE 10

John Markham

HIGHLANDER teaching boy to play the pipes; Aviemore

An interesting case of relations of incomers and older established population of the phase with which this chapter deals was investigated by S. J. Jones, then of the Bristol University Speleological Society, at Gorsey Bigbury, near Charterhouse-on-Mendip. It consisted of a circular rampart or ring enclosing an almost flat area separated from the rampart by a ditch. Both ditch and rampart were interrupted by a causeway. Quantities of flints show pygmy types as well as others, there are many fragments of beaker pots, and animal bones include those of ox, sheep, pig, dog, red deer and roe deer. The site seems to have been a settlement of Beaker people, probably with women of older elements of the population, a rustic outlier perhaps of the new cultures with immigrant elements weakening in the course of time. The site is of special interest because evidences of settlements of Beaker people are not abundant. But the further discussion of early habitations can be postponed to a later chapter (ch. 11, pp. 215 ff.).

The people of the new cultures, both easterners and westerners, must have fed themselves locally, but we have relatively little evidence on this matter. The easterners certainly had farm animals, and may have been responsible for some small-scale cultivation of little patches that can still be identified. Cultivation was probably done with hoe and spade; at any rate we have no evidence of ploughs, though it is difficult to imagine that farmers with cattle did not use animal power in their great megalith-building schemes; and, if they used animal power at all, they may have used it in their farming. The verdict then, is rather " not proven " than an absolute negative. The little plough (*aratrum*) was in use in East Mediterranean lands at the time and may have been spreading on the loess lands of Central Europe. Saddle-querns tell us that some cereal was grown even at this early stage. It may have been spelt or barley or emmer wheat.

The evidence concerning dwellings of this early time is very poor. Some " pits " hollowed out especially in the chalk of S. and E. Eng and have been called pit-dwellings. There have been suggestions that the " ditches " between the concentric banks of early camps, such as that on Windmill Hill, near Avebury, were places of habitation. The Dartmoor area and the Haldon Hill site, near Exeter, have given evidence of what are very ancient dwellings, though dating is hazardous because finds are so few. The hut-builders at Haldon must have had series of wooden posts regularly spaced to outline a rough rectangle,

F

suggesting that possibly there was a timber frame. The walls had stone bases but were no doubt wattle-and-daub above. On Dartmoor unmortared stone walls played a larger part in the structure of the huts, and they had low narrow doorways, so that anyone entering was forced to bend down.

The fact that animal rearing was a notable feature, at any rate among the beaker people, has interesting bearings. In the first place herders, accustomed to management of beasts, are often ready for war

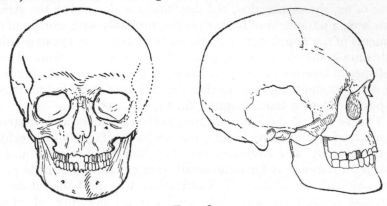

FIG. 18

Broad skull of a type found in graves with early beakers; front and side views

and have a certain discipline and strategy. The beaker people seem to have been dominant groups fading into the general population in the course of time largely through intermarriage.

In the second place, as Peake has pointed out, it is a widespread habit of herdsmen to have seasonal round-ups for counting, branding and slaughtering, and these are great social and ceremonial occasions. Seasonal round-ups are to be linked with observation of the seasons and this with study of the varying position of sunrise and sunset, so we have a hint concerning astronomical observations, which the monuments often themselves suggest, and also a hint as to the plan of Stonehenge and perhaps of its wood predecessors (e.g. Woodhenge and the Sanctuary in Wiltshire, and Arminghall near Norwich). The herders' round-up typically involved making a palisaded kraal or enclosure, sometimes subdivided in sectors or into inner and outer rings, and some of the uprights of the palisade would be provided with lintels for hauling up the carcases of slaughtered beasts for skinning and cutting up. The lintels of Stonehenge with their mortices, into which fit tenons of the uprights, may have some genetic relationship to this feature.

What of the people themselves? An old generalization still has considerable meaning : " Long barrow, long skull ; round barrow, round skull." In the round barrows of the beaker people one finds that the chief burial is often that of a strongly built male of average height or sometimes more. The face is strong, with a well-marked chin and prominent cheekbones, the nose is narrow and starts from a deep root under strong brow-ridges. The brain-case is in a finely arched curve, high and rather broad, and the length from front to back is relatively not great. Some burials of beaker people have also yielded long skulls analogous to those to be discussed next ; and this seems evidence of intermingling of the beaker people with either westeners or descendants of earlier inhabitants or both. The typical " beaker men " skull is not found in subsequent burials of prehistoric time but does occur now and then in historic burials ; and the general assemblage of characters mentioned in this paragraph occurs at the present day here and there in our population and is inherited down the generations in some families (plate X, p. 179).

Evidence about languages of those days is mainly negative. Some continental students have argued that a Neolithic group, perhaps the men of the corded ware and the battle-axe of stone, brought in an early form of Aryan speech, and that, if so, it would be probable that the beaker people had an Aryan language. As it is doubtful whether Aryan speech reached India or Persia before about 1500 B.C., and the languages of the Mediterranean people in the early Bronze Age were apparently non-Aryan, this idea had better not be emphasized. It is more probable on the whole, that Aryan speech spread later in the Bronze Age.

The western maritime people's graves were collective burials, and, it has been suggested, stores of vital essence or fertility, probably for families and farms too. They have yielded, for the most part, long narrow skulls of people of medium or rather lower stature and not very strong build. This is a type found in megalithic tombs in France and the Iberian peninsula and is highly characteristic of the general population of Western Mediterranean lands at the present time. It has therefore often been called the Mediterranean, and sometimes the Iberian type. A group of " Mediterranean " men usually includes a small percentage of the extreme longheads mentioned in Chapter 2, but the greater number are somewhat different as regards the skulls. These are not quite so narrow or high, have moderate cheek-bones, less strong temporal hollows and brow ridges, and a less gabled skull. The mouth, jaws and teeth are usually less powerful, and one might suggest that with this reduction has come a lessening of lateral pressure from jaw muscles upon early skull-growth. Whereas the percentage of breadth to length of skull in the extreme longheads of the later part of the Old Stone Age was often 68-73 per cent, this ratio in the skulls from megalithic tombs is mainly 73-77.5 per cent though no absolute distinction can be made. In the beaker people the corresponding relation is often 82 per cent or more.

In the present-day population of Britain a group of characters much like that mentioned for the majority of long-barrow and megalithic burials, i.e. a breadth-length relationship of 73-77.5 per cent on the skull (cranial index) or 74.5 to 78 or 78.5 per cent on the living head (cephalic index), is found commonly in Ireland, in the south and east of the Isle of Man, in Cornwall and South Wales, and generally scattered through Wales in the valleys around the moorlands, on the flanks of the Pennines, in parts of West Scotland and in some areas of south-east England, among which one may mention the Chilterns (see p. 17). The type is typically dark-haired and fresh-complexioned and the eyes may be brown or dark grey, while the smoothness of feature gives considerable beauty, especially of course to women and a few of the youths ; boniness develops as the men grow beyond adolescence. It is noticeable that present-day people who carry the characters, such as strong brows, deep-set nose-root, prominent cheek-bones and mouths, associated with a good number of the earlier skulls, are usually dark-eyed as well as dark-haired and tend to have a little pigment visible in the skin. Perhaps the very in-bred earlier peoples were more pigmented than the later immigrants. Perhaps the later immigrants moving along the coasts of Atlantic Europe mingled with fairer folk, and lost more pigment in our region, which does not favour pigmentation greatly. We tend to have too little ultra-violet radiation rather than too much, and pigment stops ultra-violet light from penetrating into the skin so it is actually a disadvantage amongst us.

Some minor groups of characters should be mentioned here. One group occurs on the Denbighshire moorland, in North Devon, in West Scotland and to some extent in Ireland. Its characters include tallness, a very long narrow head (index often about 70-73) and a long narrow face without prominence of brow-ridges, cheek bones or mouth. It has resemblances to a group of characters common in Castilian Spain and represented remarkably in the paintings of El Greco. It has at least analogies with a group of characters found among Sikhs, Rajputs and some others in north-west India. In India this group of characters contrasts with the features common especially in the Indian peninsula. There one finds the slightly built, smooth-featured person with cephalic index often 73-77 or so, thus showing analogies with what is commonly called the Mediterranean type, but having more pigment in the skin.

The Old Stone Age had some very tall men in its later stages. The remains of these have been found in caves on the Riviera, but the tendency among them was to have brow-ridges and cheek-bones still rather prominent. The stature in some cases seems to have been over six feet.

Another minor group of characters is worth mentioning. There are little nests of people with broad heads and faces and moderate to dark colouring, who are often strongly built though not necessarily having tall frames. They occur here and there on the coasts of Cornwall and in north-west Wales, and are a notable element in Brittany among the "Islandais," the people of Binic and Paimpol who for so long have fished cod off Iceland and the Grand Banks of Newfoundland. They are found in an area of ocean fishers near Luarca in North Spain and around Salerno in Italy, and a grave of the late Neolithic or early metal phase of culture at Anghelu Ruju in Sardinia has yielded skulls that seem to belong to this group. A few skulls of the kind have been found in French megalithic graves. We seem here to be dealing with a physical heritage from some early maritime migrants concerning whom we had better not speculate further here. It is of special interest in this connection that the famous pioneer of physical anthropology, Dr. John Beddoe, noted a type of this kind in the Long Island (Lewis) in the Hebrides, and in Orkney. Something akin to it is characteristic of the south-west coast of Norway and of parts of Holland included in the Rhine delta. A somewhat similar group of characters has been found in the Hadhramaut in South Arabia and in parts of Greece and of the Ægean Isles, in the latter of which, however, the slightly built longheaded type is more general.

Of the density of population in the phase this chapter has discussed we can as yet say but little. It looks as though considerable man-power was required to make Avebury and Stonehenge ; and the general

distribution of remains of the centuries round about the time of construction of these monuments suggests that population had increased considerably beyond the few thousands who are supposed to have inhabited
Britain in the earlier (Mesolithic) phase. The area of Britain is nearly
89,000 square miles, and a large part of its lowland was in early days
almost uninhabited because of oak woods or marshes. Much of the
highest land was too bleak and rocky to be of use to early folk. If
one dare make a guess of some 15,000 to 20,000 square miles of more
habitable land with a density of 5 to 6 per square mile in south Britain,
that gives a population of almost one hundred thousand. It will be
understood that all such estimates are very rough indeed.

The apparently habitable areas included a good many stretches of
coast, the greater chalk surfaces, the Cotswolds and some other Jurassic
limestone areas, and some moorlands if not too high. The estimate of
four or five persons per square mile is based upon the idea that all
were dependent on local production of food, with hoe and spade.
If a plough was in use the figure would be higher. Whether enough has
been allowed for flesh food and milk is quite uncertain. If all the
megalithic work was done without use of animal power it is probable
that there were more men involved than have been allowed for.
Fishing in rivers, meres, lakes and coastal waters may well have made
possible a little more population than that estimated, and maritime
trade may also have helped numbers up.

This chapter has attempted to sketch a very important phase of
British development, the effective beginning of food-production and,
with this, of civilised organization in the sense of communities with
institutions and elaborate techniques. It was long ago a common
error to suppose that all that has here been mentioned was the work of
vanished peoples, presumably exterminated by later comers. We have
on the contrary a large physical and mental heritage from those days.
Physically, the small dark people are a large element of the population
of Britain and have probably increased greatly in proportionate
numbers recently because of their relative tolerance of urban, even
crowded conditions. Psychically, one can trace the continuity from
megalithic cults to Christian practices in several details in Brittany.
In Britain the religious revolution after the Middle Ages has reduced
survivals of custom from the days of the megaliths. At Ysbyty Cynfyn
in West Wales a church connected with the mediæval order of St. John
stands in a churchyard which many think has been the site of a

pre-historic monument. Standing stones are now incorporated in the churchyard wall, and one very large one (11 feet high) may well have marked an entry into a circle, or a part of some type of prehistoric monument. Brittany has an example of a round churchyard, probably based on a stone circle, at S. Germain. It may be added that there are many churchyards in Wales that are, or have been circular, but whether this has anything to do with stone circles we cannot say.

The early Celtic Christian Church, largely isolated from the Mediterranean by Franks and Saxons, developed along its own lines, and utilised prehistoric sanctities, as did early Christianity in the north-west of the Iberian peninsula. There, it is thought, the fame of Santiago da Compostella owes something to a megalithic cult, as is explained by Messrs. Peake, Howes and E. O. James in articles in *Folklore* after 1920.

The Roman Church condemned the worship of great stones, but sometimes, notably in Brittany, compromised by setting a cross on a sacred standing stone, or placing a representation of the Virgin and Child in a niche on a great stone monument. Dedications and place-names also sometimes give traces of prehistoric cults. Beleme is a name for promontories and is supposed to refer to a prehistoric deity. St. Michael is often the dedication of a hill-top or hill-brow church or a church at a seaward view-point, St. Catherine is especially linked with headlands, and both are probably the successors of pre-Christian dedications, but of what age we cannot tell.

Appendix, concerning Domestic Animals

The dog is man's first animal friend, and is related to the wolf of northern latitudes ; and it became more or less domesticated in Mesolithic times, i.e., before cultivation became important. It is usually supposed that domestication of the dog occurred first in Northern Asia and that the domesticated animal spread thence to Europe, to Southern Asia and to North America. If the Australian dingo really is, as seems certain, a form which has run wild, domestication of the dog may have occurred even earlier than is suggested above.

The pig is not an animal suited to long migrations. Like the dog it probably became attracted to the refuse-heaps of human settlements. For Sweden and the Sudetenland it has been argued that local races of pig have arisen from local wild forms, though to what extent the idea of domestication was brought into these areas or to what extent the domestication was almost accidental it is difficult to say. The very great importance of pigs in parts of the Far East has led some scholars to think of their domestication in China or Turkestan.

In connection with cattle, we have to think of the powerful *Bos primigenius*, or aurochs, wild in the post-glacial forest glades of Europe and the wetter borders of the steppes, and of the smaller shorter-horned *Bos brachyceros*, said to belong to South Europe and South-west Asia. Both seem to be varieties of one and the same wild species, and perhaps *brachyceros* is largely a product of domestication ; it occurs in the first series (late Neolithic) of Swiss lake-dwellings. It is probable that *primigenius* was domesticated on the borders of the great Eurasiatic steppe and that it contributed greatly to the races of cattle in Europe. Crossing between more or less domesticated females and wild bulls must be considered probable. It seems likely that domestication of cattle in such places as Northern Mesopotamia was achieved to some extent by corraling calves and thus attracting their mothers, whereas, on the mountain borders of the great Eurasiatic steppe, herds migrating seasonally up and down hill were followed and, in due course, to some extent controlled by man. Probably this control became more effective as men learned to ride the horse.

The sheep is sparingly represented in Europe until the Bronze Age. It seems probable that the earliest form, *Ovis aries palustris*, first identified in the earlier Swiss lake-dwellings and later found in southern and western Europe, spread in Europe from North Africa. It may have attained to North Africa from S.W. Asia as it is found in the early phases of the Anau settlement in W. Turkestan, north of the Persian border. It is further probable that the mouflon (*Ovis musimon*) may be the wild ancestor, and it occurs in N. Africa and was once found in Mediterranean lands but has survived there only in Sardinia and Corsica. It has been thought that the Soay sheep of the Hebrides is of North African descent. *Ovis aries studeri*, thought by many to be descended from the mouflon of S.W. Asia, became more numerous and more widely distributed in Europe in the Bronze Age, probably spreading from the borders of the great steppe.

The goat is primarily a mountain animal. *Capra prisca*, wild in S.E. and E. Central European highlands, appeared early in the Swiss lake dwellings and was, for some time, more abundant there than the sheep. *Capra hircus aegagrus* of the Caucasus was also domesticated and spread to the Eurasiatic steppe but is probably less early there than is the more or less domesticated *C. prisca* in Switzerland, a mountain habitat.

The ass was used as a domestic animal in Egypt in pre-Dynastic times, and the larger Asiatic ass was used very early in S.W. Asia. It is thought that the European donkeys are derived from the former and that they spread relatively late, perhaps in several regions in historic, even recent historic, times. The donkey appears to have become common in Southern Ireland, for example, at some time near 1800 A.D.

The horse as a domestic animal is a subject of much doubt partly because it is difficult to decide whether particular specimens found in excavations were wild or tame. It has been suggested that the Tarpan variety of horse, with a short, broad skull, short snout and well rounded orbits, was tamed on the steppe-borders in S. Russia and used to pull slypes and sledges. The slype is, fundamentally, a box supported on two poles, the back ends of which trail along the ground. The sledge, on wooden runners, is a more skilled construction. The Przewalski type of horse, probably of Mongolian origin, seems to have been valued rather for riding than for pulling loads, also for the milk of the mares. The Przewalski type has contributed most to later European breeds. The horse was apparently unknown in Egypt until the time of the Hyksos (ca. 1700 B.C.), but was used in parts of South-west Asia some centuries earlier. The famous Arab horse is a much later and highly specialised breed.

A few horse-remains are known from megaliths in the west and Obermaier thought a Spanish rock drawing (probably Neolithic) indicated a domestic horse. Thence some authors have suggested a domestication of a horse in Spain.

The horses of early times seem to have been small. Breeding for size and strength is thought to have been a task undertaken within the last 3,000 years or less. The strong and heavy cart-horse associated very particularly with the Low Countries and France and Britain has been the subject of much speculation as to origins and history. The famous British breed known as the Shire horse owes something to the cart horse and something to the " Great Horse " bred in mediæval times to carry the heavily armoured knight. An element of Arab heritage is thought to have been a factor in the evolution of some of the lighter and faster breeds. Our moorland ponies were considered by Professor Cossar Ewart to have had an origin rather separate from that of our horse breeds. It should be realised that the use of the horse became far more general and attention to breeding increased when, in the late eighteenth century, roads began to be improved and horses began to supersede oxen for ploughing and other agricultural operations.

As one male animal can impregnate a number of females, and male animals are apt to fight one another for mates, the disposal of surplus males has long been a matter needing attention. Castration, that is the removal of the testes, or male reproductive glands, has been a widespread process and the result has been a heavy animal, patient and strong and inclined to put on fat. The ox and the castrated horse or gelding have been the farmers' main sources of animal power for work. The killing of young male cattle is a feature in French farming and a French menu often therefore includes veal. In Britain's " green and pleasant land " the amount of pasture has permitted farmers to keep castrated male cattle to the bullock-stage.

REFERENCES : see end of ch. 4, p. 99.

CHAPTER 4

CRAFTSMEN IN METAL

As the process of smelting became better understood, the practice of mixing ten per cent of black tin-sand with ninety per cent of copper became established and gave standard bronze as a result, harder than copper and so capable of being sharpened more usefully. Gold also came to be better worked, especially to make gold-leaf coverings for wood or other objects, gold-leaf on wood being illustrated by a fine bowl found at Caergwrle in Flintshire. Bronze became more abundant and could be used for pins with decorated heads ; and interest in metal technique to some extent replaced the old craft of grinding and polishing stone. But, for a long time, arrowheads were still made of flint very finely chipped, and in many cases shaped with a pair of barbs. In the Iberian peninsula the majority of these fine flint arrowheads have no tang and this is the case with a minority of the arrowheads found in Ireland and a few from Britain. The great majority of those found in France, including Brittany, are barbed and tanged and the same is true for Britain and for Denmark. The difference implies some diversity of method of hafting on to the shaft and so perhaps some contrast in the wood available for the shaft.

Again, some very finely chipped flint daggers from Denmark give a strong impression that they are stone copies of metal weapons. As they are found in graves, this may mean that ritual conservatism accounts for the continued use of stone for this purpose, or it may be that copper or bronze would be kept for remelting. One recalls that circumcision among the Jews was long done with a flint knife, primarily for traditional reasons no doubt, though hygiene entered into the matter ; a copper or iron surface might have compounds dangerous if introduced into the subject's blood. What is important is that we

73

should not too hastily assign a grave containing only stone weapons to the days before metal. More and more is it being recognised that the " Neolithic " period is really the dawn of the early age of metal, when copper and gold were attracting attention. In most regions it was a passing phase or prelude, perhaps two or three centuries, not the period of thousands of years that it was once assumed to be.

Another change of interest is concerned with the modes of burial. Perhaps the skill for making the great megaliths died out, but more probably a different idea about the soul or spirit spread, and made it no longer seem necessary to preserve a part of the body (the head for example) in the tomb for re-birth. In place of this the dead were increasingly cremated and in a number of cases dealt with singly rather than collectively.

Bohemia had the good fortune to have tin and copper near together, and Cornwall had tin and some copper, which latter could be supplemented from Ireland. North-west Spain and the banks of the Vilaine river in south Brittany had some tin-sand but not a great quantity ; and they do not seem to have altogether maintained their old importance, perhaps because the tin-sand was exhausted. But Irish and Cornish products—tin, copper and gold—gave our islands considerable resources in this phase of evolution.

Later on a further great change followed, a revolution almost as great as that from the old hunting and food-gathering to the organization of food-production. This change was the discovery of methods of casting metal in a mould in place of hammering it while still hot into the desired shape. The most important of these methods was that known as " *Cire perdue* " (wax lost). An object which it was desired to make in bronze would be modelled in wax and then placed in clay moulded around it. The clay was then hardened by heat ; and the wax would melt and drain off through an opening left for the purpose. A mould would be left, usually arranged in halves. Into the mould would be poured molten metal, which would take the form of the original wax model.

The increase of the amount of bronze in use not only led to elaboration of bronze axes, especially after casting had been developed, it also had further consequences. It became worth while to collect scrap bronze for remelting and remoulding, apparently by itinerant smiths. The smith moving from place to place was to continue for long ages as a feature of our European life. Some of us now living still remember the " tin-smiths " who wandered about with a small equipage for soldering and the like, and the phrase " a tinker's curse " has had a wide currency, while Tinker's Piece is known as a place-name, some-times near a church dedicated to St. Giles, the patron of itinerant vendors and craftsmen.

One of the technical possibilities opened up by casting was that of making sockets into which a wooden shaft could be thrust, a device which was stronger than the older ones of tangs and flanges. Use of the

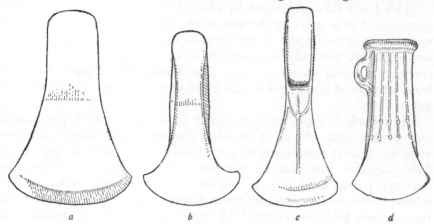

FIG. 19

Four successive stages of evolution of British Bronze Age axes: *a*. Flat axe. *b*. Flanged axe. *c*. Palstave—with stop-ridges on each face, to prevent splitting of wooden handle. *d*. Socketed axe. (*a* and *b* could be shaped by hammering; *c* and *d* were shaped by casting). (1/3 natural size)

tang involved making a hollow in the shaft and this might expand and split the shaft. A flange was not very secure without much cording or other accessory help. The socketed spearhead and socketed axe became dominant in due course, and are the mark of the late Bronze Age in Britain (after 1000 B.C.).

Another of these technical possibilities was the making of a long thin sharp edged blade, soon to be a sword for slashing. The sword, as contrasted with the dagger, is the cavalryman's weapon ; he can slash with it from his seat on horseback. The occurrence of swords in the latter part of the Bronze Age thus may imply the use of the horse for riding. The horse had been used, apparently for pulling, for some time in Eastern Europe before it was ridden by Europeans ; but the same may not hold for the people of Central and Western Asia, who may have ridden their horses earlier. The horseman's power over the man on foot suggests conquests and gives us the basis of the idea of the superior military officer mounted on horseback, which has been a feature of military life until recently. It is quite probable that the sword and the cavalryman spread westwards into Europe from the borders of the Ukraine in the Bronze Age, in 1400 B.C. or thereabouts.

This has a further interest in view of its possible connection with language. Let us note, by the way, that, whatever may be the date of appearance of the Dardic Aryan[1] languages in India, the Vedic Aryan[1] languages are generally supposed to have been taken into India by conquerors about 1500-1200 B.C. Also Iranic Aryan[1] seems to have been introduced into Persia in the latter part of the second millennium B.C.

As regards Europe, one can argue that Aryan speech penetrated into Greece with groups of invaders (Achæans and others) of 1400-1000 B.C. ; that some form of Latin had reached Italy before *Annus Urbis Conditum* (the year of the foundation of Rome, traditionally B.C. 753) ; that Celtic was in use in S. Germany long before people moved thence to Catalonia in Spain about or after 600 B.C. (it has left place-names in S. Germany). In other words, there is evidence of Aryan speech, and of some of its differentiated descendants, in various parts of Europe not long after 1000 B.C., and earlier no doubt in Greece. An old idea, to be discarded, is that successive waves of peoples spread from the grasslands of Asia carrying the various families or varieties of Aryan speech, so that the oldest would be farthest west and so on. It seems quite possible that Aryan speech spread with conquering horsemen and travelling smiths and the general economic and political revolution of the period this chapter is discussing. New processes, new objects and new methods and rituals were being developed and a new vocabulary was necessary.

[1] Sir George Grierson and other scholars think that a very old form of Aryan speech was spread by conquerors of the second millennium B.C., erupting from Turkestan. Into India, they think, came two waves of invaders using languages of this class. The earlier wave has given a good deal of their character to the languages mainly used by Hindus of Bengal, Bihar, Orissa, Central India and a part of the west coast ; it is said to have influenced Gujarat as well. Its speech is retained among the peoples of the north-west frontier of India and of parts of Kashmir and the Pamirs. This group of Aryan languages is called the Dardic group. The Vedic Aryan languages of most of north-west India are thought to have come in as a later wave ; they are called Vedic because of the language of the Hindu sacred books called Vedas. Other Aryan-speakers penetrated Iran or Persia.

That the new words would be diversely pronounced by people according to the shapes of their mouths, the lengths of their lips, the size of the tongue and so on is self-evident. One may instance in passing that a long-lipped person finds it easier to say p and b clearly whereas a short-lipped person is inclined to make them f and v or even q(k) ; quattuor, vier, four ; pater, vater, father ; quinque, pimp, five, are a few examples here. Dr. Darlington has recently drawn attention to the importance of the th sound in Britain, especially around the Irish Sea and St. George's Channel. It fades into v in Cockney and into a dental d in West Ireland. It is a feature of the dialect of W. Jersey and is notable in the Iberian peninsula. One cannot but draw attention to the relation of this distribution to that of the passage-grave megaliths. The same sound seems to have been important in ancient Greek, and it is notable in modern Danish though difficult for Germans. Greece and Denmark may be described as the two ends of the coastwise trade route of prehistoric times. The relations of s, sh, and sch, not only in standard spelling in different languages but also in actual pronunciation, are another notable feature, the sch sound being far more abundantly used in German, for example, where in French or English, we should use s. Adaptability to fashion set by leaders must, of course, be considered as a potent factor of standardization in language. Not only pronunciation but syntax, i.e., the construction of sentences, would be affected diversely in different regions, in this case according to previous custom. Syntax often retains older features in spite of large new introductions in vocabulary. One can find Welsh people who have learned English using a Welsh structure for a sentence with English words. Sir John Morris Jones thought that the syntax of the Celtic languages owed a good deal to pre-Aryan speech, and he was disposed to look for links with Basque and with Berber in so far as the Celtic languages of Atlantic Europe were concerned.

The revolution hinted at above was accompanied by another, of even greater import to European and British life. When men had settled to the life of cultivation beside the Nile, Euphrates, Tigris and a few other rivers of south-western Asia, one of their problems was that of keeping the silt of the cultivable flood-plain from caking as it dried after the floods subsided. Repeated hoeing would do this ; and, in places where a further elaboration was feasible, they learned to fix the hoe to a frame to be pulled by one or two animals. This is the ancestral plough (Latin *aratrum*, French *araire*). In those climates strong evaporation brings salts in solution up to the surface of exposed soil, so there was no need to plough deep, but, if the salts include carbonate of lime, the danger of formation of a hard cake of lime and iron is very great ; and oft-repeated ploughing along and across is the best treatment for the land. Away from the flood-plains with their annual deposit of silt, the soil in those climates is often yellowish to reddish, because iron salts have been drawn up and the surface becomes stained with iron hydroxide. In Mediterranean lands, also, these reddish, limy soils abound and are called in Italian *terra rossa*. The lime salts, however valuable as plant food, are often a menace, as they so easily form a hard crust.

The character of the soil makes the plough already mentioned for S.W. Asia useful in Mediterranean lands as well ; and it may be taken that this little plough spread to the Eastern Mediterranean, at least, fairly early in the third millennium B.C. It is doubtful whether any cities of non-food-producing population could have been fed by the produce of hoe agriculture, though fishing, tree cultivation and the use of the spade would help.

The little plough spread in the course of time to other parts of Europe where, in some cases, it needed adaptation to the different circumstances. On the porous loess, in regions with a warm summer, the little plough could be useful ; the soil is light and friable and the little vertical canals in loess help, with evaporation, to bring nutritive salts up. Before men could attack the lowland oakwoods they had little deep loam in use, and were often restricted to relatively thin soils in patches from which they had cleared the stones. In such places the little plough might be most suitable. In deep marls and clays the nutritive salts are apt, north of the Mediterranean sunshine, to remain distributed through the whole depth, while further north the long duration of low temperatures lessens evaporation still more ; and there, especially in rainy or snowy areas, the nutritive salts tend to accumulate in the lowest layer of soil. This type of soil is called podsol, while that with nutritive salts distributed at all levels is called brown earth. If podsol is to be cultivated, it is obvious that the lower soil must be brought up to the surface. This is true also of brown earth, especially because promiscuous weeds or grass will usually have taken some of the food that was near the surface. The adaptation of the plough to this new task of turning up the soil seems to have been a long process, including attempts to make bigger ploughs pulled by more animals.

PLATE II

John Markham

WELSH WOMEN in national costume; Bettws-y-coed

PLATE 12

A heavy deep-furrowing plough was difficult until the ploughshare could be iron-shod. For the moment we are concerned with the little plough and perhaps with early experiments on larger ones, if the relevant Ligurian rock-drawings are really dateable to the Bronze Age.

In the later part of the Bronze Age a considerable increase of population occurred, especially on several loess lands in Central Europe. There were fairly large settlements of cultivators who had cemeteries, called urnfields from the deposition of the ashes in urns after cremation, and the burial of the urns in a special area set apart for the purpose. There was also considerable settlement on the alluvium of Swiss lake-shores, the lakes being apparently rather low at this period, perhaps because of a phase of rather dry warmth. These are the second series of Swiss lake-dwellings. On the hills, people who apparently relied more on flocks and herds, buried their dead in tumuli, i.e., mounds derived from the round barrows of the Early Bronze Age. They are often assigned to the Middle Bronze Age, but probably persisted into the Later Bronze Age among rather backward and old-fashioned folk perhaps more apt for war than were the urnfield cultivators.

Whether or no the plough in Central Europe came into really widespread use before the urnfields idea spread, it is difficult to interpret the larger populations of the Later Bronze Age without thinking that the plough had then become commoner on the loess lands and perhaps larger, too. There is, however, another probability to be taken into account. Early wheat in S.W. Asia was of the type known as *emmer* ;[1] the variety known as engrain (French), little spelt (English) or einkorn (German)[1] was an early introduction into Europe, but the common bread-wheat[1] of Europe north of the Mediterranean is a hybrid that

---

[1] The late Professor Vavilov had a famous collection said to include some 26,000 varieties of wheat. Many of these varieties fall into one or other of 3 groups : (*a*) Little spelt (*engrain* in French, *einkorn* in German) with bearded flat ears, one grain in each spikelet, seven chromosomes in each haploid nucleus ; (*b*) Emmer, also with bearded flat ears, but with two grains in each spikelet and fourteen chromosomes in each haploid nucleus ; (*c*) Bread-wheat, some races bearded, some beardless, often more than two grains in a spikelet, 21 chromosomes in each haploid nucleus. Little spelt is a very ancient food-plant now found only in backward localities in Europe and south-west Asia and Morocco. Emmer is a wheat of ancient Egypt and south-west Asia and is grown still in a few spots in Europe. Bread-wheat is thought to be a hybrid between emmer, or some other allied ancient type, and some grass related to little spelt. One theory suggests that the hybrid arose in the region between Northern Mesopotamia (early home of emmer) and the Caucasus. A great deal of information can be gained from *The Wheat Plant* by J. Percival (1921), and from contributions by H. J. E. Peake to the *Journal of the Royal Anthropological Institute* (especially 1927 and 1940). Students who wish to follow this matter further will find it useful to consult Dobzhansky, T., *Genetics and the origin of species*, New York, Columbia University Press, 1941.

G

seems to have taken some time to settle in as a standard crop. It is likely, though not yet clear, that it spread a good deal in the late Bronze Age, probably with better cultivation, and especially dung-manuring, for it is well known to be an exhausting crop. Barley and probably a little millet have been grown in parts of Europe as long as wheat. Rye and oats are thought to be of later date, as crops ; and there is a widespread surmise that they were at first weed-intruders in fields of the earlier cereals, becoming valuable, probably, in the pre-Roman Iron Age phase of cool wet summers (often dated 500 B.C. onwards for some time). Whether men learned to alternate wheat and barley, or wheat and fallow, barley and fallow, or wheat, barley and fallow at the time under discussion, we have no knowledge.

Still another aspect needs to be noticed. The early agriculturists of Europe, in addition to dogs, had semi-domesticated pigs, and also cows, which probably were impregnated by wild bulls, perhaps of the great wild cattle (*Bos primigenius*). The breeds of most of our domestic animals of later prehistoric and historic times are of Asiatic origin, though the pig may be an exception. It is likely that the horsemen who seem to have come from the steppe border in the latter half of the second millennium B.C. had Asiatic-Pontic steppe breeds of animals and that the period therefore witnessed an improvement of the flocks and herds, including especially a large increase in flocks of sheep, valuable for wool, flesh, and dung. An appendix to the previous chapter discusses domestic animals in more detail.

We thus have the probability of a combination of factors of change. Horsed swordsmen conquering and organising, ploughs or at any rate larger ploughs, either just introduced or becoming more general, travelling bronze-smiths and probably other specialized craftsmen, improvements of crops and of domestic animals. These were not accompaniments of the introduction of bronze ; that change was mixed up with changes due to the melting of the beaker people (p. 50) and the groups of megalith builders into the general population through marriage with women of the older populations. The advances in technique and organization discussed just above came later.

As regards Britain we have the clearest evidence of the introduction of bronze swords, probably via northern France and south-eastern England, but spreading far and wide. Some students think that the swordsmen were Celtic-speaking. Some go even further and suggest that the Celtic thus brought in was ancestral to the later Gaelic languages, thus returning in part to an old opinion of Sir John Rhys which had been rather neglected, but we shall revert to this later (p. 92).

Small mound graves (tumuli) of the Bronze Age are still numerous in Britain and no doubt many have been destroyed. A speculation concerning some may be permitted here, but should be lightly held, if held at all. In parts of Africa the claim of a group to its territory depends considerably upon whether the group has buried its dead on the land in question for some generations, i.e., whether the land and its people are under the influence of the ancestral spirits of the group. Sometimes tumuli in Britain are found in lines or groups near some ancient trackway, and trackways have long been used as boundaries, e.g., between manors in the Middle Ages. It is thus just possible that trackways and tumuli may be related to boundaries between groups of the Bronze Age people. The trackways of Megalithic, Beaker and Bronze Age peoples were not very closely defined zones ; they were green roads, along hill-crests or hillsides that were not too thickly wooded. The great Ridgeway along the crest of the Berkshire Downs (plate Vb, p. 82) and the Icknield Way along the N.W. flank of the Chilterns both are probably very old, may indeed be Neolithic in origin in parts here and there. Whether porterage or traction by animals had developed to any extent in the Bronze Age in Britain we are not sure. Some axle-ends and a few other items have been, not too certainly, ascribed to the late Bronze Age. If this is correct, the late Bronze Age in Britain knew the wheel.

Fox in his *Personality of Britain* and in his archaeological studies in Cambridgeshire has emphasised a very interesting and important point concerning our Bronze Age life. It is that, apart from graves, the finds of this period are chiefly near the line of springs at the base of the chalk or where the chalk downland meets the fens, i.e., where fresh water could be obtained. The same is true for Northamptonshire, while on the Lincoln Edge finds are almost confined to the neighbourhood of stream-gaps. In some other regions Bronze Age finds are characteristic of patches of river gravel, again suggesting the same inference. There is some indication, admittedly not very conclusive, that the later part of the second millennium B.C. was a period of rather dry climate, perhaps even with drought in some Mediterranean lands. It is fairly certain that the climate was warmer and drier than it became for a while in the Iron Age (see p. 85), but it would not be wise to insist too much on the warmth and drought of a phase of the Bronze Age.

Peake inaugurated a great catalogue of finds of the Bronze Age in Britain. It is greatly to be desired that they should be mapped on large-scale maps, whence the soils on which they occur could be determined, in order to test these hypotheses. There is no doubt that Bronze Age people buried their dead on the uplands in many cases, and they probably pastured flocks and herds on the opener parts of the downlands. The relative paucity of Bronze Age finds on the Cotswolds is a puzzle; it is just possible that the Megalithic culture with little metal long survived there in a somewhat isolated fashion, but this is not a full explanation. In the Late Bronze Age the importance of Salisbury Plain may have declined to some extent, as seems probable *a priori,* when we reflect on the new immigrations with new cults.

Simple direct substitution of one culture for another over any considerable area is rare. There are nearly always vital remains of the older one. When not destroyed, its sacred places become objects of awe, and, especially if there is intermarriage between intruding men and local women, the older rituals resurge, often in modified form. The fact that rites centring around the great stone monuments (pp. 174-75) seem to have persisted through millennia right into Christian times is important here. It would not be at all surprising if at any time evidence was found which dated one of these monuments to a late pre-christian date. There is also the important economic fact that the equipment of a new culture may penetrate only slowly and partially into remoter areas. It is thus likely that, at a time when bronze-casting and the various accompaniments noted had become important in South Britain and probably parts of Ireland, remote areas were still in a condition that could be described as " Stone Age."

Gordon Childe has made a notable study of such a remote and backward settlement, excavated at Skara Brae in Orkney. It had rectangular huts of stone slabs, but the corners were always rounded, though one cannot say that this was in the interests of cleanliness. There are inner and outer wall-facings, giving a total thickness of wall of 5-8 feet. There was a narrow entry, a central hearth, built-out beds apparently with posts supporting some kind of canopy and a storeplace above this. The frontal slab of the bed was apparently a seat. The dwellings were connected with one another by stone-roofed passages. The people ate limpets, but no seal-bones have been found ; they

PLATE V

Aerofilms, Ltd.

a. MAIDEN CASTLE, Dorset. The greatest earthwork fortress of the pre-Roman Iron Age in Britain

Aerofilms, Ltd.

b. WHITE HORSE, UFFINGTON, Berkshire Downs. Below an earthwork of the pre-Roman Iron Age the chalk has been laid bare by cutting away the turf, giving a representation of a horse

PLATE VI

Aerofilms, Ltd.

ANCIENT FIELDS AND FIELD PATTERNS revealed by aerial photography. The small field seems characteristic of the days before the coulter and iron-shod ploughshare came into use

appear to have used stone to pound fish-meal. There is some rough pottery apparently rather like that of the Scottish Bronze Age. The village was eventually overwhelmed by sand, but whether it had already been deserted is a question.

Curle investigated a settlement at Jarlshof in Shetland which showed evidence of cultivation of barley. Scattered bronze swords have been recovered, some from the Long Island (Lewis and Harris) of the Outer Hebrides. Buchan district has stone circles with a recumbent stone as a special feature, no doubt a local modification of older cults of the Beaker people who were an important element there.

Generally speaking it seems likely that the Bronze Age continued in Britain down to about 500 B.C. but no doubt persisted longer still in some remote regions. It is almost impossible to think that Celtic languages had not been introduced into Britain before that period came to an end.

Improvement of metallurgical furnaces made it possible to treat some iron compounds. With adequate draught a sufficiently hot flame could be achieved, and men appear soon to have learned to mix lime with iron ore and so to get a calcium silicate replacing iron silicate, and as a consequence, easier reduction of the iron to the metallic condition.

One of the earliest regions for working iron ores seems to have been the territory of the Chalybes on the south side of the Black Sea, and iron played a great part in the life of the Hittite Empire. Iron compounds are very widespread but of varying value to the smelter; some containing phosphorus remained useless until the Gilchrist-Thomas process was developed in 1879; sulphur in others has been another trouble. Nevertheless, once the draught of the furnace could be made strong enough, a good many iron compounds could come into use and the apparatus required was not unduly complex; also, there was no longer the need of an organization to bring together such items as copper and tin which, so often, were found in widely separate areas. In other words, iron-working of a simple type could spread more easily than bronze-working. It is one of the outstanding facts of human affairs that bronze-working remained almost unknown in Africa south of Abyssinia until much later, whereas iron-working spread almost all over that region probably one or two thousand years ago ; a few people even think it may have originated somewhere in Africa, but this is usually doubted. The iron-workers are sometimes itinerant groups, who may not be considered members of any of the communities they serve. They may be highly regarded in some cases, or treated as doubtful strangers in other areas, and there may be tabu ideas connected with them and their work. In intertropical Africa the iron-worker has lacked the background of bronze-work characteristic of most parts of Asia, the Mediterranean lands and Europe, where iron came in as a supplement to bronze. Cases in Europe are known even of a bronze sword with an iron pommel, though of course iron was eventually to be valued especially for the blade. The fact that wood was the fuel for smelting iron ores made easier the discovery of steel, which is primarily iron with a percentage of carbon. It is useful to remember that legendary history makes great play with magic swords, and, in this connection, to realise that a bronze sword with a blade thin enough to have a sharp edge would buckle and become useless very much more quickly than a steel one. And one can realise that steel would be likely to be an accidental (and therefore magical) result of smelting as well as a secret until the process was a little better understood. Robert Browning in *The Englishman in Italy* has a picturesque reference :

> " . . . . Look out, see the gipsy,
>   Our tinker and smith,
> Has arrived, set up bellows and forge,
>   And down-squatted forthwith
> To his hammering, under the wall there ; "

This reminds us of the wandering smith and the continuity from bronze to iron in Europe. The legends of Wayland the Smith as a mysterious being outside the community should also be recalled. The fact that " Wayland's Smithy " near Lambourn, is a megalith is interesting partly because it suggests the continuation of awe of ancient sacred places into the Iron Age.

One centre of iron-working in Europe in early times has yielded so much information that the first phase of the prehistoric Iron Age has been given its name—" Halstatt ", a site in Austria where, as the root " hal " implies, salt was mined. The association of salt-getting with the early phase of iron-working in Central Europe and France is an interesting fact. Herders living on flesh and milk got salt in these foods, but grain-eaters greatly value salt as a condiment. The preservation of meat for winter consumption is often done with the help of salt. Salt is also used as a flux and is important for glass-making. These considerations need to be borne in mind in thinking of the importance of salt to the peasants of early Europe. Imperfect salting of meat promoted the use of flavourings and condiments.

The idea of iron-working spread to Britain across the Channel ; it seems not to have affected Atlantic Britain for some centuries ; our West was of course a stronghold of the life of the Bronze Age, and its links with the continent were maritime rather than landward. Like those of earlier immigrants, the Iron Age ideas and objects probably came to our south-east coast from the Rhineland, and to the Christchurch entry (Hengistbury Camp) from northern France ; their arrival seems to be not far from 500 B.C. Whatever may have been the condition of life on Salisbury Plain in the Late Bronze Age (p. 82) it certainly was important in the Early Iron Age. Mr. and Mrs. Cunnington, of Devizes, investigated All Cannings Cross, in Wiltshire, a prehistoric settlement with an earthwork fortification near to it, as if for shelter in time of danger. Earthworks on the Polish plains were analogous centres of refuge in historic times ; and some, like the Wawel at Cracow, have been nuclei of towns. In south-east Britain, earthworks, such as the Trundle of the early age of metal (p. 49), were reoccupied and fortified afresh. Outlines of small cultivated fields have been identified through air-photographs and these outlines may date from the late Bronze Age or early Iron Age or later (plate VI, p. 83).

Apparently the early phase of the Prehistoric Iron Age in Britain (Iron Age A) was not particularly prosperous, and on this subject the botanists have given us valuable information from studies of pollen-grains, leaf-impressions and other details in the soils of the time. In Switzerland the pile-villages of the Late Bronze Age, which had been built on platforms on the alluvium of lake-shores, were flooded by the growth of the lakes. The Norse legends speak of the "Fimbul Winter" when winters succeeded one another and there was no real summer in between. Memories of the summer of 1946 in Britain help us to appreciate the difficulties of farmers of those days ; and we can understand both that it made cereal harvests poor and that rye and oats, probably at first chance weeds in a wheat or barley field, might come to be important contributors to the food-supply as they thrive in cooler conditions. The special association of both with Scotland in particular, and of oats also with Wales, seems significant here,

Apparently, then, a period of wet cold summers adversely affected Western Europe and Britain for some time. Its dating has been variously estimated as after about 700 and about 500 B.C., and, towards the latter date, the use of iron seems to have spread into south-eastern Britain (Early Iron Age A of the archaeologists, a phase of comparative poverty).

At some period probably not very far removed from 300 B.C. the climate seems to have improved somewhat, probably earlier in France and Switzerland than in Britain.

If we think of the date provisionally given to this improvement of climate, we shall realise that at this time the classical Mediterranean was in full career. Western Europe was a remote fringe, and ideas, objects and designs from the classical civilizations spread into the west. Greeks and Carthaginians were active in the Western Mediterranean ; Pytheas (fourth century B.C.) travelled to north-west Europe, and an order of priests and, in Gaul and Britain, lawgivers had arisen. They are known as Druids. They had major centres at or near Chartres in France (a place sacred to the Mother-Goddess and later specially sacred to the Virgin Mary) and in Anglesey. The Anglesey Druids seem to have been venerated by many tribal groups, and the Chartres Druids had a sort of Appeal Court with widespread prestige. Their teaching emphasised reincarnation, an idea which they may have inherited from Megalithic cults, but which was very widespread. The Druids faded out in Roman times.

At La Tène, between the lakes of Bienne and Neuchâtel in Switzerland, so much has been found that the name is given to the phase of culture in the west from about B.C. 400 for some centuries. It is really an infiltration of ideas into a tradition of the early phase of the Iron Age and that infiltration varied greatly in degree in different places. The Middle Rhine, south of Bingen, and north-eastern France show the newer features most clearly. In north-eastern France, parts of what much later became the province of Champagne increased considerably in population and outstretched burial in flat graves was substituted for cremation ; some of the immigrants seem to have come from the Upper Saone area (Burgundy), where salt and iron had already for some centuries attracted population. Communications, some think even fairly definite trackways, were developing and iron axes made the clearing of bush and woodland somewhat more effective.

It was at this time that bronze safety-pins, or fibulæ, as they are called (Fig. 44), became widely used as ornaments and fasteners for cloaks. Their styles are highly characteristic and help archaeologists to subdivide the Early Iron Age into shorter periods.

Iron also found utilization for the armature of ploughshares which, henceforth, could be large and cut deeper into the soil, with added

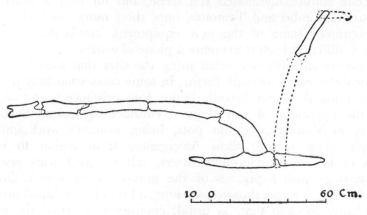

10   0   60 **Cm.**

FIG. 20
Early Iron Age plough

devices and manipulations for turning the soil over, an important consideration in Europe north of the Mediterranean lands. The coulter, an iron knife cutting the sod just ahead of the ploughshare, was a special feature.

Whereas, in Mediterranean lands, strong evaporation draws up dissolved matter in the soil to the surface (soils yellow and red with iron), in lands farther north where the soil is sometimes deep loam, rain in summer tends to wash nutritive salts down as much as evaporation tends to draw them up, so they are here spread through the thickness of the soil. The food-stuffs near the surface are taken up by plant-roots, and renewal must be sought by bringing up and overturning the deeper layers. An iron-armed ploughshare and especially one with a coulter working ahead of it thus meant a considerable advance in cultivation and food-supplies. Overturning of the soil on the deep loams is related to development of the long strip system to be discussed later.

The people thus equipped spread east and west, south and north, from the Mid-Rhine and N.E. France, with horses and apparently with chariots, betokening ways made for wheeled traffic. Eastwards to Transylvania, westwards to Spanish Galicia, southwards to Rome and northwards down the Rhine, Celtic-speaking peoples with the iron implements and weapons just mentioned as belonging to the La Tène culture dominated the scene, but for only a short time. Pressure of Cimbri and Teutones, once these more northerly peoples had acquired some of the new equipment, combined with feuds between different leaders to create a phase of warfare marked by much fortification on hillbrows, often using the sites that long before had had neolithic earthworks on them. In some cases what may be called towns, using the name broadly, came into existence ; and weapons and the apparatus of war show a considerable resemblance from Britain to Transylvania, but pots, being women's work until the potter's wheel spread, show divergences from region to region. Tales of heroes, warrior-adventurers, tell of great feats rewarded by marriage with a princess of the group among which the hero finds himself ; he may thus become king, a hint of matrilineal survivals. We clearly see also that, as usual, conquerors married the girls of the conquered folk. Patrilineal succession was developing and replacing matrilineal ideas, as the Greek dramas, especially the story of Orestes, indicate.

As this La Tène culture spread to the Atlantic shores of Gaul and the Iberian peninsula, it must have come into touch with, and re-vivified, the old coastwise trade. Fortresses of rough stone, *citanias*, abound in the northwest of the Iberian peninsula near the coast, and there are fortresses of this period in Brittany. Both regions favoured a bird ornament on their pots. These fashions spread to the south and west coasts of Britain by 200 B.C., and are the fashions of Iron Age B. The British Museum shows two splendid bronze shields of a later phase of the La Tène culture. One, found in the Witham, has a bead of red coral, probably from the Mediterranean, as a central ornament. The other, from the Thames, has red cloisonné enamel as its decoration. Did the trade in coral decline between the making of the Witham and of the Thames shields ? A number of finds link Cornwall with the Mediterranean in this period.

From about 300 B.C. objects of the La Tène culture had come into south-east England, and Fox has shown that the West Hants, and

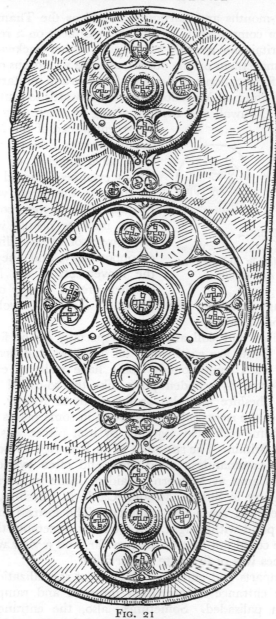

FIG. 21

Bronze shield with red enamel inlay, found in the Thames near
Battersea.   It belongs to the immediately pre-Roman Iron Age

Dorset river-mouths and harbours as well as the Thames may have been used for communication with the continent on a relatively small scale, but Britain for a while remained a rather backward area. The Iron Age B movement on the other hand was a vigorous one, spreading intercourse, fortification and designs of artistic and military importance. The coins of Philip of Macedon spread westwards to south-east France and then to Cornwall and Britain, giving an interesting analogy with

FIG. 22

Macedonian gold coins. These were very feebly imitated in Iron Age Britain

the recent spread of the Maria Theresa dollars into the Ethiopian region where these have lingered on to our time, having even been minted by the British in India in the recent war for use in Ethiopia. The western coastwise movements indicate people with initiative and power of adaptability to diversity of opportunity, and they differ from the movements of the Neolithic Age by their greater power of penetration inland using especially the Jurassic scarp (Cotswolds, Edgehill, Northampton, Lincoln).

Adaptability and skill are shown especially in the fortifications of the period. Some are earthworks on hillbrows and headlands, some have stone walls (unmasoned), some have walls of earth or small stones supported by wooden posts, like the so-called *murus gallicus*, notably in Cheshire but also as far north as Moray. But the full-complexity of the *murus gallicus*, as found in some places in Gaul, with a wooden framework held together by iron pieces, has not yet been identified in Britain. The situation of an Iron Age fortress is generally such that it commands a good view and often overlooks a slope ; The British Camp at Malvern, Maiden Castle in Dorset (plate Va, p. 82), Cissbury in Sussex, Maiden Castle in Cheshire, Almondbury near Huddersfield are a few instances. The fortress may not be on the highest point within sight, but we must remember that projectiles of that time could not be thrown very far, and a view with command of approaches was of first-rate importance.

The ramparts and entrances underwent specialization. The rampart at the entrance is sometimes inturned and ramparts were no doubt often palisaded. Sometimes, also, the entrance is oblique, exposing an attacker to cross-fire if he tried to enter. Sometimes the

PLATE VII

J. Chettleburgh

a. THE DANCE OF THE DEERMEN at Abbots Bromley, Staffordshire

J. Chettleburgh

b. THE MORRIS DANCERS giving their annual performance on Whit-Monday at Bampton, Oxfordshire

PLATE VIII

rampart and ditch system was duplicated or triplicated in the course of time. The enormous shifting of soil and stones, sometimes even rock, involved in digging the ditches and heaping the ramparts implies a very considerable labour-force. Within the fortress are pits which were probably storage places that were ultimately given up in favour of clean new ones, the disused pits being then filled with rubbish.

Further north along the west coast of Scotland and among its isles there are structures possibly of this age but of quite another type. Brochs, as they are called, are cylindro-conical towers with two concentric walls bound together by slabs going across from one to the other at intervals. Sometimes remnants of poor huts are near the brochs. We may suppose that they were the centres of seafarers of Iron Age B and later times, not, however, extending to the days of the Vikings. The possibility that the lords of the brochs may have been " pirates " on the fringes of the Roman Empire should not be excluded.

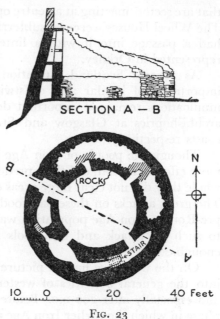

SECTION A — B

FIG. 23

A broch, W. Scotland; vertical section and plan

Galloway, Arran, Kintyre to Skye, the Great Glen, Beauly and Dornoch, Aberdeen and Angus also have what are called " Vitrified Forts ", the stone rampart having apparently been subjected to fierce heat that affected the surface of the stone. The thought of vitrification as a possible result of the burning of a *murus gallicus* springs to the mind.

These are some of the many varieties of construction attempted in what must have been an adventurous time.

In Cornwall hollowed-out passages and chambers called Fogous ; in Ireland, Souterrains, in north and north-east Scotland, Earth Houses, and, in some Scottish areas, Wheel Houses, with compartments that are sectors meeting at a centre open to all, give hints as to dwellings. The Wheel Houses were not subterranean. The Earth House typically had a passage into it with a lintel about ground-level : it is well represented in Orkney.

As regards Scotland, attention may be specially called to the importance of insular and coastwise distributions ; maritime communications remained important down to the Middle Ages with the archbishoprics at Glasgow and St. Andrews for the west and east coasts respectively.

Though the people of Iron Age B were obviously able to cut trees more effectively than did their predecessors, Fox has shown that on the whole they did not clear large areas of damp oakwood in clay lowlands. The great attacks on these oakwoods was to come later. Probably the pre-Roman Iron Age population was hardly large enough to spur men to such an attack and iron tools may not yet have been common enough.

On the whole we have a picture of Britain being drawn once more into the general activities of western Europe from perhaps 300 B.C. and especially after 200 B.C. Before that there had apparently been a phase in which the earlier Iron Age and the Late Bronze Age peoples of Britain had faced serious difficulties, probably of climate, and had lived on a relatively low level.

There can be no doubt that the bearers of the La Tène culture were Celtic-speaking and that they entered Ireland as well as Britain. Here we touch upon a problem that has been discussed many times. The Aryan family of languages, which includes what developed into the Celtic, Greek, Latin, Teutonic, Gothic and Slavonic varieties of speech, appears to have spread from the South Russian steppe as already stated, and the Celtic form of speech was important in the Mid-Rhine country of S.W. Germany and in adjacent parts of France and may have taken shape there. Surviving Celtic languages include two groups—the Goidelic or Gaelic, spoken in Ireland, Western Scotland and, until recently, in the Isle of Man, and the Brythonic spoken in Wales and Brittany and until two centuries ago in Cornwall, as well as in earlier times in south Scotland and north England.

Some hold that the Gaelic tongues (see p. 81) were brought by earlier immigrants than the Brythonic, and the swordsmen of the latter part of the Bronze Age and even the makers of beaker pots have been credited with Gaelic speech or something akin to it. On the other hand, some believe that the Brythonic variety was the type that was introduced, probably mainly with La Tène culture. They think that the Gaelic forms arose through fusion of this introduced speech with older languages, whether Aryan or pre-Aryan, in the west, that is in Ireland and western Scotland. Considering the importance of Ireland in neolithic and early bronze times, there is some probability in this view. The Gaelic languages emphasise the q sound where the Brythonic emphasise the p sound (see pp. 76 ff).

It is necessary to add that the surviving Breton language is believed to have reached Brittany from south-west England with refugees and the preachings of the Celtic Saints after Roman times ; and it is thought that the older Celtic speech of the Breton peninsula had died during Roman times. The north and west of Brittany are full of place-names with first syllables based on Plou and Lan ; Brythonic Welsh equivalents are Plwyf and Llan ; but it is also noteworthy that in South Brittany there are numerous Q place-names such as Quimper, Quimperlé, Quiberon, Questembert, etc., and South Brittany was of special importance from the days of early megaliths. With the sugges-tion therefore that old forms of speech emphasising the q sound, whether Celtic, or Aryan pre-Celtic, or pre-Aryan, may have been important in the west before La Tène times, we must leave this con-troversy. A philologist might find clues by mapping ancient place names with first syllable Cor, Car, Tam (and variants) in Europe. He might also consider whether the evidence for Celtic speech among the Belgic rulers of south-eastern Britain in the days of Julius Cæsar is really satisfactory.

Legendary history as strung together by Geoffrey of Monmouth is interesting in connection with the movements of peoples in the centuries just before Roman times. He writes of Dunwallo of Cornwall trying to establish a King's Peace in Britain, and of his sons Belinus (whence Billingsgate) and Brennius being concerned with the Celtic raid on Rome (about 390 B.C.), a connection it would be unwise to emphasise in view of Geoffrey's unreliability in chronology. Brennius is made the ally of the Allobroges (of the Marne district in France) and he is brought back to Britain *via* Neustria (Normandy). After reconciliation with his brother he is said to have proceeded to Trino-vantum (the future London). Belinus is credited with having organised a system of roads ; and this is to be brought into relation with the widespread opinion that the immediately pre-Roman centuries in Western Europe did witness a development of communications both by land and by sea. It is further noteworthy that, in the stories of the successors of Belinus, Orkney and migrants along the way from Spain to Orkney are mentioned. Indeed it would be no surprise if evidence of people of this period should be found in Iceland or Greenland. It will thus be seen that archaeological inference, however incomplete, and legend, however confused, do show some approximation to one another, an approximation, we must however, refrain from taking into too much detail.

Folk-tales, especially in Wales, are also suggestive here. The Black Mountains of Carmarthen are a moorland area on which lies a picturesque little lake, Llyn y fan fach. A folk-tale tells of a farmer from the vale of Towi going up to the moorland with his cattle in spring and of his wooing of a fairy girl (of the moorland peoples). Her father ultimately sanctioned the marriage, but, if the husband struck her with iron, she must return to fairyland. The tale goes on to speak of the prosperity of the marriage until one day, in trying to capture a runaway horse, he threw her the bridle and the iron struck her. He drowned himself in grief, and the lady was allowed to meet her sons in the lanes and teach them her herbal lore. Herbal lore was handed down for many generations in that area among the " physicians of Myddfai ". It is possible that the link between the story of the physicians, who actually existed, and the fairy woman is an invented one, but it is likely that the iron tabu and other features of the tale are very old. The idea of the Iron Age intruders along the valleys and of their contacts and intermarriage with the people of the moorlands is one to be borne in mind in thinking of the movements and changes of peoples of those days. The fairies are transmutations of the indigenous moorland folk living from ancient times above the lowland oakwoods.

Some of the migrations were probably movements of a group of warrior-adventurers melting into the general population through inter-marriage and thereby giving opportunity to a new intrusive warrior group. Tribal names thus change though populations may not change with them, and there may be considerable continuity of custom and tradition. Grimes and Fox have described finds from Llyn Cerrig Bach, Anglesey, approximately dateable within the last century B.C. These are thought to include gifts to a sacred centre in the traditional isle of the Druids and some of them come from Belgæ of south-east England, intruders of the generation or two before Julius Cæsar's advent, using probably the Thames and Chichester, Christchurch and Weymouth entries.

The name Belgæ remained attached to those who seem to have made themselves masters of Salisbury Plain and the Hampshire Avon Others, with indigenous underlings, were Regni (Chichester), Trinobantes (Essex and Middlesex), Cantii (N. and E. Kent), Atrebates (Berks.), Catuvellauni (Herts., Beds., Bucks.) and Durotriges (Dorset). Of non-Belgic groups (that is, using Belgic fairly narrowly) we hear of the Parisii coming apparently from the middle Seine to East Yorkshire and burying their chieftains with chariots, the Brigantes of West Yorkshire and the Pennines, the Iceni of Norfolk and N. Suffolk, the Boritani and Dobuni of the Northants and Cotswolds areas of the Midlands, who, together with the Dumnonii of the southwest, must have been ruled by Iron Age B peoples (p. 88). The Cornovii of Shropshire and the adjacent parts of the Welsh border and the Ordovices of Mid and North Wales were probably also under Iron Age B rulers and the surmise is permissible that the Silures of S. Wales included older elements in considerable proportion.

The Belgic immigrants, probably the last pre-Roman immigrants, seem to have used larger ploughs than were previously at all general, but to have come into a country already provided with a property system, so far as south-east England was concerned, and to have considerably influenced the Iceni. We have in Kent and East Anglia field-divisions which differ from the long strips which established themselves apparently under the Anglo-Saxons in much of the rest of S. England, as will be discussed in a later chapter. But in Denmark in La Tène times the long strip was apparently beginning to spread.

Earthwork fortresses and probably the nuclei of towns came into existence such as Colchester (" Old King Cole "), the future Verulamium, the Trundle and the future Chichester, St. Catherine's Hill and the future Venta Belgarum (Winchester), Llanmelin and the future Caerwent and so on. The more Roman of these centres were creations of Roman times replacing older pre-Roman settlements, as notably in the cases of Chichester, Winchester, Caerwent and Verulamium. Estimates of population will be discussed later (p. 115).

The late La Tène period immigrations had no doubt a considerable influence upon the quality as well as upon the numbers of the

H

population which had inevitably been much inbred in small communities. The immigrants, many of them vigorous young warriors, took to themselves the virgin women[1] of the country and the sons born to them may well have been above the average of the country. We know little of the physical type of the immigrants, but the balance of probability is in favour of there being a good number of big, fair-haired men. At least this is how most classical authors described the Celts they knew; but Tacitus knew that Celtic-speakers in Brittany were not so blond as others. The Gaul of the Capitol was broad-headed, and one can have no doubt that, among the bands of migrating warriors, typically gathered together around a supposedly lucky leader, there was a considerable range of head form and probably of colouring ; but the latter was lighter than that of the populations of the Mediterranean lowlands.

We may picture the people of the hillbrow camps gathered together with their flocks and herds at the coming of spring warmth and sunshine that was making the rich fresh grass grow on the hillsides above the forests still occupying the lowlands beneath. The more venturesome trees might have risked possible returns of frost, but the oak and the ash are the safer guides ; when they come out and the hawthorn is in bloom, man feels safer from returns of winter. The sight of the lowland forest in May, looked at from above, was one to gladden the hearts and stir the emotions of our forefathers. Winter's privations over, there would be milk for the babes, grass for the cattle, wild game to be hunted, crops to be tended, calm seas for fishing and trade. No wonder May Day became one of the great events of the Nature Calendar. We must here remember that the reform of the calendar in the eighteenth century cancelled eleven days and thus made May Day a little too early for the Nature Calendar. It is May 12th that is the old " Calan Mai " in Wales, and that date has remained as the date for various hirings in some parts of Britain.

[1] In this connection one should recall the ancient superstition to which the name of telegony has been given. That fancy suggests a lasting influence on all that a female might bear, exercised by the first male to whom she submitted herself, or sometimes the first male who made her pregnant. The fancy has been applied both within our own race and to domestic animals. It seems to have no foundation in scientific fact. Yet, no doubt, the young conquerors would pick desirable virgins, and the sons born might well be physically and mentally superior to the children other women might bear to native men. Even when the more desirable women had been discarded by the conquerors and had associated with native men, the sons they bore might be fancied to be superior. As it was supposed by many that the women merely germinated the male's " seed ", superiority of this kind would be associated with the mother's early connection with the conquerors, rather than with her own qualities.

The Maypole, primarily a phallic or male-sex symbol, and many related traditional ceremonies were put down by the Puritans between 1644 and 1660, and were in several cases revived at the 1660 Restoration. But, as Charles' return was celebrated on the 29th of May, that day to some extent and for a time replaced the old May Day. The habit developed of wearing a sprig of oak in remembrance of Charles' escape through hiding in the oak at Boscobel on 29th May, 1651, after the battle of Worcester, and there was added the custom of whipping with bundles of nettles those who did not wear the oak. But some of the old customs remained attached to the 12th or, later on, the 1st of the month. The gathering of hawthorn (going a-Maying) and its distribution to decorate the houses, apparently with an idea of protection against witchcraft, but with a tabu against having it in one's bedroom, is about the most general of these customs. There are also many records of the blowing of horns and the making of sycamore whistles illustrating the universal love of noise at a festival. Jack-in-the-green, personifying the vegetative force, persisted until recently as a man surrounded by boughs in chimney-sweep processions on May Day.

The autumn would give another magnificent spectacle viewed from the hillbrow camp with the leaves gold and brown and red before they fall. 13th November, the old All Souls' Day, with its memories of tributes to the ancestors, is the celebration of the death of the spirit of vegetation to be re-born next spring. The Church fixed its All Saints' Festival for the previous day, and, again, much as " Restoration Day " altered and captured some of the old May Day ceremonial, so celebrations of 5th November, the day when the Houses of Parliament were saved from the Guy Fawkes plot, captured some of the All Souls' tradition. The burning, in effigy, of the dead spirit of vegetation became the burning of the Guy ; but the Channel Islands have kept " Le Bout de l'An " (the End of the Year) as the name for the effigy which is burnt (on 5th November, however). As in the case of the May festival, hirings of various kinds took place on 12th November or 13th and that day is called " Calan Gaeaf" in Wales. The begging of fire from an aristocratic house, the collecting of firewood, the making of soul cakes are all suggestive details. In Latin countries ceremonial meals at the tombs have been a feature.

About midway between the May and November celebrations comes Mid-August with its varying relation to harvest in different European latitudes. In parts of France it marked the completion of harvest with celebrations emphasising fertility cults. The Roman Church attempted to assimilate this festival by making it the celebration of the Assumption of the Virgin Mary, and Napoleon in his turn tried to make it the celebration of the foundation of his Empire. It is very interesting that this date does not gather any special associations in British life, perhaps because of the variability of our harvest.

The solstices and equinoxes are other dates for special festivals, some of them, especially the winter solstice (Christmas) assimilated by the mediæval Church. Bel, Baal or Beltane fires in public places were long a feature of midsummer eve. Dancing around the bonfire, and leaping over it as the flames burned low have both been widespread. Midsummer eve was also a great day for divination, especially divinations to determine future husbands by girls. The Yule Log, the Boar's Head, Begging by Widows, Carol Singing and many other features are characteristic of the winter solstice.

The Dance of the Deermen at Abbots Bromley (plate VIIa, p. 90) and Morris Dancing, for example at Bampton (plate VIIb), are survivals, and in some measure revivals, of ancient local customs.

The May and November festivals like most others, have traditionally been occasions for " divination ", especially concerning future husbands and wives, and there has survived to the twentieth century a remnant of some old tabu condemning marriages in May, a tabu that seems linked with a fear of a birth nine months later, in February with its combination of cold and old-time scarcity, as the provision laid in for the winter was vanishing (note the institution of Lent as a factor in hindering slaughter of animals for food towards the end of winter). The instances here given of the attempts to link the nature calendar with religious associations and political commemorations show the vitality of folk tradition and illustrate the notable fact that ritual has been apt to persist though the creeds or explanations attached to it may have altered. A new myth for an old rite has often been a device of priests and potentates ; and one may recall from an earlier chapter the references to modified survivals of megalithic sanctities transformed for their own purposes by Celtic saints and Roman priests. It is clear that increased mobility and diversity of contacts must reduce the power of local custom to a memory, or give it a chance of a semi-artificial because self-conscious revival. More will be said about folk custom in chapter 8 (p. 174). It has been mentioned here because it is believed that a good deal lingered on from pre-Christian and pre-Roman times, but we cannot always assume that a folk custom is of this antiquity.

REFERENCES TO CHAPTERS 2, 3 AND 4 : Antiquaries' Journal, Antiquity, Archaeologia, Archaeological Journal, Armstrong (1939, 1940, 1947-48), Breuil (1939), British Museum (Stone, Bronze and Early Iron Ages), Bulleid and Gray (1911, 1917), Childe (1931, 1935, 1947), Clark (1932, 1936, 1940), County Archaeology Series, Crawford (1928), Cunnington (1923), Curle (1932), Darlington (1947), M. Davies (1945-46), Fox (1923, 1946, 1947), Gardner (1926), Garrod (1938), de Geer (1940), Godwin (1940, 1940b), Hawkes (1940), Hencken (1932), J. Morris Jones (1899), S. J. Jones (1938), Keith (1948), Kendrick and Hawkes (1932), Lockyer (1901 . . .), Marston (1937, 1938), Milankovitch (1938), Oakley and Ashley-Montagu (1949), Ordnance Survey (Neolithic Wessex, South Wales, Trent Basin), Peake (1927, 1940), Peake and Fleure (1927 . . .), Percival (1921), Piggott (1939, 1947), Prehistoric Society's Publications, Rhys (1900), Royal Commissions' Reports, Sollas (1913), Stamp (1936), H. H. Thomas (1923-24), Varley (1940), Vavilov (1926), Victoria History of the Counties of England, Wheeler (1925, 1943), Wright (1939), Zeuner (1946).

CHAPTER 5

ROMANS AND BRITONS

So MUCH has been written by specialists concerning Roman Britain that it would be inappropriate to go into great detail in a general survey such as this book attempts. Attention will therefore be concentrated mainly on some general features of relationship to environment.

Whereas pre-Roman social life in the west seems to have been dependent very particularly on the occurrence of a strong personality as leader, on the transmission of oral tradition, on rather rudimentary specialisation of crafts and trade (if we may judge from the feeble development of urban life), and on engineering still in a preliminary phase, Roman rule altered all this. It brought in on a larger scale the ideas of the city, of written tradition and institutional law of general application, of a standing army with hierarchical organization, of road engineering based on systematic surveys, and of trade in greater bulk than had been previously thinkable with the limited communications of older times. It seems that indigenous peoples who were prepared to adopt Roman ways and language (e.g. many of the Belgæ of S.E. England) were soon treated as Romans, a feature that has to some extent characterised several of the peoples of Latin tradition in their contacts with some non-Europeans in modern times. It was the pre-Christian Roman tradition to tolerate most religions that did not claim exclusive allegiance, and this helped the process of Romanization.

A considerable element in Celtic languages that was cognate with Latin made the introduction of new words to a Celtic-speaking people easier and facilitated the melting of Celtic into Latin, at any rate among the peoples of the cities, attracted by Roman culture. In addition to elements cognate with Latin, Welsh has direct borrowings such as *pont* and *ffenestr*. But the Latinization was probably largely urban, and could not be as complete as in Gaul and Iberia, because the Romans left remote parts of the Island mainly in the hands of the non-Romanized peoples of Wales, parts of north-west England and Caledonia. In mid-Wales, for example, they seem to have attempted little beyond guarding communication lines. The cutting-off of East Britain from the Mediterranean world in post-Roman times through the large scale immigration of the early English was another factor that limited the linguistic heritage of later Britain from Roman times.

The *pax Romana* substituted itself for the local feuds of earlier times, but only with awful slaughter and savagery, as in the case of the Iceni under Queen Boudicca (A.D. 61) and the massacre in Germany recorded on the column of Marcus Aurelius at Rome. It was the Iceni, one of the more civilized groups, in what was later Norfolk, who revolted. Kent, described by Cæsar as the region of highest civilization (the Belgæ) in Britain, was apparently rather more amenable, and, as in later periods, had special interest in communication and trade with the continent. It is likely that there is some exaggeration and hearsay in his account of the people of the interior of Britain described as living on flesh and milk, being clad in skins and staining themselves with woad. All this may be true, but it hardly conveys an adequate impression of the people who built Maiden Castle, Uffington, Eddisbury, Almondbury, Tre'r Ceiri and many more fortresses, and apparently carried on long distance trade. It is certain, too, that there was a Belgic immigration via the Solent a few years after Cæsar's attack on the British people in 51 B.C., and that the Catuvellauni in Hertfordshire were engaged in prosperous commerce and were spreading their coins over a good part of the south-east interior (especially Hertfordshire, Bedfordshire, Buckinghamshire and Oxfordshire, with some doubtful instances from Surrey and Sussex). The coins of the Belgic lords of the Solent entry are less widely distributed. The Catuvellauni indicate their development of mercantile life by their abandonment of their old fortress capital at Wheathampstead and their building of Verulamium (later St. Albans) in a forest clearing. Their famous king Cunobelinus (Cymbeline), probably great-grandson of the Cassivelaunus who had resisted Cæsar, evidently spread his power fairly widely in south-east England and made Colchester (Camulodunum) his capital. He died (A.D. 43) just before the Claudian invasion of Britain, and the lack of orderly succession left his kingdom weak in spite of the bravery of one of his sons named Caratacus (formerly written Caractacus, in Welsh Caradoc) in defence of the Medway crossing. The fact that Cassivelaunus, Cunobelinus and Caratacus appear in a direct line of inheritance, so far as we know, within the space of 100 years is an interesting illustration of patrilineal succession and of hereditary quality which we shall find again in later Saxon times (see p. 59), but which has not been conspicuous among rulers in historic Europe ; psychological qualities of leadership have become a very subtle and complex matter.

The Belgic peoples of the interval between Cæsar (B.C. 54) and Claudius (A.D. 43) were, then, commercial and political to a considerable extent. They used mainly wheel-made pottery, and it is doubtful whether they greatly valued the art of the La Tène phase of the Iron Age. After the Claudian conquest their people seem rather to have been ready to adopt Roman styles, as they adopted Latin for their language.

The defeat of the Belgæ at the Medway crossing, after a very fierce and long struggle, soon gave south-east England to the Roman armies, and some Belgic leaders appear to have fled to the west, to what is called in Chapter 1 Moorland Britain. Here the old-fashioned life persisted, in some places not yet much affected by the elements of La Tène culture. Caratacus went to Wales ; the Brigantes were a fierce group in the Pennines ; beyond were the wild warriors of Caledonia, to be known later as Picts, and already being supplemented by Scots from Ireland. The Romans spread quickly (after A.D. 43) over the land to the south and east of the Jurassic scarp and, after the horrors of the Boudicca episode (A.D. 61), they were supreme there. The names of Boudicca, Queen of the Iceni, and Cartimandua, Queen of the Brigantes, suggest that women might play very important parts in political and military affairs in those days.

The Romans, soon after the Claudian conquest, developed the mineral resources of south Britain. They smelted iron in the Weald and the Forest of Dean. They mined lead in the Mendips, in the northern part of the Welsh Marches and in Derbyshire and Yorkshire. They extracted copper in Anglesey and in north Wales and its marches, while tin was obtained from Cornwall. A little gold was found at Dolaucothy, in Carmarthenshire.

The struggles of the Romans to extend control beyond the Jurassic scarp (see pp. 1, 15) went on after the establishment of Roman power in the south-east, with the interruption of Boudicca's revolt in 61. It

appears that, though Caratacus was defeated on the borders of Wales in
A.D. 50, Welsh peoples, especially the Silures of South Wales, resisted
until A.D. 75 or a little later. The West Midlands of England were,
however, occupied and Chester and Caerleon were established as
legionary fortresses which developed Roman towns that have left
interesting ruins excavated by modern archaeologists. They were at
strategic points controlling lowland lines along the Welsh border and
into Wales. Farther in that country were some regimental forts, with
a number of minor posts. Apparently native life went on within the
rather thin Roman network and it is possible that Tre'r Ceiri (see p. 3
and plate 9, p. 62) and other earthworks were built or at least much
developed by native peoples in Roman times, as Willoughby Gardner
has so well shown. Calls upon Roman strength on the Scottish border
led to diminution of garrisons in Wales in the second century A.D., but
they were strengthened again towards the end of that century, probably
as a reminder of Roman power and as a concomitant of severe troubles
from the Scottish border when invaders came across the frontier into
England.

The contrast between Wales and Scotland in Roman times is very
marked. Wales with the possibilities of entry along the north and
south coasts and up the river sides, notably the Severn, could be
fractionated, and the hill masses were not sufficiently large to make
their people really formidable once a Roman network was established.

On the Scottish border there was a very different state of affairs.
Either the Newcastle-Carlisle frontier or the Forth-Clyde frontier invited
concentrated attack from northern invaders, while the Romans had
little opportunity offered by physical geography for division of Scottish
hill folk from one another. Under Hadrian there was built the great
wall in 122-127 A.D., which still excites the wonder of the student both
for the splendour of the work, and for the evidence that it marked the
failure of Rome to draw Scotland into its system. That failure is still
further evidenced by the building of numerous native hill-forts in
south Scotland, apparently in the earlier part of the second century A.D.
Both the building of Hadrian's wall and the native building of the
hill forts can be looked upon broadly as results of the evacuation of
Scotland ordered after Agricola's Scottish victory in A.D. 83. Obviously
that victory did not have much durable effect. A fresh advance into
Scotland led to the building (A.D. 142-43) of the Antonine Wall (Forth-
Clyde) provided with many forts to watch for invaders. The Antonine

Wall seems to have been destroyed in the great irruption at the end of the 2nd century A.D. The Romans were on the defensive in the north, and not very successful in their effort ; the contrast over against the Welsh border is dramatic.

The Romans expected assaults on Hadrian's Wall. It had a great ditch in front and the defenders hoped to corral the attackers in it and so to capture many alive for sale as slaves. The Wall was altered more than once. It was provided with Mile-Castles through which defenders might go out to deal with an assault, and there were great camps at Chesters and Housesteads. The expense of the wall and its garrisons must have been very high, especially when Roman currency devaluation became serious. Soldiers of the garrison were given land and settled down and handed on their duties in the army from father to son. So the men of the garrison came to be less Roman than British and the defence of the wall lost its efficiency in the later years of Roman rule in Britain. But the Wall and its story is a very special and complex subject that cannot be discussed in any detail here.

Within their territory the Romans developed roads primarily for moving troops and equipment to legionary and regimental head-quarters ; but these, and the roads, came to be used also for commercial purposes. The construction of the roads will be mentioned in a later chapter ; here it is necessary rather to indicate very broadly something of the general lay-out of the network so far as it has been worked out. Richborough (Kent) and Portchester, with Noviomagus (Chichester) behind it, were two main entries from the continent ; they had store-houses and general mercantile activity. Thence roads led to London, that from Noviomagus (Stane Street) crossing the Weald, which was not such impenetrable forest as has often been alleged. From London roads led to what are now Exeter, to Wroxeter and Chester and from Chester on to Carlisle and the Wall, to Lincoln and York (Eboracum) and the Wall, and to Norwich. The south-west was linked, near the Jurassic scarp, with Lincoln by the Fosse Way, and with Wroxeter and Chester as well, and another cross road linked Chester with York. These are but the main lines, the network had a much smaller mesh, especially in the south-east, and the newer investi-gations, notably those of Mr. Margary, promise to add much new knowledge.

London became important as a road centre, bridge town, port and merchant's city and may have had nearly 20,000 inhabitants in prosperous days. Eboracum (York) was a base fairly near the Wall and could then be reached by ships up the Ouse. Bath was obviously an important resort. Stations along the roads were in some cases military police posts. In some cases they were towns and the major ones, to the number of perhaps a dozen or so, probably had, in the second century A.D., two to five thousand inhabitants each, and some forty minor ones may have averaged fifteen hundred or so each (see further details of population pp. 115-116). These towns were settlements of Roman, more often Romanized British, officials; ex-legionaries settling down, and socially ambitious Britons, more or less Romanized, came in. Potters in the towns made common ware ; finer stuff was imported in early days. But during the second century imports seem to have diminished and currency problems were aggravated by inflation and unwise finance. It is probable that the Roman authorities hoped to develop the amenities of what they valued as a corn-supplying province. They " planned " towns, but it is very doubtful whether some of them ever filled the plan ; and the grave troubles round about 180-200 A.D., when invaders passed the Wall, must have shaken a still half-developed commercial economy hampered by poor administration in a country that was a distant outpost. Decline became more marked in the fourth century, when Roman order was shaken by the defeat of the Roman fleet and the break-through of northern invaders (367 A.D.), but the walled town still had power of defence even if defenders were few. It was the economic difficulty that was most severe. Farms were left derelict ; slaves escaped. Bankruptcy followed the disorganization of the slave system on which farming was based. In the third century A.D., energy had been given more to the development of rural life and production of corn and wool and probably leather, and to sale of slaves. The well-to-do town-dweller in Italy might draw supplies from his own or his neighbour's vineyards and olive groves, and he could at need go out to inspect the managers whose slaves did the agricultural work ; and the city in Italy could buy food and sell manufactured goods on a fairly large scale, apart from difficulties due to inflation. It was otherwise in Britain, a land of mixed farming needing continuous attention to the animals which were and are such a large factor in our island agriculture. Stockraising became more important in later Roman times in Britain. The uncertainty of our climate makes it necessary to adjust dates of farm processes and to exercise a responsible judgement at every stage.

An important scheme of Roman rural development in the west of Europe was the establishment known as the villa. This was an organization of fairly large-scale agriculture, probably in some cases developed from farms established under the Belgæ and other lords of immediaely pre-Roman times, when, it seems almost certain, there spread a plough larger than the little ones of earlier periods and provided with a coulter (p. 124). The villa included a residence for the Romanized owner and outbuildings for staff, including many slaves. Villas had partial

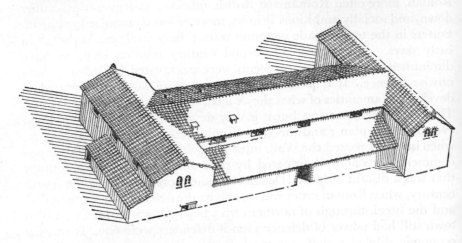

FIG. 24

Roman villa in Britain. (After Dr. Norman Davey). Second century A.D.

analogies with the later haciendas and estancias of Spanish America and some modern plantations of other warm lands. It is doubtful whether many owners of villas were Roman immigrants ; some may have been Romanized Gauls, many were Romanized Britons. The Romans certainly introduced several new plants, including fruit-trees.

South and east of the Jurassic scarp, villas were developed in con-siderable numbers in the territories of the Cantii (N. Kent), the Regni (W. Sussex), the Durotriges (Dorset), in the Belgic area in Hampshire, and the neighbourhood of Camulodunum (Colchester), all near important entries from the narrow seas, as well as among the Dobuni (Cotswold country), the Atrebates (Berkshire), and the Catuvellauni (parts of Bedfordshire and Hertfordshire). They are less numerous

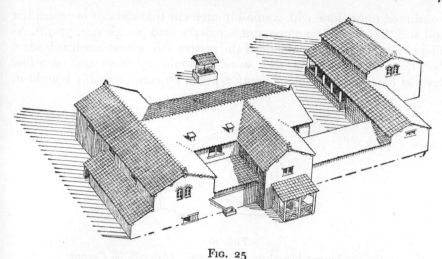

FIG. 25

Later Roman villa in Britain. (After Dr. Norman Davey)

in the territory of the Iceni (Norfolk) and in Lincolnshire. Generally speaking, agriculture at that time specialized on the lighter soils ; and Fox in his *Archaeology of Cambridgeshire* has shown that, in Roman times, only a moderate mount of clearing of damp oakwood was as yet undertaken, but Margary has emphasised the importance of Roman roads in the Weald. To the west and northwest of the Jurassic scarp villas are much less numerous in the English Midlands with their ancient forests and marsh, but they spread in the south-west across the Severn and through South Wales.

Apart from Wales, the regions named as being notable for villas were mostly regions in which pre-Roman populations had become fairly considerable under Belgic and other presumedly Celtic lords of the last century or two before the Roman conquest, but this linkage is not universal. Maiden Castle, near Durnovaria (Dorchester, Dorset), seems to have been the very strong fortress capital of the Durotriges, and was probably stormed by the Romans and to some extent replaced by Durnovaria. Groups of British descent, less Romanized than the people of the villas, went on living in villages or hamlets concerned mainly with farming but, in some cases, with mining, e.g. of lead in the Mendips. These villages had little fields around them, and, in the parts remoter from the south-east coasts, it is likely that ploughing continued to be done with a small implement that did not overturn the soil and that was taken along and across the field (see also pp. 77-78). As these hamlets were the homes of the poorer folk whose natural leaders had become Romanized, they were no doubt unkempt and on a low level of life. But one finds Roman types of objects, probably bought in

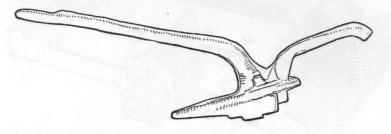

FIG. 26

Roman bronze plough-model, Sussex.   (After F. G. Payne)

flashes of prosperity or acquired by theft, and there are cases of roofing with Roman tiles and of writing in Roman fashion. So the hamlets may be looked upon as the poor relations of the villas, less completely Romanized, but yet dependent on Roman order rather than on any native scheme.

Salisbury Plain and Cranborne are notable areas for dwellings of native folk in Roman times, mostly on high spots, and they belong to the pre-Roman heritage of settlement (see Fig. 29, p. 114). It is interesting that the Cotswolds, another old area of settlement, again on light soils, was a region of villas. One must not argue dogmatically from physical conditions to social facts, and it is necessary to bear in mind that negative evidence is far from conclusive ; discoveries may alter the picture in several ways. From the existence of the little fields, revealed especially by aerial photography in the last thirty years (plate VI, p. 83), thanks largely to the pioneer work of O. G. S. Crawford, one might argue that the land was in family holdings, or perhaps in household lots re-allocated from time to time among groups of kinsmen, somewhat as has happened even in quite recent times in the western Highlands and Isles of Scotland (p. 8) and in parts of Ireland.

Among the more Romanized elements we may picture the replacement of the old habit of pursuit of local military power by the pursuit of administrative prestige and economic power or security. Military efficiency among the Romano-British declined ; and, when the Roman power weakened, the need for an overall organization proved to be crucial, as in Gaul, and difficult to achieve in both cases. There was no one among Romano-Britons after the Roman connection disappeared who could effectively take the lead and organise the people in their own defence. Moreover there was not much general British feeling ; the population was very diverse in outlook and in problems in the different regions.

On the east and south men had to ward off attacks from people who came across the North Sea and in the 3rd century we hear of a Count of the Saxon Shore. Fortresses and watch-stations were built along the coasts and such places as Richborough (Rutupiae), between Kent and Thanet, and Cissbury were refurbished for defence. Picts (Highlanders) and Scots (from Ireland and perhaps W. Scotland) raided into Roman Britain from the north and west, and Roman towns beyond the S.E. region of the villas became refuges for displaced persons, to use a modern term. Exeter, Caerwent and Caerleon, Gloucester, Wroxeter, Leicester, Lincoln, York may be mentioned here. Apparently the border of the more fully Romanized Britain in the neighbourhood of Caerwent (S.E. Wales) was not very disturbed, even towards the end of the Roman power in Britain, for a temple of a local god, Nodens, with supposed healing powers, was built at Lydney, near Chepstow, after 360 A.D., with a guest-house for pilgrims. One must remember, however, that religious centres have often claimed a certain amount of respect even in unsettled times.

Tradition tells that Cunedda, a British warrior who apparently had been concerned with the defence of Hadrian's Wall, led his people into North Wales and drove out the Scots (invaders from Ireland). Charlesworth dates this as late as 450 A.D.

Of the coming of Christianity to S.E. Britain we know very little save that it was already strong in the early third century, and that its martyrs suffered under Diocletian (284-305). Already early in the fourth century Roman towns in Gaul had bishops as heads of local clergy (epi-scopus—overseer) and we hear of British bishops going to the Church Council at Arles (314) and to that at Ariminum (360). It is also known that the British Christians accepted the results of the victory of the Athanasian party at the Council of Nicæa (323). Picts, Scots, Saxons, and no doubt a good many people in outlying rural areas were for a time little affected by Christianity. The name Roman

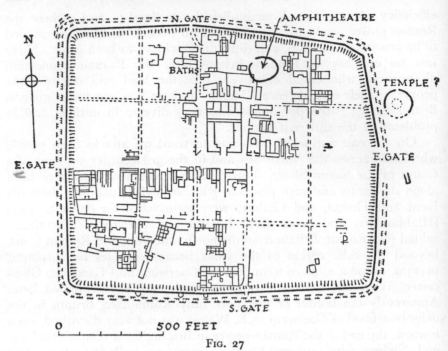

FIG. 27

Ground plan of Caerwent; a Roman urban settlement, Monmouthshire

thus came to imply that the person was of the Christian faith while many rural folk (pagani), still following their traditional rites, were the cause of the change of meaning whereby pagan has come to mean a follower of old rites not expounded in books. Jews, Christians, Muhammadans, Buddhists, Parsis and a few other groups would be excluded from the " pagan " category, they follow " religions of the book ".

We know that Christianity came to Atlantic Britain before 400 A.D. A few students of the subject think it may have come much earlier and fancy that the legendary history of St. Patrick may be a compound of two biographies, but the evidence for any Christian effort in the Irish Sea region before Ninian is non-existent. Ninian studied at Rome and under St. Martin of Tours, and he founded Candida Casa (the White Cottage : probably whitewashed) at what became known as Whitern or Whithorn in Galloway in 397. He dedicated his church

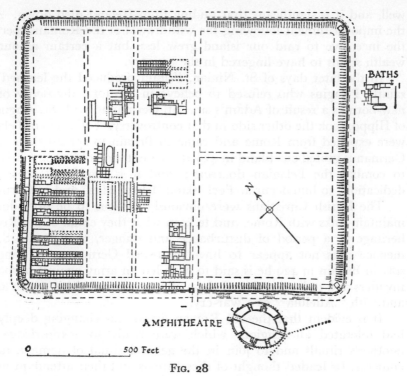

BATHS

AMPHITHEATRE

0   500 Feet

FIG. 28

Ground plan of Caerleon; a Roman legionary fortress, Monmouthshire

to his master, St. Martin. Several St. Martin dedications are early,
and his festival, 11th November (Martinmas), has special traditional
importance ; it was for a long time the day on which animals were
killed for salting down for winter provision, as it was about the end of
the vegetation year (p. 97).

Patrick was a son of Calpurnius, a Decurion who was a Christian
deacon at the unidentified site of Bannavem Tabernae, near the
western sea. Patrick was carried off by Irish raiders but later returned
home and then went to study at Lerins, an island of S.E. France and
an early monastic centre. Then he was taught by St. Germanus of
Auxerre, who was interested in Atlantic Britain, as we shall see below,
and visited our island in 429. St. Patrick became leader of the effort
to Christianize Ireland in 432. Apparently the mission succeeded

well, and it is significant that raiding from Ireland died down. After the impoverishment following the withdrawal of the Romans, perhaps the incentive to raid our island grew less, but a certain amount of wealth seems to have lingered in the country.

In the later days of St. Ninian, Britain produced the learned and saintly Pelagius who refused to believe in the total depravity of the new-born as a result of Adam's sin. St. Germanus, with St. Augustine of Hippo, took the other side in that controversy. Followers of Pelagius were expelled from Rome and came to Britain to spread their ideas. Germanus visited our island in 429 at the invitation of British Christians to combat the Pelagian doctrine ; and it is significant that early dedications to him occur at Peel Island (Isle of Man) and in Cornwall.

The British Christians were obviously anxious to be orthodox, to maintain links with Rome, and to keep what they could of the Roman heritage in a period of disturbance and danger, though the Saxon menace does not appear to have impressed Germanus. During his stay in Britain in 429 he is said to have led an army against barbarian invaders and to have defeated them after a baptism of his whole army, and with " Alleluia " as a war-cry.

It is evident that the old Roman world was changing deeply. It had tolerated all religions which were ready to acknowledge one another's rituals and to join in the general ritual of homage to the emperor. Its leaders thought of these rituals and their attendant myths as ideas and practices of social utility. They had little desire to press any one ritual forward exclusively. The new movement was on the other hand inherently exclusive and full of missionary zeal, and was apparently beginning to develop that ecclesiastical totalitarianism, the attendant hatreds and cruelties of which were to be such a ghastly feature of European life for many centuries.

We must now go back to the days of the decline of Roman connections before trying to piece together some picture of the sub-Roman period.

The towns declined and appear to have become places where a few romanized Britons lingered on in poverty. Silchester and Wroxeter died out completely. Some students believe that London itself was virtually uninhabited for a century or more, while others think it survived in some, rather feeble, measure, and caused the early Saxons to avoid it by keeping on the south side of the Thames ; the water then spread more broadly than it does now. Lincoln is a case of special interest here ; its Newport Arch is a Roman town-gate still surviving and there is mention of Caedbaed, a Celtic king, in Lindsey in the fifth century. Did Lincoln survive through the Dark Ages ? It is, nevertheless, important to remember that a number of British towns and cities are on Roman sites ; so the question of survival of towns may not yet be finally settled.

The villas may be said to have died out ; no case is known of a villa underlying a later settlement. They obviously depended on the presence of a settled government favourable to property-owners and on a complex economic system recognising social privilege. In disturbed times the relations between owner and labourers or slaves would become difficult, slaves could escape.

The less Romanized population living in villages may sometimes have suffered intensely as disorder spread ; sometimes on the other hand they would find opportunities to raid villas and towns, the Romanized people of which had probably treated the villagers as inferiors and may have exploited them. The rural risings in sub-Roman Gaul are a notorious fact, the bands concerned being known as Bacaudae.[1] Sometimes a leader appearing from the moorlands might organise these bands, or employ mercenaries, and even be accepted by Romano-Britons as seems to have been the case with Vortigern (pp. 117-18). It is even possible that groups of villages may have maintained some measure of organized life for a time, especially in the east of Kent.

Of areas that were less Romanized and had British villages rather than Roman villas, Salisbury Plain south of Wansdyke, together with Cranborne Chase, stands out. Wansdyke was made by men who had some Roman equipment, and it is probable that it was made at the latest not long after the Roman connection had disappeared (see fig. 33, p. 128). Its ditch is on the north side of the vallum or raised bank, so it was made to protect the region of British villages from attacks coming from the north. Whether these attacks were those of one-time Anglo-Saxon mercenaries turned raiders, or of early Anglo-Saxon immigrants entering at the Wash and spreading south-west we cannot be sure ; the Salisbury-Cranborne area of ancient settlement may have attempted to protect itself against some still earlier enemy. It seems best to avoid trying to link Wansdyke with the conquests of Cerdic (p. 128).

[1] Bacaudae. Apparently a name for wandering groups of makers of wickerwork frames and possibly of other things.

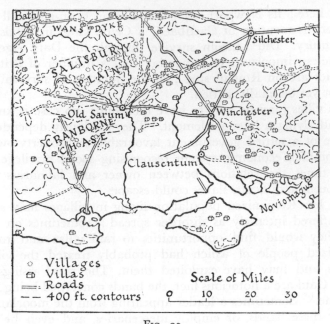

FIG. 29
Roman villas and British villages in Hampshire and
Wiltshire

Parts of Devon and Somerset, the Chiltern Country and Elmet in
Yorkshire may be named as other regions in which little-Romanized
villages survived within what was nevertheless considered Roman
Britain. A reference to Lincoln (p. 113) above and to a Celtic king
Caedbaed, in Lindsey, in the fifth century, cannot but hint at a considerable element in Lindsey that was not very Roman. There is, however
also the fact that coastal marshes limited the chances of useful landings
for Anglo-Saxon farmer immigrants, so that Lindsey at any rate, was
not likely to feel the effects of the earliest of these immigrations.
Mattingly has interpreted coins apparently minted in the sixth and
seventh centuries in Britain as copies of late Roman coins, another
hint of Romano-British survivals.

Cornwall, Wales, parts of the Pennines and Cumbria together with
Strathclyde were among the least Romanized areas and could provide
or give opportunities to adventurers to take advantage of unsettled
times, especially as chiefs of moorland pastoral groups.

In Atlantic Britain it is likely that maritime activity tended to increase as the communications across the Straits of Dover declined. In this way intercourse along the old time S.-N. route (p. 88 ff.) between Brittany and Cornwall and on to Pembrokeshire, Anglesey, Man, Galloway, the Isles and the Clyde, and Ireland seems to have become more important in sub-Roman times, especially after Christianity had spread. This subject will be taken further at a later stage (p. 119). Here it is necessary merely to point out that there seem to have been movements both ways, but especially southward, between south-west Britain and northern Brittany. It is thought that Brittany owes its surviving Celtic language to this immigration, and that it had lost its older Celtic language during the Roman period.

Before proceeding further we may give some estimates of population with the reserve that befits such guess-work. At the height of its prosperity Roman London may have had 20,000 people. Verulamium (a *municipium*), Colchester, Lincoln, York and Gloucester (all four coloniae), Caerleon (with Caerwent) and Chester (special legionary headquarters) and Bath (health resort) may have averaged 3,500 each. A dozen other towns may be credited with 2,000 each, and some forty or even fifty other places with 1,000 each. This rough calculation suggests 120,000 as the urban population. If it was about 20 per cent of the whole, that gives a total of 600,000 for prosperous times, in the area south of Hadrian's Wall.

If we realise how the entry of India and Egypt into modern commercial life has increased population we shall appreciate the idea that Roman activity in Britain led to a large increase. It is probable that the introduction of larger ploughs in the late La Tène period had already made possible a considerable increase, as did the west coast trade of Iron Age B. (p. 88). If we eliminate an urban 120,000 from the 600,000 total estimated for Roman times in prosperous phases, and halve the remainder, we have a fairly generous estimate of 240,000 for late La Tène times—and something considerably less, shall we guess 150,000!—for the antecedent period, i.e. before the larger plough or the west coast trade of Iron Age B.

It is probable that the population had increased when bronze-casting had spread, and that numbers had tended downwards in the wet cold centuries. One may therefore estimate a population under 100,000 for the Middle Bronze Age, and probably for the dawn of the age of metal. At the same time, we must realise that population may have been larger and may have declined especially during the phase of cold wet summers about 500 B.C.

It is likely that the 600,000 estimated above for Roman times would tend downwards in the unsettled days after the Roman power over Britain ceased and town life and its productivity declined. How far the downward trend may have gone is beyond our reckoning, at present, but we may estimate the sub-Roman period's total at less than half-a-million (A.D. 400-500).

Speech and writing had been largely Latin in Roman Britain save in the villages, and even there Latin names for new items of equipment must have come in. Celtic speech was thus deprived of standardising and enriching factors on the educated level, it must have become in parts of south-east Britain largely a kitchen and farmyard dialect, and, without written documents, such dialects are too weak to resist new languages. This is one reason for the slightness of the influence of the Celtic heritage on Anglo-Saxon, though one suspects that there is more Celtic in our place-names than is commonly allowed. Another is the fact that many Anglo-Saxon immigrants came as families to settle near the water-meadows, or, in the south-east, on the lighter soils rather than as conquerors to rule and intermarry. The new settlers' families in the course of time drew in labourers and so on from the older population, but the immigrants' language was firmly fixed by the character of the migration, and the older population was not firmly rooted in either Celtic or Latin. The prestige of Latin led to its survival in Gaul as the language of the church, and to its reintroduction by the Roman church into Britain.

The dating of Anglo-Saxon immigration is a difficult subject even for specialists, and the reader who wishes to pursue this question may be referred to R. H. Hodgkin's *History of the Anglo-Saxons* with its many references to other work and its foundation upon the pioneering researches of E. T. Leeds. The lamentations of Gildas written about 550 give some hints of the story but experts think he knew little of what happened in the period 350-450. Bede's history has other references, and the compilations of Nennius and of Geoffrey of Monmouth may also be mentioned. The *Anglo-Saxon Chronicle*, compiled under King Alfred in the ninth century, gives details concerning Wessex, but has little relation to the stories told by Gildas and others. The multiplicity of the immigration-movements is one factor of the difficulty of interpretation ; and another is the probability that the Anglo-Saxon immigrants gave up depositing goods in graves some considerable time before they were Christianized. This last probability carries the implication that the " pagan " Anglo-Saxon cemeteries, identified by grave-goods, give us only some stages of the immigration, generally speaking early ones.

The Wall of Hadrian was abandoned by the legions when Maximus took the troops away to fight for his claims in Gaul in 383. It is just possible that Cunedda (p. 109) tried to hold it some years later. Stations on the east coast were under Roman occupation until near the end of the century. Roman troops were withdrawn for war in Europe in the early years of the fifth century. 410 was long accepted as the date when the last Roman soldiers left Britain ; it seems clear that a locally created emperor Constantine had gone from Britain to Gaul, that the Britons were trying to organize their own defence at that time, and that the Roman Emperor, Honorius, could not help them and told them to fend for themselves. Few Roman coins of date after 395 have been found in Britain but that does not necessarily date anything at all closely.

Apparently Britons hoped for Roman help at any rate until 446, and Collingwood and Myres think there may have been some reoccupation of south-east Britain during part of the period 410-446, There was no Roman army in Britain in 429 when Germanus (p. 112) paid his first visit. The *Notitia Dignitatum*, of 428 or later, considers Britain a part of the Roman Empire ; but was the script a copy of an earlier one ? These dates are given not for any purpose of discussion of their validity, but to suggest that a more or less Romanized community with Celtic-speaking accessories was struggling to maintain the Roman connection through and perhaps beyond the first half of the fifth century. The menace of Saxon immigration and the development of Saxon military power in Britain is the other side of the picture, and in that respect again dates are unsatisfactory, as might be expected. The process was a gradual one and quite possibly had begun even earlier than the departures of the legions. The early separateness of English from Romano-British life is an important feature as will be suggested (p. 137), and one reason for difficulties of dating.

The traditions of Vortigern, living in the middle of the fifth century, help to give a picture of some relations of men and environments at the time. He seems to have been a leader on the Welsh moorland or border, very likely head of a frontier guard like Cunedda (p. 109), and to have spread some sort of domination over south Britain. Geoffrey of Monmouth calls him Earl of Gewiss (confederation), a name applied to the West Saxons ; this is probably another muddle of Geoffrey's, but one may bear in mind that Salisbury Plain and Cranborne Chase, later the heart of Wessex, were regions in which a British population living in villages was specially important. Tradition curses him for a pact with Saxon adventurers called Hengist and Horsa for the purpose of getting help against barbarians from the north and against a rival from Brittany. It should be borne in mind that the Empire had long drawn barbarians into its military personnel and probably Vortigern was following this custom. Further, one cannot expect too much solicitude on the part of a man of the west concerning Kent. That county had probably witnessed a drift of its more Romanised elements in the disturbed times back to Gaul ; and it may have seemed to need immigrants to cultivate its fertile lands. The connection of the Vortigern-Hengist arrangement and subsequent quarrel is made responsible for the Anglo-Saxon conquest : but, whatever the truth of the story may be, it is probable that Vortigern's action as regards the Saxons was only a minor incident.

The other part of the Vortigern tradition is of considerable interest. It tells of Constantine, in Brittany but with obvious British connections, and of his sons, among whom was one called Ambrosius Aurelianus, who defeated the Saxons. The date is within a few years of 475. Some are inclined to think that Ambrosius had Salisbury Plain, the old British centre, as his base after he came over from Brittany, and that the Wansdyke (p. 127) from Clevedon to Newbury, on the south side of the Kennet valley, has a connection with this. Tradition connecting Ambrosius' victory, no doubt fictitiously worked in by Geoffrey of Monmouth, with the bringing of the "foreign stones" to Stonehenge, (p. 56) may be recalled here. What is of special interest is the tradition of connections between Brittany and the west of England, and of the military prowess of Ambrosius and his Britons as well as of the relative weakness of the Saxons. The Saxon burials north of Wansdyke show a good number of cases of cremation, and are therefore probably early ; they give no evidence of cremation south of the Wansdyke, on Salisbury Plain. But further consideration must be left to the chapter that will deal with Anglo-Saxon Britain.

If historians have a maze of difficulties in dealing with the sub-Roman period, the bards and romancers, on the other hand, have rejoiced in it. We gather that in those days bards sang the triumphs of the kings, and marvellous stories were woven about their wars and the prowess of the knights. Naturally, in the west, the bardic tradition was found among the less Romanized elements, especially therefore among the people of wider outlook connected with the commerce that was carried on between Brittany, Cornwall, Wales, Ireland and South-west Scotland. This intercourse, we have already seen (p. 115) accounted for voyages of the early Christian preachers, the Celtic saints of the west. The struggles with the Saxons furnished another source of stories of which there are many divergent constructions in prose and verse. One reason for their persistence and elaboration is that they belong to the period immediately before it became customary to set them down in writing. The *Historia Brittonum* of Nennius for example is thought to have been compiled at some time near 800 A.D.

Ambrosius Aurelianus is credited with victories in north England. Legend makes Uther succeed him and beget Arthur, borne by Igerne of Tintagel. And it is around Arthur's fame that romance has played. He and his knights are linked with Brittany, Cornwall, Somerset, Wales, Cambria and South Scotland, that is with the British side of the Irish Sea route. In the twelfth century the stories were embroidered not only by Geoffrey of Monmouth in Britain but by Wace and others in France. Ireland is not touched directly by the Arthurian legends, though it is mentioned here and there. The Irish connection is much more explicit in the *Mabinogion* stories of Wales.

Legend at any rate suggests that the Anglo-Saxon immigrants did not have an easy time in early days in Britain, that Salisbury Plain was still British for a while, and that Stonehenge was supposed to be a centre of ceremonial. Knowing that the great stone monuments in many parts of western Europe were ritual centres at this period, we may be allowed to think that Stonehenge was in use in some way. Perhaps even construction of rough stone monuments may have gone on in some areas, for example in Ireland.

While struggles between more and less Romanized Britons, Britons and Picts, Britons and Anglo-Saxons were continuing, Atlantic Britain and Ireland were witnessing much religious activity. The region was no doubt cut off from much connection with Rome and Lerins (p. 111) by the advance of heathen Franks and Saxons, but the coastlands of the Irish Sea and St. George's Channel, as well as Cornwall and

Brittany, had considerable intercourse among themselves and built up what has come to be known as Celtic Christianity. It had monastic leaders, but hardly bishops in the full sense of the term ; the earlier bishoprics of Britain (p. 109) had faded out. The monastic leaders had centres of training : for Britain, one may specially mention some, namely the isle of Iona, Whithorn in Galloway, and the coastal site of Llanilltyd Fawr, now Llantwit Major, on the south coast of Glamorgan-shire. Information about the so-called Celtic Saints in the various compilations of lives of the saints is often dubious. Professor Bowen has recently tried, and is still trying, another line of enquiry, through mapping ancient dedications to individual saints, although the verification of the antiquity of some dedications is admittedly difficult. His provisional conclusions, thus far, show that there seems to be a measure of parallelism between the coastwise intercourse of Celtic Christian time and that of Iron Age B and the period of the megalith-builders. Probably, if we knew more about intervening periods, we should find analogous movements going on then. Generally speaking, the Irish Sea north of Bardsey and Anglesey was one province of this intercourse, and this province included the Clyde and S.W. Scotland. St. George's Channel, especially south-east Ireland, the South Welsh coast, Cornwall and Brittany were another province ; but the two had links. The details of this interesting line of research, which, apparently, also has importance for the interpretation of economic development, must be left to Bowen's articles and his promised book on the subject.

Celtic Christianity in Atlantic Britain and Brittany made much use of pre-Christian ideas, and the contrast between Atlantic Britain and Moorland Britain (see fig. 1, p. 15) comes out in this matter as in so many others. We may think of leaders such as Vortigern in their relation to Moorland Britain, perhaps nominally and superficially Christianized, but at times using a veneer of Christianity as a means of securing support from the Romanized remnants still in the south-east. The contrasts between the Atlantic coasts and the moorlands should be in the minds of those who try to look into the subject of the post Roman west.

As an instance connected with the northern region one may cite the aristocratic St. Columba of the sixth century, son of a member of the royal houses of Ireland and Dalriada (Argyll). He was trained at Moville (Strangford Lough) and Clonard and founded monasteries at Derry and Durrow (King's County). He seems to have had relatively little connection with Antrim.[1] In 563 he founded the famous community at Iona, from which his influence spread into the Scottish Highlands.

An instance from the southern province is that of Samson or Sampson who moved between Llanilltyd Fawr, Cornwall, probably the Channel Islands, and the north-east of Brittany where he worked at Dol. The cathedral at Dol is dedicated to him.

The equipment and influence of Christianity in the sixth and seventh centuries in Atlantic Britain and Ireland is shown by the famous manuscript Book of Kells, now in the library of Trinity College, Dublin, perhaps the finest, and certainly one of the earliest, manuscripts of the west. Celtic Christianity, being cut off from Rome, came to differ from the Roman usage in certain practices such as the fixing of Easter and the appointment of bishops. The idea of bishops was primarily associated with that of a Roman city as administrative centre of a district. While Roman influence remained weak before the days of Saints Gregory and Benedict, Celtic Christianity sent out missionaries to the Rhineland, Burgundy, Switzerland and even as far as Vienna. It is therefore important to realise that Atlantic Britain, at any rate, was by no means in a low state during the period of immigration of the pagan Anglo-Saxons into south-eastern Britain, and one should remember that, in what is called Iron Age B, i.e., the pre-Roman period, Atlantic Britain was evidently already on a fairly high level of achievement.

REFERENCES, see end ch. 8, p. 181.

---

[1] It is noteworthy that, already in the days of megalith building, Antrim was specially important for its gallery-graves while the region from South Down around to Derry had chiefly passage-graves, including the imposing group on the Boyne (New Grange, Dowth, etc).

CHAPTER 6

THE EARLY ENGLISH AND THE
CELTIC WEST

T HE WEAKENING of Roman power, as already mentioned, led to irruptions of warriors from outside the Empire, but there was going on at the same time a good deal of movement of families and groups. In all this change the more widespread use of the iron axe and the iron sword and also the larger iron-shod ploughshare played notable parts. Barbarian warriors coming within the Roman frontiers might think of trying to maintain what could be maintained of the Roman system of communications and law, or they might be out for plunder, or both. In any case, however, the multiplication of local sovereignties and the general poverty of legal and engineering experience militated against Roman systems of roads, wheeled carts and commerce, and accelerated the decline of cities. The iron axe made forest-cutting on a larger scale more possible, and the larger iron-shod ploughshare, with a coulter in front, was useful on the heavier lowland loams and clays, largely covered in earlier Iron Age time with damp oak wood in the west. Rural life on a low level found quantitative scope, urban life was weakened. Many of the barbarian groups coming into Roman territory were little able to understand the factors of city maintenance, but a number of cities in Gaul and the Rhineland by this time had bishops, and several of these managed to survive. Köln, Mainz, Sens, Rouen, Tours, etc., are examples here. The importance of this fact for the future redevelopment of civilization as the " Dark Ages " passed away can hardly be overestimated.

The old-established rural cultivators of the loess belt of east-central Europe, notably around the north-east and north of the Carpathian and Sudeten ranges, also became able to attack the denser woodland

THE EARLY ENGLISH AND THE CELTIC WEST 123

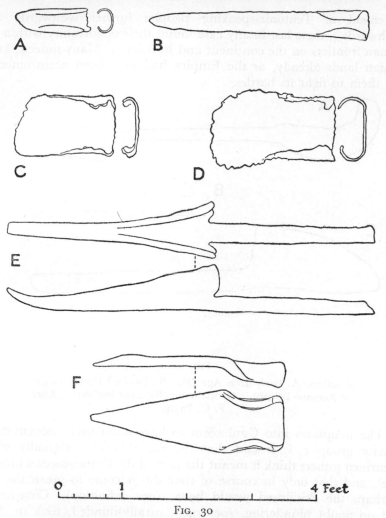

FIG. 30

Ploughshares: A. Caburn (Early Iron Age). B. Bigbury (Early
Iron Age). C. Bigbury (Iron Age). D. Eckford (Romano British).
E. Box (Romano British). F. Moorgate Street, London (Romano
British). (After F. G. Payne)

on the plains and thus to multiply and spread. It is from this time that
the Slavonic languages increased in importance ; and probably west-
ward pressure of Slavonic-speaking peoples was a factor promoting

movement of Teutonic-speaking peoples further westwards and southwards ; these last in any case found their opportunity within the Roman frontiers on the continent and in Britain. Many indeed, knew Roman lands already, as the Empire had long been accustomed to hire them to fight its battles.

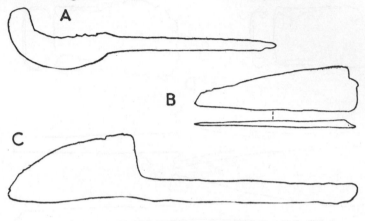

FIG. 31

Coulters: A. Early Iron Age (?). B. Twyford Down (Belgic or Romano British). C. Silchester (Romano British). (After F. G. Payne)

The irruptions into Gaul seem to have often been movements of warrior groups ; it is said that the name Franks originally meant Spearmen (others think it meant the men of the Francisca or Throwing Axe), and that only in course of time did it come to mean the Free (perhaps the Privileged would be a truer definition). Conquering, and no doubt plundering, spearmen, rurally-minded, took to themselves indigenous, more or less Romanized women, and thus the Latin tradition in speech survived, leading to the evolution of the French language in Gaul and eventually to the overawing of the barbarians by the Church. Later on, the spread of Islam on the Mediterranean coasts became a further factor of urban decline in Gaul, the people of which for centuries were little able to develop communications with or to exercise influence upon Britain as they had previously done.

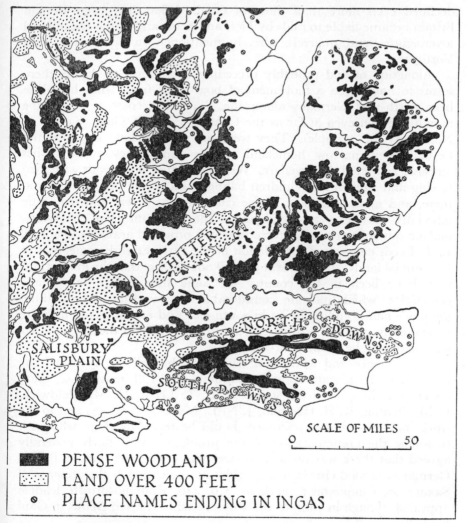

DENSE WOODLAND
LAND OVER 400 FEET
PLACE NAMES ENDING IN INGAS

FIG. 32

Map of distribution of place-names with the old suffix -ingas, now -ing

For a while the heathen Franks and Saxons cut Britain off from its old links with Rome, and British cities, mostly weaker for various reasons than those of Gaul, seem to have lost their idea of bishops and to have declined even more than those of Gaul. What had been Roman Britain became liable to raids by Picts and Scots and to the rise of local sovereignties and quarrels, already mentioned in connection with Vortigern.

Alongside of and probably preceding these military events there seems to have been a movement of boat-loads from what has since been north-west Germany along the North Sea coast to the Rhine mouths and on even as far as the Channel coast of Gaul (Bayeux in Normandy for example). They were probably seeking opportunities beyond their narrow homeland, where sand-dunes and marshes seriously restricted their welfare. We may picture boat-loads with men rowing and women and children baling, with a cow or two here and there, and some iron tools. Some came up the rivers and fed cattle especially on the water-meadows of the alluvium near the rivers, making settlements on river terraces which provided arable land above. E. T. Leeds emphasises the relation of the early English cemeteries to the alluvial lands, an important point if one realises that the immigrants may have been in the country for some time before they made cemeteries, which indicate considerable communities. Many think the place names ending in *ing* in south-east and east England indicate a very early phase of settlement; usually they are on the lighter drier soils and will be mentioned later on.

The whence and whither of what may be collectively called the early English migrations and conquests are still matters of great uncertainty in spite of the studies of E. T. Leeds, H. M. Chadwick, F. M. Stenton, R. H. Hodgkin, J. N. L. Myres and others, and to the works of these scholars reference should be made by those who wish to follow the argumentation of the problems. It is fairly generally agreed that there was no sudden sweeping conquest ; indeed Bishop Germanus' second visit (A.D. 447) gives no indication of the presence of Saxons as conquerors ; and, in A.D. 446, Romano-British leaders appealed, though in vain, to the Romanized barbarian Aetius in Gaul for help.

Some time after this, Kent seems still to have had commercial contacts with the Rhineland, as finds of jewellery have shown. Some of the post-Roman jewellery of Kent is probably of British make, and we have already seen that there has been a measure of continuity in Kent, and, probably also, in East Anglia from pre-Roman times through the Roman period and onwards to mediæval and later times.

PLATE 13

S. C. Porter

LAVENHAM, the Hall of the Guild of Corpus Christi. March

PLATE 14

John Markham

Military help to Romano-Britons against Picts from Scotland was given by Saxon bands who later disagreed with their allies and began a spreading conquest not long after 446. They did not quickly attain a general victory over the Britons ; there must be some truth behind the tradition of a British victory at the Saxon siege of Mons Badonicus about 500 A.D. (various calculations place it between 493 and 516; E. T. Leeds suggests a later date). In Nennius' *Historia Brittonum* and in Bede the hero of that fight is Arthur (p. 119) ; in Gildas we have only one doubtful reference to such a person. Archaeologists are in agreement that the " English " conquerors did little between 500 and 550 ; and this is an indication of the magnitude of their defeat at Mount Badon (the site of which is still unidentified though some believe it was near Bath).

Arthur has become the basis of legends that, at any rate, emphasise features of Atlantic Britain (pp. 2-4). Coastal life along the Irish Sea at this period was active and apparently prosperous in some measure, though the times were too disturbed for large scale organization. Stories from several sources relating to different men have gathered around Arthur in the course of time.

The Wansdyke, from near Newbury and Marlborough westwards to Clevedon, probably began in the time of Roman decline, perhaps even as a protection to a British community gathered chiefly on Salisbury Plain. If one may think chroniclers are right in associating the British victory in the siege of Mons Badonicus with the Britons of Salisbury Plain (p. 119), Wansdyke may have served as a defensive boundary against English onsets from the north. There is considerable ground for thinking that some " English " advanced from the Wash south-westwards, as well as from Thanet westwards south of the Thames in fairly early days. The latter may well have been mercenaries of Romano-Britons at first. The neighbourhood of Dorchester-on-Thames has yielded hints of this advance from graves of the fifth century's second half, if not even earlier. The immigrants had previously practised cremation, but, apparently, in Britain they came into contact with the custom of interment and with the idea, specially developed under Christian influence, of putting no grave-goods with the dead. This change of custom and some transitional cases give a warning not to argue dogmatically from regional customs in other matters.

The chroniclers speak of West Saxons landing on the south coast and use the name Cerdicesora, conjecturally placed on Southampton

K

Water. The *Anglo-Saxon Chronicle* under the year 495 mentions the leaders Cerdic and Cynric, names that have given rise to much discussion because they seem Celtic. In 519 there was a battle at Cerdicesford which may have become Charford on the Avon ; but it is chiefly after 550 that Wessex really looms up. Probably before that time the newcomers were struggling for footholds, founding valley villages (p. 8) and intermarrying with native women. The landing of two ships at *Portes mutha* has been construed as a reference to Portsmouth, but this

FIG. 33
The Wansdyke, Marlborough Downs

must not be taken as certain. The whole story is difficult to interpret, and it is just possible that we have here another of those associations of Briton and Saxon that have already been noted for Vortigern and Hengist above, perhaps combining to defend Salisbury Plain and its southward links with the coast against people advancing from the north-east and also up the Thames (p. 130). The chronicle allows us to infer that disaster fell upon Wessex later in the sixth century in the reign of Ceawlin (584-593), another Celtic name, it seems, perhaps corresponding to later Colin. A battle of Fethan leag (584) was probably in north-east Oxfordshire, and Woddesbeorg at which Ceawlin was routed in 592 is Woodborough in the Vale of Pewsey.

The " Early English " remains on the south coast of what became

Wessex and in the Isle of Wight suggest links with Kent and the supposed Jutes, and it is well to remember again here that Kent is a region with much continuity from Romano-Celtic times. Whether this or some continental mingling with Celtic elements has anything to do with the supposedly more or less Celtic names Cerdic, Cynric and Ceawlin is anyone's guess. The ultimate defeats Ceawlin suffered may be supposed to have been inflicted by his English rivals from farther north and north-east, or from the more easterly part of the Thames basin. The thought of an " English "- Celtic combination of some sort in sixth-century Wessex (Salisbury Plain, etc.) seems worth entertaining, but not at present emphasising.

An interesting statement in the *Anglo-Saxon Chronicle* mentions that Cuthwulf in 571 defeated the Britons at the unidentified Bedcanford or Bedeanford (Bedford is a much disputed identification) and took towns near the Chilterns (Limbury, Aylesbury, Bensington and Eynsham). This suggests, if it be taken as a statement of fact, that the Chiltern Hundreds (p. 194) were a centre in which British life lingered on, a very probable inference.

Another survival of British life was in Elmet, Yorkshire, stretching from the west end of the Humber to the Pennines. This British area was of special importance in that it separated the conquerors of north-eastern England (who came to be known as Northumbrians) from the conquerors of the Midlands. Both are traditionally known as Anglian, but Anglian, Saxon and Jute may be names that came to be applied to mixed groups probably because of the name and associations of a leader, or of some considerable element in an aggregate of families. Another possible British survival is that to which reference has already been made in connection with Lincolnshire (p. 113).

It may be thought surprising that so little Celtic influence penetrated into early English speech, if these possible survivals of the pre-Saxon population actually occurred. But it was not primarily a Celtic, it was rather a Romano-British survival ; the people had largely forgotten their Celtic or it was at any rate decadent, and one doubts the command of Latin by the ordinary folk. Moreover the English often came over in families,[1] so that intermarriage was probably not very general just at first though it soon became common. Hampshire and Dorset have apparently preserved a few traces of Celtic place-names, but they are generally rare, except for names like Avon, Ouse, Axe, Exe.

[1] The use of the kinship suffix " ing " in their early place-names suggests this.

Professors Wooldridge and Linton have published interesting studies bringing out environmental, and especially soil-type factors affecting the spread of the early English into the country and the former has given a valuable summary in the chapter he has contributed to the *Historical Geography of England* edited by Professor Darby. South-west Essex, north-west Middlesex, the boulder-clay (or related deposits) on the top of the Chilterns, and a good deal of Surrey and Berkshire and the Weald had dense woods on heavy clay, and formed, one might say, a partial barrier around north Kent and London ; while sterile, rather acid soils with the water-table deep down characterised the Bagshot area, the Blackheath plateau of south-east London, the gravel areas near Beaconsfield and near Chelmsford, the sandlings of Suffolk and the Breckland of Norfolk.

The lowland between the Blackheath plateau and the Thames had much more water-cover than now, and may thus have allowed boatloads coming up the river to bypass London and so to reach western Surrey which has place-names with the *ing* suffix (see fig. 32, p. 125. This suffix was appended to family or stock-names on the continent and was used by early settlers in Britain for a habitat of a man's kinsfolk-group or of a man with subordinates. Lethridge thinks it was used for a summer settlement, but only before the seventh century. It is important on the more porous soils above the Medway, which seems to have been a significant entry for some of the megalith-builders, and is an area in which loams are not too heavy. It is historically and pre-historically very different from east Kent. The heavy clays of Essex and the clay lands of the north Kent coast have fewer *ing* names. Names with the suffix *ham*[1] are common both on the continent and in

---

[1] *Ham* seems to have been used for a farm or estate and it went out of use in later Saxon times. It is rare beyond the Jurassic scarp; it is commonest in East Anglia, Essex, Cambridge, Surrey and Sussex. It is often found on the clay-loams and sometimes suggests a clearing and settlement under a leader. *Hamm* may be allied to Hem (to shut in) and apparently means an enclosed possession ; *hamm* also meant the bend of the knee and is sometimes used for a meadow bounded by a river-bend. *Tun* (*Ton*) came to be the commonest Anglo-Saxon suffix and was at first an enclosure containing a village or at least a group of dwellings. It is possible that the change from the early use of *ing* and perhaps of *ham* to the later use of *tun* or *ton* has some relation to the change from kinship to neighbourhood as the commoner basis of a group or cluster of householders. It may be noted here that in regions of more persistent Celtic tradition, especially in Ireland, an old type of cluster is the Clachan (p. 242) and this is supposed to have been originally a group of kinsfolk. Suffixes such as Hurst, Der (pasture for pigs), Holt, Wood, Ley are fairly common in the cleared woodland of the interior, including the Weald. Some of these settlements may have been almost as small as single farms, probably with serfs. The higher lands in the centre of the Weald (Hastings Sands) did not encourage settlement. See Professor Wooldridge's book on the Weald in this series.

Britain, but those with the suffix *tun* (*ton*) are almost absent from the continent. *Ham* occurs especially at creek-heads in N. Kent, e.g. Faversham, Teynham, Luddenham. *Ingham*, a combined suffix occurs notably in N. Kent, west of the Stour. *Ing* names do not occur west of the Goring gap of the Thames.

Ing names are common in Sussex along the coast except between the Adur and the Ouse, where old villages seem to have been lost through invasion by the sea. The northern foot of the South Downs, thanks to springs emerging from beneath the chalk, was another zone of early settlement, enriched by the presence of downland pastures above.

The woodland-on-heavy-clay barrier zone above mentioned was to some extent broken by the Roman roads from London and by a few natural features such as the Hog's Back in Surrey, and the water and gravels of the lower and middle Thames and the Lea. Lowland gravels, and river terraces with the water-table near the surface, but at the same time reasonably good drainage, were favourable to the English settlers, who specially valued the water-meadows for cattle, but lighter land for sheep, as the wet lands are infested with water-snails that carry parasites of sheep. Zones around the foot of the chalk, where chalk outwash lightened otherwise heavy clay, were also useful, and so were areas covered by chalky boulder clay in Hertfordshire, Essex and East Anglia once they were cleared. The land lightened by calcareous outwash on either side of the Northamptonshire scarp was also valuable, and became the centre of characterization of the Middle Angles. This area was separated from East Anglia by the Fens, with a way across south of those fens *via* what became Cambridge ; the East Anglian region was further marked off from the south-west by a good deal of dense wood. The sandlings of Suffolk helped to divide East Anglia from Essex. Though Cambridge was a place for landing, that region is without *ing* place names.

The relation of the Middle Angles (from their Northamptonshire centre) to the other early English who went into the upper Thames basin is a matter on which opinion is not settled. E. T. Leeds thought of an advance from the Wash area where the water then reached further inland, and he pictured an advance right away to the Upper Thames. This remains a probable inference ; but it is likely that the way up the Thames may also have been used, perhaps, so far as Oxfordshire is concerned, after the custom of using *ing* as a suffix in place names had declined, that is, after the small family group had given place to the larger less closely related cluster. The penetration from the Middle Anglian region may thus have been an earlier one, if, again, the episode which culminated at Mount Badon about 500 A.D. was a conflict between the people of Salisbury Plain and its margins, on the one hand, and people to the north (and north of the Wansdyke), on the other.

West and north-west of the Middle Anglian country of Northamptonshire was an area with much heavy clay and dense woodland— one thinks of Sherwood and Arden. Beyond this, on the slopes around the southern end of the Pennines for example, the glacial deposits are often gravelly or sandy, and there is much sandstone outwash. Here, again, was a relatively favourable area, generally allowed to have been the nucleus of Mercia, bounded to the south-west by the forest of Blore near the boundaries between Staffordshire and Shropshire.

North of the marshes of the Humber and the woodlands of Elmet (S. Yorkshire lowland), York, the old northern capital, the " Street " to the Roman Wall, commemorated in place names such as Chester-le-Street, as well as the Pennine uplands themselves, all suggest lingerings of Romano-British and even Celtic elements. Northumbria, too, or, in early days, Bernicia (Northumberland, etc.), and Deira (E. Yorkshire), was probably Anglo-British rather than purely English. The historic Archdiocese of York, and the political power of the bishops of Durham suggest respectively the early separateness of the north, and the later need for close attention to what became the Scots border. West of the Pennines and north of the Mersey mosses English penetration was slower, but Anglians appear to have come through Pennine gaps, and probably related Mercians spread northwards to the east of the mosses (i.e. via what became the Stockport-Manchester area). It is characteristic that the Mercian diocese of Lichfield once reached northwards to the Ribble, beyond which the country was then in the diocese of York. Early ecclesiastical provinces no doubt look back to folk groups in many cases, and, in view of what was said a little above concerning the Middle Angles, it may be relevant to recall that the diocese of Dorchester-on-Thames at one period (not the earliest) reached north through Northamptonshire and Lincolnshire to the Humber.

We may next try to picture some of the villages of the English settlers as they developed beyond the pioneer stage. They might choose the edge of a gravel terrace above the water-meadows as the site for habitations. These might be grouped in linear fashion along the edge, or, sometimes, but more rarely, gathered in irregular fashion, but close together, on some part of the terrace or other relatively well-drained spot. The rest of the terrace, perhaps with gravelly soil or with loam lightened by calcareous outwash from chalk or oolite outcrops above, would become the village arable. It might verge upon oak woodland where gravel gave place to clay, or upon grassland and bush, especially if near calcareous strata. Woodland would give timber for the frames of houses and acorns for the swine, also fuel for domestic use, and for smelting. Grassland gave pasture for cattle and sheep (these latter on drier soils to avoid parasites), and, on the one hand, enriched the stock-raising side of agriculture, but, on the other hand, might mean that the cattle and sheep were less often on the arable fields which would therefore be less manured. Wheat had been exported from Roman Britain ; that export ceased, wooden bowls replaced earthenware, leather replaced woven stuffs, clogs replaced hob-nailed boots.

When the church organization developed, the village as an economic unit tended to become the parish and in some cases its lands would stretch from the pasture land just mentioned through the arable and the habitations and also the water-meadow to the river, making a long strip. If the river was a very small one the parish might stretch across it and include water-meadow, arable and perhaps down-land on the other side, on which, at some place on a porous surface, a subsidiary hamlet might develop. In the case of some rivers of more consequence, less easily bridged by mere villagers, strip parishes are, in some places, in double series, one on each side of the stream. But it must be borne in mind that arrangements of villages and parishes vary greatly with circumstances. All that can be said in a general way is that a habitation site, land for hay, arable fields and if possible some pasture land and some woodland would be included in a parish, the village of which had to be nearly self-sufficient.

The quite irregular agglomeration of houses into a village is much rarer and seems to have been less characteristic in the early days of what had become England than in north-west Germany, from which many of the early English came. There the *Haufendorf* is a character-istic feature ; among us the village around a green or along a trackway of some kind (for example along a river-terrace) is far commoner. Perhaps we may venture the opinion that the quite irregular *Haufendorf* of north-west Germany owes its form to an older time[1] than that of the migrations of the post-Roman centuries. During those centuries villages were established east of the Elbe where we pass through a zone noted for villages around a green (the *Rundling* type) to a zone in which the houses are along a trackway (*Strassendorf* or street village). The form of the village is probably far more closely related to circumstances of topography and soils and of the time of its establishment than to the ethnic, often miscalled racial, factors that have sometimes been invoked. August Meitzen's wonderful treasury of data (1895) concerning villages must be used with care for this reason; he was too apt to bring in ethnic factors to explain distributions that depend on quite other things. Early English villages notably avoid the immediate vicinity of Roman roads, which were no doubt the means whereby conquerors, itinerant craftsmen, traders and marauders pursued their often nefarious aims. We must also remember that wickerwork and probably clogs were important and were no doubt often made by itinerant groups (Bacaudae, see p. 113).

Little has been said so far in this chapter about brooches and other ornaments buried with the early English dead in their pre-Christian days, or sometimes, in the quite early stages, burned with the dead who were cremated (see p. 127), and placed in the urn containing the ashes. One reason is that the subject is going through a transition phase in its study, owing to the discovery of most remarkable jewellery in a memorial, apparently to an Anglian king of about 650 A.D., at Sutton Hoo in Suffolk. The find has revealed workmanship and beauty of a grade hitherto hardly equalled from any early period in our country, but perhaps paralleled or surpassed in Ireland ; and the study of the many objects found is actively proceeding (1948-9) : As, however, 650 A.D. is well after the idea of cremation went out of fashion among the early English, it is perhaps not very likely that new views to be reached through research on the Sutton Hoo material will seriously affect opinions about the very early brooches. Material of the fifth century has been found to a notable extent south-west of Cambridge, an early landing-place.

What are called equal-armed brooches are well known from north-west Germany, and fine specimens are known from near Cambridge and are dated to the fifth century. As has been well said,

---

[1] Some of the British villages of Roman and immediately pre-Roman times seem to have been examples of a poor variety of this type.

if they were made in England, the people concerned must have been in the country for some time previously ; they are no work for the pioneer phase. The brooch may be described as a T standing on a base nearly as large as the cross-bar of the T ; the curvilinear decoration is very elaborate and characteristically covers every bit of the brooches. The style had not evolved to the more refined phase of appreciating a plain background for a pattern of ornament such as the prehistoric craftsmen in Irish gold, and the makers of the splendid pre-Roman shields found in the Witham and the Thames (see fig. 21, p. 89) and prehistoric Chinese ceramic artists had loved.

The Cambridge area has already been mentioned as the way from East Anglia into Middle Anglia. It may be said to have been an isthmus between those two important areas, with marsh and water (Ouse, Cam, etc.) on the north and a considerable proportion of woodland to the south. Before the drainage of the fens, boats could come near Cambridge's site, so it is appropriate that the brooches of a type known from north-west Germany, west of the Elbe, should be found near such a landing place in Britain. Similarities in urns containing ashes are also generally accepted for " Saxon " Germany west of the Elbe and the Cambridge area. This area furnishes some of the quite early evidence for the English in Britain, not only of objects also known from the Elbe-Weser (i.e. Saxon) area of Germany, but also of cruciform brooches like those found in Anglian areas in Schleswig. It is probable that families from both areas came over, brought some of their valuables with them and intermingled in this Cambridge area, becoming Anglian (Middle Anglian) in due course through conquest by Mercia. It would be tempting to state that people who landed here went on along the scarp-side of the Chalk (Icknield Way) to the upper Thames which also has fair evidence of Saxons before 500 A.D. (see also p. 127), but it is possible that that region was reached via the Thames, perhaps by groups of men who came first as mercenaries. Discoveries are occurring so quickly that we may well leave this question undecided ; it may merely be added that old views concerning a fifth century approach to the upper Thames from the south (i.e. through Wessex) seem to have faded out. The dearth of really early English graves in Wiltshire and their absence from Hampshire is significant. The absence of place names ending in *ing* is a Cambridgeshire feature, and this suggests (see p. 130) that research is still very much needed.

O. G. S. Crawford's air surveys have shown that, on Salisbury Plain and some of its margins, British villages were sited on hilltops and other prominent spots, whereas English settlements are mostly near the rivers. There seem to be no cremation graves of early English style south of the Wansdyke. (p. 127). It seems as though early attempts to spread the English life into Wiltshire from the south were slow and that the making of new settlements using the valleys proceeded rather piecemeal, probably from the middle of the sixth century, but all such opinions are very tentative and subject to revision as more discoveries are made. Air surveys and the study of early English cremations and burials have already produced so much new knowledge that it is difficult to say more than that the older accounts are, at the least, subject to considerable revision.

The question of the continuity of Saxon London from Roman and possibly pre-Roman London has often been debated, and it may be hoped that examination of sites laid bare in the raids of 1940-45 may shed new light on the subject. For the present, the old opinion championed by G. L. Gomme seems to gain favour, namely that some sort of continuity did occur, but whether there was at times more than a remnant clinging to the old city we cannot say. R. E. M. Wheeler thinks the Grim's[1] dykes or ditches on Harrow Weald and the Chilterns and the Aestendic of Bexley indicate boundary lines of sub-Roman times ; and the Chilterns were a traditional hunting ground for London, quoted in early medieval documents ; they are also a region in which the British population seems to have lingered on.

The *Anglo-Saxon Chronicle* speaks of the flight of the British from north Kent to London in 457, but one must not place too much confidence in this. At the other end of the time-gap in our information, it is evident from the records of the Christianization of the early English that London was of some importance about 600 A.D. or a little later. The almost complete absence, up to the present, of finds from the fifth and sixth centuries in London is an important fact to be weighed in this connection. The absence of early English burials in the London area is another fact ; some might say they have been destroyed, others think they never were there because the site remained British until the late sixth century. It is at any rate probable that early

---

[1] Grim, Grime and related forms are derivable from a Saxon word for demon. The use of this in place names illustrates the widespread habit of ascribing anything mysterious to demons or supernatural powers.

English families in boat-loads would not be attracted to London. They wanted arable and pasture ; they were seeking new homes as farmers. The boats could row on, passing a decayed London, for the river was then spread much more widely southwards than it is now.

Anglo-Saxon farming has already been mentioned here and there. It has probably been a mistake of some writers to picture Anglo-Saxons setting out a land system as soon as possible after they arrived, and to discuss the selected system in a particular region as an ethnic feature. We may imagine that the earliest English immigrants, perhaps even before the so-called ending of Roman rule, were inclined to avoid areas of Romano-British population, and naturally had little or no interest in towns as such. In Kent, Essex and East Anglia the local systems of compact fields of the Middle Ages, so different from the large open fields of many areas further west, may go back to the Anglian Immigration. If the Anglians came from Angel (S. E. Slesvig), as one may judge from later evidence, compact fields may have been the scheme there. The compact fields of East Anglia may go back even farther to Roman and pre-Roman times. One must, however, beware of taking the " compact farm " system of a region in later centuries as necessarily implying such a system in sub-Roman days. Meitzen set out several regions as characterised by the tradition of the compact farm (*Einzelhof*) where later workers have found that the *Einzelhof* has succeeded a communal system of some kind akin to those to be discussed below. Nearly everywhere the " little men " in farming find they must exchange services and sometimes implements. Some kind of co-operation, not necessarily enthusiastic or even good-humoured, is often dictated by circumstances. And the circumstances of sub-Roman times forced forward that idea.

The iron-shod ploughshare with a coulter was apparently spreading considerably after some centuries of use, probably since a century or so before the Roman conquest of Western Europe. It was to be pulled by four or even six oxen and this of itself suggests collection of animals from more than one farmer. The turning of the team of oxen in a small field has been thought to have militated against the small field, since the turning area, or headland, would have occupied a considerable proportion of the side, and, it has been assumed, would have had to be left waste. This argument attempting to account for big communal fields has probably been somewhat overdone. At the same time it must be allowed that ploughing a large field would take less time and be more efficient than ploughing the same area cut into small enclosures occupied and worked by different households. Also, once the coulter and the iron ploughshare had come into use on the deeper loams, they overturned the soil along the furrow and there was no point in ploughing "along and across" as had apparently been customary with the little plough of earlier times. We cannot but think, however, that the pioneer phase of English settlement in England was still dependent on a small plough in many places.

Wheat, in particular, is an exhausting crop, and, in our western climates, can be grown effectively only once in two or three years, even with the help of dung. The little man with only half or a third of his land under wheat would often have only a small area to plough, and dunging by his few beasts would not be very effective. On the other hand ploughing of one third of a large communal field could be more successful ; and the cattle of the village turned in after harvest to eat the weeds growing in the stubble would spread dung fairly generally over it.

It is permissible to think that the big iron ploughshare and coulter, the ox-team, and the dunging of the fields all played their part in the development of the communal fields so characteristic both of N.W. Germany between Elbe and Weser and of the English Midlands and their margins. At the same time it is also permissible to suppose that the systems of communal agriculture and large open fields so prevalent over a zone of Britain from Dorset to Durham owed something to the similar systems in N.W. Germany. There is evidence of long strips in Jutland from a date well before the first English movement to Britain. That these systems developed in the English Midlands but not in Kent and East Anglia can be ascribed to the existence already in the latter regions in pre-English times of cereal farming on established lines, as well as perhaps to the coming of people from Angel (p. 137).

A word must be added here about Wessex. If what was said earlier (p. 128) about British villages and survivals in this area was reasonable, why should not the old system, whatever it was, persist here as, it has been suggested, it did in Kent and East Anglia? The answer is that it was not the same system. Kent and East Anglia apparently had a fairly large plough with coulter before Roman times ; and Roman villas, especially in Kent, must also have had considerable influence on agricultural development. In western Wessex, on the other hand, the British villages were on hilltops with relatively minor cultivation, and probably no, or very few, really large ploughs. Moreover, the English came into Wessex or at any rate spread over Wessex some time after 500 A.D., by which time they were moving as clusters larger than the small groups of kinsmen of the earliest phases. The paucity, even absence over large areas of Wessex, of *ing* place names and of cremation burials, supports this idea of general lateness of the occupation. Further, it has already been said (p. 136) that Crawford has shown that the English villages in the valleys developed a scheme of land division and farming disregarding the old and doubtless decadent system of the British villages higher up.

It should be borne in mind also here that societies which cultivate but lack an effective manuring scheme are apt to decline as they exhaust the available soil, unless the cultivators can move to fresh fields. The decline of the Maya civilization of Central America was probably due to this, and it is a menace in several African areas. Regions of loess soil, among which one may include parts of East Anglia (" Brickearth "), feel this difficulty less ; the organic matter in the loess derived from decayed grass gives plant food for a very long time.

A heavy iron-shod plough could be directed with the share edge oblique, and this would help to overturn the soil, or, more effectively, " ears " could be added on one or both sides of the ploughshare, or a board (mould-board) could be placed on one side to throw the lifted earth down again. We know that medieval ploughs had mould-boards ; probably some of the ploughs of sub-Roman days had some device to the same end.

A communal scheme of agriculture lends itself to the development of an aristocracy, whether it be of officials as in some modern cases, or of war leaders as was likely to be the case in periods of ignorance and disorder. The genealogies of Offa, those of the dynasty of Cerdic, and many others tell of the importance of leaders, sometimes of a leader who was *primus inter pares* rather than a despot with a legal and administrative scheme under his control. Genealogies are apt to be treasured by emigrants, as we know from New England. One can easily see that groups with leaders for defence were more effective than a gathering of families landing from boats, struggling with a new environment in jealousy of one another, squalor and fear of indigenous demons, watching increasingly against encroachments as settlements grew and new fields became more difficult to acquire or redeem from forest or waste. The leader or king would usually have to rule along customary lines if he wanted to carry the people with him ; and the group of sub-leaders (eorls or king's companions—earls) might declare the custom of the people which should be followed rather than initiate experiments on new lines. And the people (ceorls—churls) would be called upon to furnish food, farm labour and war service for their masters, both the lesser lords of villages and groups of villages and the greater lords or kings and their relatives (ethelings).

The need for years of rest for the soil (fallowing) had already made itself felt in N.W. Germany, it was at least as great in the English Midlands west of what has been called above (p. 135) the Cambridge isthmus. On some lands of calcareous Jurassic rocks and some chalk lands (when not too heavily covered with the boulder-clay) most notably in the Midlands, i.e. from the Humber to Dorset, but not in East Anglia and the Chilterns and North and South Downs, large open fields, in which families held strips, were ploughed in alternate years, and thus left to rest and to be dunged by cattle one year in two. This is the two-field system and it probably was as much as most of this soil could stand under the then conditions.

On the moderately heavy clays of the Midlands north-west of the Jurassic line (beyond Lincoln Edge, Northampton, etc.), it was possible to put in a " spring crop " of barley or oats, later sometimes of beans, in a year interpolated between that of the wheat (or rye) crop and the fallow year. This is the three-field system—wheat, oats (or some alternative) and fallow. It used two-thirds of the land for food in each year, and allowed the land some time for rest and dunging between the harvesting of the wheat and the ploughing for oats or another spring crop towards the next Easter. In the introductory regional survey (p. 14) reference has already been made to the dominance of the three-field system in Staffordshire and parts of Shropshire where the two-field system either never existed or at any rate does not seem to have left any traces. Two and three-field systems seem to have occurred side by side in some areas. In every region there were also other, often quite special, arrangements, made, for example, between partners in a wood-clearing effort.

It seems impossible to argue profitably how far the above communal systems of cultivation were founded by co-operation of heads of families and how far they were imposed by lords ; the probability is that, in the beginning, a good deal of consent was necessary, as people might escape easily and join itinerant groups of marauders, while, as the scheme developed and spread, controllers gained an advantage. This hierarchical scheme became more important as the village of neighbours superseded the older hamlet of kinsmen. The association of hunting with the training of warriors has been very widespread, and hunting in the woodlands or on the waste was linked with the defence of people and crops against rovers of the wild. This function of the warriors and especially of their leaders helped to make the authority of the aristocracy more secure, especially as wild life became a little less abundant, varied and dangerous, and hunting came to be more especially a pastime and a sport for those who could escape the more menial tasks of the farming routine and could keep a horse for riding and a falcon or goshawk trained to help to bring down prey. These considerations help us to picture the broad features of the later development of the lordship of what became known as the manor, specially characteristic of areas under the open-field systems, whether two-field or three-field (p. 246). In these cases the lord and his agents might contribute to the direction of the communal system, which involved imposition of a measure of uniformity and completion of ploughing, sowing and reaping by certain dates often marked by festivals. In lands such as Kent and East Anglia the manor tended to be smaller. and in the persistently Celtic west and north it was weaker and the routine was different.

In spite of much new light of recent years from the field study of archæology, from geographical studies of the local environments in different parts and from what may be called the higher criticism of the writing of Gildas and of the great Bede as well as of the poem of Beowulf, lives of the saints and other lesser sources, the general picture is still a confused one. It is quite probable that it will have to be redesigned after another generation of work on the subject.

We see Romano-Britons struggling in the east and south-east to hold on to what they could from the Roman heritage ; and less Romanized and non-Romanized Britons further west setting up kingdoms and employing mercenaries from Germany, while families were probably already spreading into the creeks of north Kent and East Anglia and up the Wash to the Cambridge district. Mercenaries employed by Romano-Britons became conquerors on their own account and took more than their share in the fighting for local power. But it seems increasingly likely that the immigrants, fighters and farmers, did not come in whole tribes or nations and that their traditional ritual and ceremonial were not strongly maintained. The names of Jutes, Angles and Saxons should not be held to imply total diversity of origin or culture ; groups attaining consciousness-of-kind in England may have come to be named from leaders or large elements within a mixed population. Whether much of the Romano-British element was left, consciously as such, by about 700 A.D. is doubtful, but the fact that London was already again of some importance is at least suggestive. Struggles for power between English and Britons (Romanized or not), and among English as well as British groups, make a tangled story, with the successes sometimes on the British side, and with the possibility of temporary English-British combinations, especially in Kent, Wessex and Northumbria.

Christian effort found both British and English without very definite religious tradition. The Roman heritage had weakened, the English heritage had got muddled in the migrations. The monastic tradition from Egypt spread to Lerins, off the Mediterranean coast of France, and from Lerins to western Gaul and Britain ; and there was also the powerful influence of S. Martin of Tours, in west Gaul. The old sea-route of Iron Age B and of early megalithic times came into importance again ; and the Celtic saints preached and wandered, but apparently developed little ecclesiastical organization save under the proud Columba from his centre at Iona. In 597 the Roman Church sent St. Augustine to Canterbury and others came later to other areas. In 664 the synod at Whitby decided in favour of certain Roman usages and against those which Iona favoured. Our islands were thus brought into the culture-stream which the Roman Church maintained and developed from the Imperial Roman heritage. The English conquest went on, with the Roman ecclesiastical tradition as a mainstay, but also a good deal from the Celtic Christian tradition of learning and skill so notably shown in the Book of Kells and the Lindisfarne Gospels, and also evident in the remarkable reverence paid to St. Cuthbert and his tomb, now, after many journeys, in the great cathedral of Durham, and in the sanctity of Glastonbury carried on from Celtic through early English to medieval days.

It seems that, after about 600 A.D., struggles between English and Romano-British in what was, in the stricter sense, becoming England had little importance ; and the next phase was characterised by the spread of the power of the Roman Church and by struggles between

PLATE 15

Robert Atkinson

PARGETTED PLASTER between the beams of a timber frame house,
probably seventeenth or early eighteenth century, Saffron Walden

PLATE 16

John Markham

a. COURT BARN, West Pennard, Somerset. Mediaeval manors and monasteries, dependent on dues paid in kind, had to build barns. Windows were reduced to a minimum. June

Robert Atkinson

b. JORDANS MEETING HOUSE of the Society of Friends, an eighteenth-century building near Beaconsfield. September

various English rulers. This phase covers practically two centuries, during which monasteries and cathedrals under the Roman Church came into existence and accumulated treasure from gifts. The cathedrals in several cases were founded by monks, but the founders were not expected to live the monastic life ; they were too busy with church affairs for that.

Rulers made defensive boundary ramparts and ditches, sometimes called running earthworks, and a number of these have been studied in exemplary detail by Sir Cyril Fox. The most important of all is Clawdd Offa (Offa's dyke) built by Offa, king of Mercia, and, more or less, overlord of England south of the Humber during the later part of the eighth century. It still runs continuously from north to south near Ruabon and Buttington and Clun, but apparently only fragments were built on the plain of Hereford. Fox thinks the gaps in this part of the dyke occur where there was then almost impenetrable forest. Beyond the plain of Hereford to the south the entrenched meanders of the Wye formed a sufficient barrier. East of Offa's Dyke in the north there runs for several miles a smaller and possibly rather older earthwork now known as Wat's Dyke. It may be an earlier effort superseded by the great design of Offa, which, we must note, left various villages with undoubted English names on the Welsh side. Fox in his *Archæology of the Cambridge District* gives a study of running earthworks there, and these dykes were the scenes of many struggles.

The construction of these earthworks, the growth of abbeys and bishoprics, the efforts towards a supreme kingship, the style of the few documents surviving from the courts of rulers such as Offa and Egbert, the occurrence of English coins in Frisia and the mention of Frisian merchants in Britain in the seventh and eighth centuries, all show that the English were evolving towards a more organised and civilized condition. Offa was able to treat on fairly equal terms with Charlemagne, who, in one crisis of their mutual relations, closed the ports of his empire for about three years against trade from England.

We can picture the English now (towards 800) settled as farmers, after much intermarriage with the descendants of Romano-Britons, with less military aptitude than their forebears of the fifth and sixth centuries, but with better equipment and more craftsmanship, though urban development seems to have been slight. The country lay open to attack once more and ominous events occurred in the last years of the eighth century as will be discussed in the next chapter. The

L

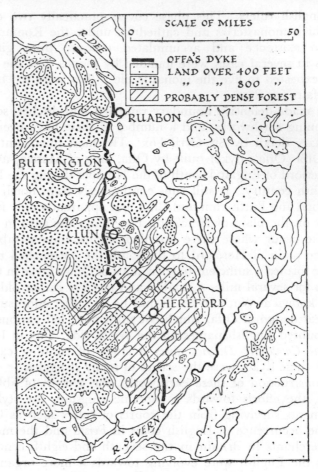

FIG. 34

Offa's Dyke.   (After Sir Cyril Fox)

English in Wessex had cut off the Celtic-speaking people of Wales
from those of Cornwall and Devon already before the end of the sixth
century ; and by the eighth century the Welsh were also cut off from
their old connections with Cumbria and Strathclyde. Only in the eighth
century, however, did the Welsh clergy agree to accept the Roman
scheme for the calculation of Easter ; and, as we hear of the martial
prowess of Rhodri Mawr (Roderick the Great) in the ninth century

and of the codification of laws by Hywel Dda (Hywel the Good) in the tenth, we realise that Wales was still largely independent. Indeed, it is thought that Offa's Dyke was built while Mercia and Wales were at peace ; and, certainly, its plan and execution do not suggest the emergencies of war. The language of Wales by this time could be called Welsh and probably had obliterated traces of Gaelic used for a

0   12 Inches

FIG. 35

Inscribed stone, Cymyn, Carmarthenshire, with both Latin and Ogham script

while after the third century in Pembrokeshire, and also used on some Ogham[1] Stones, chiefly in south-west Wales in the sixth century. Those Ogham[1] inscriptions need not, however, imply much use of Gaelic in common speech ; they may have ecclesiastical associations.

The Welsh lived in kinship groups (Gwely, plural Gwelyau); they depended largely on cattle which they took to the moorland pastures for the summer and brought down to the lowlands for the winter. There were schemes of strip-utilisation for crops here and there probably on an Infield and Outfield system (pp. 148-49). Communications via Anglesey and Pembrokeshire with Ireland indicate some attention to the sea, but in this matter they could not match the Northmen who threatened them in the ninth century. (ch. 7.)

The north of Britain was, in the Dark Ages, hardly as yet to be called Scotland. In the Highlands were clans which have been called

[1] Ogham is a system of writing with long and short strokes (or strokes and points). It was much used in chiselling names on memorial stones in South Ireland and South Wales in the fourth and sixth centuries A.D., i.e. in what may be called the sub-Roman period, during which Irish groups (Deisi) were apparently in Pembrokeshire.

FIG. 36
Map of distribution of Ogham
inscribed stones in the British
Isles

Pictish. In the west, Scots from Ireland had settled and one judges that they must for a while have held main lines of communication, with Iona as one of the foci. In the south, in Strathclyde, Brythonic Celtic-speaking people were a diminishing element between Scots to the north-west (Dalriada, largely now Argyll) and the Anglians of Northumbria, whose sub-kingdom of Bernicia included the south-east of what was to become Scotland. In the ninth century the onset of the Northmen (ch. 7) brought many crises, and Kenneth MacAlpine in 844 became king of the united Picts and Scots, who sought repeatedly to destroy the Northumbrian power in the south-east. They attained this aim only in the early eleventh century (1018) under Malcolm II. His son Duncan succeeded to the kingship of the Picts, the Scots, the Brythonic peoples of Strathclyde, and the Bernician kingdom. Henceforth, the whole territory was known as Scotland, and the rivalries and feuds of the different parts from which it was built up loom very large in Scottish History.

The Scottish people seem to have lived in small hamlet-like groups of inter-related households with an infield and outfield system of cultivation (pp. 148-49) in strips called runrig, and to have depended largely on cattle, which in the cold winter had to be kept in the stable in many parts. The custom of transhumance[1] or booleying seems to have been less suited to the conditions here than in Wales and Ireland.

The human story is woven of so many threads that in order to tell it one must often depart from both the regional and the chronological sequence and one must be allowed to repeat parts of it in their different connections. With this excuse a very short outline of some major phases of evolution of West European cultivation is given as conclusion to this chapter.

The extension of cultivation to many parts of Europe had as its typical first stage *Shifting Cultivation*, the use of a patch for a few years and its later abandonment for recovery of its fertility. This probably occurred in non-forested areas as well as in clearings. On the loess of Central Europe, with patches extending into eastern England, fertility maintained itself better because of organic matter in the soil and of the facility of digging as well as of the drawing up of food-salts to the surface by evaporation (through the vertical channels left after decay of grass-stems as loess accumulated). Deeper loams in which nutritive matter

---

[1] Transhumance is the custom of seasonal movement of herds by settled peoples. Nomadism implies movement of herds by people without settled abodes. In Switzerland and Norway the uphill summer movement is short and the herders are near home, but in a few places in Switzerland (Val d'Anniviers) many people move long distances up and down with the herds ; they have, however, a permanent village below. In parts of the Balkans the permanent village may be on the higher summer pastures. In Spain and the Carpathians, and parts of the Balkans and Albania, the herds may be moved long distances on plateau-pastures in summer, and the herders rough it in huts for months away from their families. In mediæval Wales cattle were moved up to the hill pasture (Hafod) for the summer, the permanent habitation (Hendre) being below. Since the late seventeenth century, more and more sheep have been kept in Wales ; they move up and down seasonally but often belong to a farmer who lives near the upland summer pasture. The increase of sheep was linked with the increase of the woollen industry, helped to some extent by Huguenots. Sometimes the sheep are taken to coastal pastures of sea-thrift in spring. In Ireland the moving of animals seasonally is called Booleying. There are several variants of these seasonal movements of herds in France.

was washed down were more difficult to use until the plough was improved so as to overturn the soil, and these deeper loams were also largely covered by large forest (oak, etc.), difficult to cut until iron came into use.

Closer settlement made adjustments necessary, especially in regions in which the drawing up of salts in solution from the lower layers of the soil by evaporation was not very effective. Where it was effective (e.g., on *Terra Rossa*, etc., in Mediterranean lands), time had to be allowed for that drawing up, and arrangements evolved towards using a patch in alternate years, or sometimes one year in three, and towards frequent scratching of the surface with a small light plough to prevent crusting, and at the same time to leave the deeper soil undisturbed. Where animal manure was available in sufficient amount, a patch might be cultivated year after year. The planting of olive and other trees brought further adjustments. The settlements of agriculturists there are typically concentrated clusters, sometimes almost urban in character even if small. Tall buildings and narrow streets give protection from excess of sunlight and were valued for possibilities of defence. Wide distribution of calcareous rock tends to localise water-supply and to promote clustering around springs. Fishing and trade encouraged settlement over harbours ; and coastal clusters had possibilities of salt-supply from evaporation of sea-water.

In brown earth and podsol regions agriculture generally remained on a low level until the plough was enlarged and adapted to overturning the soil. This enlargement and adaptation of the plough was perhaps begun in the Bronze Age but went ahead when an iron coulter and the iron ploughshare came into use, no doubt a long-drawn-out process. On the loess the drawing up of salts in solution was on the whole more effective than on brown earth or podsol, and the loess was easy to dig and it contained organic matter. Settlement on the loess increased faster than settlement of cleared forest and hill lands. The concentrated cluster is highly typical here ; and crop-growing is very important, though animal husbandry is important, too. The taking of stock to a distance from the growing crops in summer has been a desideratum everywhere. On the brown earth, and still more in podsol regions, and on many hill lands, much has depended on the stock/crop relations. With enough manure, a patch on which the animals were folded at appropriate seasons might be cultivated year after year (" onefield " and infield schemes), while outlying patches might be cultivated turn-about, with strip-shares for the co-operating villagers (outfield contrasted with infield). The moving of the animals away from the crops made a common pasture or the use of the waste an important part of the economy.

It is important to remember that, whereas in late neolithic settlements the animal bones found include a large proportion of those of pigs (probably only half-domesticated), in the Bronze Age and subsequent periods sheep and cattle (beasts needing to be folded more definitely) play a greater part. The iron ploughshare and heavy plough with coulter made oxen and horses more important in farming.

Broadly, the outfield may be looked upon as a modified heritage from early shifting cultivation. It is found especially in regions which have temperatures just high enough for cereals, and which have a good deal of moisture. The infield may be looked upon in the same broad way as an added specialization. The infield and outfield may both be shared between inhabitants of a cluster. The cluster may be under a tacksman or headman who may be the agent of a military lord. This agent may make (or recognise) a cluster, usually of one or a few households, so the cluster will usually be a group of relatives and/or resultants of intermarriage. The kinship bond is typically strong, and we have the clan as one type of group, consisting of a number of clusters of 4 to 30 households. The cluster is a sub-group co-operating in cultivation and sometimes in herding to a certain extent. In Ireland it is traditionally called the clachan.

Where herding predominated very markedly, the arrangements may have been somewhat different. A looser group of cottages seems to have occurred near the upland pastures in the damp west with its lowland forests. But there were, and are, marsh pastures and shore pastures with a great deal of thrift (*Armeria*) and other maritime plants complicating the variations of arrangement.

The results of conquest, etc., have often brought about a distinction between a more servile and a more lordly group, and many intermediate grades with, correspondingly, groups of more or less adjacent cottages.

The headman or nobleman in some regions seems to have had a large establishment (Hall in England, Rath in Ireland), and to have been often primarily concerned with beasts, following the widespread custom of the domination of herders over cultivators. Whether the ' Celtic House ", of which remains are found in the Isle of Man, etc., is in some way analogous with Hall or Rath or both, is an interesting question. The large ancient Scandinavian establishment is another example of the same scheme. (See Chapter 11 for further discussion of these larger early dwellings of various types).

Either infield or outfield patches or both could be divided into parts to be cultivated in succession with or without rotation of crops,

FIG. 37

Elaborate Anglo-Saxon homestead (imaginary reconstruction)

and there seems to have been a fairly widespread idea of dividing a territorial unit into " Quarters ". The Treens and Quarter-lands of the Isle of Man may be recalled to memory here.

After clearing of woodland from brown earth regions the quality of the soil was often good, and the two-field and three-field systems of communal cultivation in such areas may be looked upon as a further specialization. The outfield has not survived here ; it may once have occurred, but if so it seems to have disappeared. The fields were cultivated in rotation, with rotation of crops, typically under a leader (lord of the manor, etc.) Such a leader was more necessary when

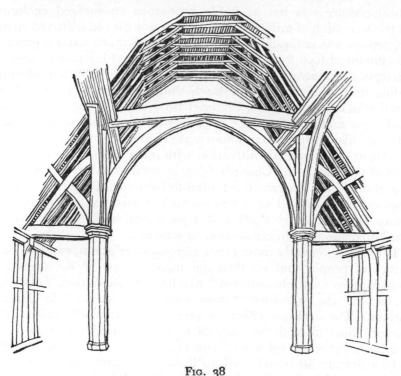

FIG. 38

Diagrammatic cross-section of an Anglo-Saxon hall

winter wheat with its long period in the ground, and the need for a
year's fallow before the sowing of wheat, were established procedure.
This is the great region of the Manor.

In the regions which had oats and barley as chief cereals conditions
were simpler, the crop was a shorter time in the ground, the animals
could be folded on the land for a longer time in the mild autumn
(but less so in the Highlands). The leader here was usually less separate
from his followers. The Manor was less developed or absent.
The widespread occurrence of natural pasture emphasised stock-
farming with seasonal migration (transhumance, booleying, etc., see
p. 147) to keep the animals away from the growing crops.

The introduction of root-crops and potatoes in the eighteenth
century has interfered fundamentally with the scheme of manuring
by folding animals on the fields after harvest. In some regions where

natural pasture was less available root-crops encouraged enclosure and the formation of unified farms, in place of the old scattered strips. This process was naturally slower in areas with much natural pasture. The amount of food from a potato crop promoted increase of population, especially among people who also had cattle for milk. The parsnip, needing deep ploughing of the land, sometimes led to increased co-operation of cultivators (e.g., Channel Isles), but this co-operation was on adjacent unified farms ; the impossibility of stubble pasture where root-crops like parsnips were important (1630 or 1640 onwards) killed old systems of communal cultivation with open fields and strips. The traces of this last in the Channel Isles, apart from Alderney, are very few and dubious. The swede, adapted to loose soil, the potato tolerant of heavy wet soils and of a considerable variety of conditions, the parsnip liking rather rich soil and a good deal of sunshine, have all contributed towards differentiation of schemes.

The cluster, in early times often a group of relations, came to be a mixture of people, and we thus get many a case of the transition " from kinship to neighbourhood " as a basis of association. Following this we get the transition " from status to contract " in human relations. The common effort to take in a portion of outfield, the common effort to send the animals to pasture outside and to bring them back, the whole scheme of communal cultivation, as well as the need for defence all contributed to make the cluster important. The lord also would both gather dependents around his hall, for personal service and care of his animals, and make a distinction between these and the cultivators in a cluster perhaps near, perhaps a little way off, but preferably from his point of view a cluster, because he and his armed men could control them more readily.

The cluster must vary in size with the amount of land, the proportion of stock to crops and so on. Generally the arable cluster has been larger and closer, and often more servile, than the more pastoral cluster, in which the man and his animals must be very close to one another. The lord or chief in a pastoral area seems often to have divided his land under sub-chiefs or headmen, e.g., the quarterlands in Ireland and the Isle of Man.

REFERENCES : see end ch. 8, p. 181.

CHAPTER 7

THE SEA ROVERS

To TRY to understand the phase of British Life most affected by the Sea Rovers we need to picture both the decay on the southern, Roman or Mediterranean side, and the increased enterprise and human pressure on the northern side.

The Roman Empire had fallen and Rome and Constantinople had become headquarters of sections of the Church with fierce mutual hatred, the basis of the problem of east and west in the Europe of 1948. The western or Romanist section of the church profited by the fact that there was no longer an Emperor at Rome, but, through its bishops, it kept some of the Empire's ideas of administration from absolute disappearance. The eastern or Byzantine (usually called Orthodox in later centuries because it objected to the addition of *filioque* to the Nicene creed) section of the church had little of such a scheme of administration to help it, and the continuance of an Emperor at Constantinople was another limiting factor. Division and consequent weakness of the Mediterranean peoples gave an immense opportunity to Islam, and Italy, instead of being a unifying link in the Great Sea, became a projection from terrified Europe into a hostile unknown. Trade and towns declined and, some centuries later, Islam penetrated deeply along the zone of hatred and conflict between Romanist and Orthodox, up the Danube to the walls of Vienna.

In the west, even before Islam advanced through Spain to its defeat by Pepin at Poitiers (732 A.D.), towns and trade had already declined as Roman law and order and Roman roads lost their efficiency, so Roman decline and Islamic advance both weakened the west. The Franks in Gaul and, as we have seen, the early English in Britain, all rurally minded, were not ready to organize effectively until

Charlemagne (800 A.D.) on the continent and, in Britain, the successors of Egbert of Wessex started their none-too-successful efforts. The west, in fact, lay open to fresh attack.

Turning now to the northern side we have a picture of plough cultivation spreading as woodlands were cleared by iron axes. In the Danish peninsula and islands and in Norway the land was in small fractions with local feuds that naturally were more serious in the fjords of west Norway, because, with improvement of boats, Denmark could more easily achieve organization of its more open lands by coastwise boat communication. The improvement of boats was promoted not only by the abundant supply of timber as woodland was cut, but also by the development of iron tools and thus of carpentering. Boats came to be built with boards overlapping below, giving strength and a reduction of leakage ; this is known as clinker-building. Later on, the Mediterranean peoples were able to improve the scheme of boards fastened edge to edge and their style is called caravel-building. Men learned to steer with a rudder (still for a while at the side, later at the back end) instead of with a movable oar, to fix a central mast securely into a lock so that they might hoist a transverse sail, and to work the oars in a slot instead of against one pin or rowlock. The clinker-built boats increased in size until they had 16 oars on each side. Perhaps most important of all was the improvement of the keel of the boat by better carpentering. We know a little about the boats of northern Europe in the post-Roman era because of the custom of burying the great dead in their boats, several of which have thus been preserved. Increased ploughing and better boats led to increased population in northern Europe, a region in which subsistence under the conditions of those days demanded great and persistent effort, and also a region without very great possibilities of taking up new land near home. Pressure of population arose quickly and led to adventure, especially of young men, abroad.

Among the earliest people to feel this pressure were the Frisians in their homeland of marsh and dune, but with the sea at hand for men ready to cope with the riddles of the sands by skilled seamanship. The Frisians seem to have been fairly peaceful and commercial, and to have developed trade around the North Sea. Through their activity, gossip about Britain and Gaul spread to the Danes and Norsemen, who had already made expeditions across the Baltic into what has become Russia, and soon learned to raid and trade, with Britain and

FIG. 39

Modern model of a Viking ship, the "Hugin," which sailed from
Denmark to Britain, 1949

Gaul as objectives. In Britain, a raid on the coast of Wessex in 785 and
one on the sacred Northumbrian isle of Lindisfarne in 793 were
presages of the terror to come, when Charlemagne's grandsons let
his empire break into disorderly fragments. Adventure from Norway
and Denmark was also promoted by the fact that rulers were trying
there to impose order on their wild subjects and many escaped to sea,
going to Iceland, Orkney, Shetland and the Hebrides and no doubt
Faeroe as well.

Meantime, adventurers favoured island stations for several reasons.
Birds and fish were sure sources of food, especially in regions where
puffins abounded. An island was less open to sudden attack than a

camp on the mainland. An island depot for plunder and slaves and for refitting of boats was considered desirable. Tory Island off north-west Donegal is a famous case, and the Isle of Man illustrates the same fact on a larger scale.

Ragnar, the most famous raider of the ninth century, took his boats up the Seine to Paris in 845, slaying and looting, and finally carrying off a large amount of precious metal, a bribe given him to leave folk alone. Various raids on the east coast of Britain followed that on Lindisfarne. Sheppey was attacked, and, later, in 850 and 854, first Thanet and then Sheppey were used as wintering stations by raiders who were not minded to return home as yet.

In 865 a much greater effort by a whole army took possession of East Anglia. This was an isolated area cut off by the Wash and the Fens from Mercia and by forests from the southern and south-western lands, save along a narrow belt between forest and fen near Cambridge. It is probably significant that the raiders became more menacing after the deaths of Egbert (802-839) and his son Ethelwulf (839-856), both able men. The parallel with Charlemagne and his son Louis is interesting here. Alfred, born in 849, was in 865 hardly as yet ready to lead a resistance. Once established on land in Britain, the Danes rode from East Anglia to Lincoln and to York, and what was soon to be known as the Danelagh or Danelaw began to take shape. The Northumbrians, north of the Humber, seem to have had more affinity with the invaders than had the Mercians south of that estuary, and the Danes attached great importance to their control of the five boroughs of Lincoln, Stamford, Nottingham, Leicester, and Derby. The first four kept their pre-Danish names, but the Danes renamed the last, using their favourite suffix *by*.[1] Whereas the early English had avoided the Roman roads and had been completely rurally-minded, the Danes used the remains of those roads freely and valued towns and trade, however rough they may have been at first. Raiders and warriors were followed by farmers, and Stenton notes that in the district (soke) of Bolingbroke (a pre-Danish name) twelve out of nineteen villages have Danish or Norse names, eight of these having the suffix *by* which, he thinks, implies a village rather than a hamlet. Probably Danish warriors settled there and became, and also brought in, farmers. In many districts, however, the Danes were few in number

---

[1] *By* in Icelandic meant a farm; in Danish it came to mean a village. In Britain it may have been used with both meanings. It was later used by non-Danish people in the north.

FIG. 40

The Danelagh in Britain in the
days of King Alfred

and merely formed a military aristocracy, which melted into the local
population through marriages with native girls. The warriors who
settled in seem to have kept some personal status and some measure
of freedom.

Danish armies spread south-westwards and Alfred, King of Wessex
(i.e., the land south of the Thames, west of Sussex), had to retreat to the
isle of Athelney in the Somerset marshes ; but later on he recovered
and refortified London ; and about 886 a treaty with the Danes traced
a frontier along the Thames from the estuary to the Lea, up the Lea, on

to Bedford and along the Ouse to Watling Street. The Danes later advanced in what are now Bedfordshire and Buckinghamshire. Guthrum, king of the Danes in East Anglia and the chief Danish leader, was induced to treat his English subjects on the same basis as his Danish subjects in the matter of land tenure ; and it is clear that Alfred had considerable influence in Danish territories south of the Humber. He had won some sort of recognition from all the English not within the Danelagh.

Of old, the ceorls or free landholders had owed military service in the local fyrd or militia for the defence of their homes, but were not liable for service at a distance. Alfred seems to have organized an army of nobles and their retainers, supplemented by a part of the local militias, as a means of defence against the mobile and organised Danes. He also built ships larger than those of Danes and Norsemen— they are said to have had at least 30 oars on each side. He and his son Edward and his loyal son-in-law Æthelred showed skill and courage in defending the land against Danish attacks ; but, for the rest of Alfred's life (he died in 899), the Danes had the initiative nearly all the time and their marches across England made warfare very different from what it had been previously. They felt secure with East Anglia and Northumbria firmly in their hands and the sea at the back of these.

Thus for a while South Britain was English in the south and southwest, with Cornwall and Wales Brythonic-Celtic, while the north-eastern and eastern Midlands were Danish with an English flavouring, and East Anglia and Deiran Northumbria were more thoroughly Danish. North-western England and Bernicia may have been independent but English. To judge from the number of later Scandinavian place-names in north-western England (p. 166) it was probably sparsely peopled at this time. Edward, Alfred's son, eventually regained territory as far north as the Humber ; the Danes were not organised on a unitary basis, their various armies were apt to act separately save under great stress, and Edward's men managed to defeat the Northumbrian Danes heavily when they were raiding in the western Midlands, at Tettenhall (Staffs.), in 910. In all this late phase of the first Anglo-Danish struggle we cannot but get the impression that it was approaching more and more the character of a civil war ; the Danes and English were mixing, the Danes were becoming Christians, the royal organisation of English Wessex was

PLATE 17

Ightham Village, Kent. November

PLATE 18

The Cotswolds yield limestone which has been used in attractive housebuilding at least

spreading ; the local hundred-courts were probably in existence ; earthwork refuges, developed under Alfred, were multiplied in Mercia by his daughter Æthelflæd, the wife and, later, the widow of Æthelred who long held London for Alfred. In some cases hill-fortresses of Iron Age date (p. 90) were used once more under Edward and Æthelflæd ; Eddisbury in Cheshire is a notable instance here.

The work carried on by Alfred and Edward and Æthelflæd was pushed on under Edward's son Athelstan, whose ability and activity in western European affairs show fairly clearly that the Danes of the Dane-lagh were no longer troublesome. They had come to look upon them-selves as English, with some customs of their own still continuing, and they showed their English adherence in their opposition to Norse raids from Ireland during the reign of Edmund, Athelstan's son. It is a very remarkable fact that there was a great inheritance of ability, industry and strength of character through so many royal generations—Egbert, Ethelwulf, Alfred, Edward, Athelstan, Edmund, Edgar. A comparable succession of able sons to able fathers in the kingly office has probably never occurred elsewhere. It is generally considered that Alfred was the greatest of the series, while Ethelwulf, Athelstan and Edgar added to their work as kings a special interest in church affairs. Æthelflæd, Alfred's daughter, seems to have had the mental quality of the men of her line.

Alfred had visited Rome as a youth and was imbued with a desire to learn : he made himself acquire the ability to read Latin and to write English. His translations into English with his running comments and his added notes, especially those added to the geographical facts in Orosius, give him a remarkable and a solitary place in English life. His desire to spread education seems far ahead of his time, and his effort to dignify the common language is most remarkable, though no doubt he would have urged the superiority of Latin. His edition and revision of the laws of the English marks a great step in the unification of England, and the earlier part of the famous *Anglo-Saxon Chronicle* was written in his reign. He is supposed to have improved clocks and other things. If we put this alongside of his defence against the Danes, his military and naval organization, the building of fortresses, his vigour in defeat and his moderation in victory we have to own that Anglo-Saxon England had indeed risen far above its barbarous beginnings.

The inherited ability in the family in all probability had much to do with the accession of the English part of Mercia to the kingdom

M

founded on Wessex, and with the rapid assimilation of the Danes of the Danelagh. The great succession ended with Edgar (d. 975) and in a few years Danish raids began again, this time an important factor being the desire to escape from an attempt to organise Denmark. How these raids led on to the conquest of England by Cnut (Canute) who reigned in our country from 1017 to 1035 is more a matter of political than of social history and we shall leave it aside. What does concern us is the vulnerability of Anglo-Saxon Britain save when its defence was under exceptionally good leadership.

It is notable that, at any opportunity, the English, emerging from the barbarian phase, strove to increase contacts with the regions of Europe which had belonged to the Roman Empire, and with the Roman Church. The links with the northern side of the continent (fig. 2, p. 20) were obviously very strong, as well as dangerous to settled folk in Britain. Under Offa of Mercia, and under the great succession from Egbert, efforts were made time after time to develop continental links. Edgar and his archbishop (St. Dunstan) tried hard to restore monasteries enforcing the Benedictine rule, and there were criticisms of both King and churchman for favouring foreigners. Apparently their breadth of view also led them to recognise Danish custom to some extent. Cnut, in his turn, took up the same ideas. It is probable also that by the tenth century the social hierarchy was becoming more definite, with noble territorial families of non-royal rank, now that the royal title was becoming reserved for the ruler of the whole country. One notes, however, that Edgar was chosen king of England north of Wessex by people discontented with the rule of his elder brother who retained Wessex until his death shortly afterwards.

Though territorial units and towns were becoming far more definite in the tenth century there was still no acknowledged capital city and centre of administration, and the court of the king was perambulatory. His council seems to have been becoming more definite in its composition ; in earlier phases it had been largely the king's companions, whoever they were at the time.

In the ninth century the distinction between Danes and Norsemen appears to have been less sharp than it became later on. Ragnar, a leading figure in the ninth century, was born in Denmark and trained in Norway. But the distinction grew with time and was accompanied by hostility between the more settled Anglo-Danes and the still raiding Norsemen.

In west and south-west Norway there was only a little arable land, mostly on the shores of the fjords. These patches with their fisher-farmer communities were almost self-contained, dependent on the harvests of land and sea, the coastal waters being sheltered in many parts by outlying chains of islands. Communities were separated from one another by barren and difficult highland, possessing, however, patches of summer pasture and hay here and there on ledges. In these circumstances the problem of surplus population appeared early, and the problem of a common organization for a number of communities was specially difficult, in spite of communication by sea. Research has suggested that to belong to a land-holding family was a mark of social distinction in ancient Norway, and that, accordingly, a farm might come to maintain several related families with dwellings around a common courtyard. In west Norway, however, the skilful boatman or hunter had his own prestige in comparison with the landholder of a small patch of none-too-fertile land in a none-too-favourable climate.

With the improvement of boats from the sixth century onwards, Norwegians moved about and made contact with more southerly lands, and, before and after 800 A.D., surplus population of the free farmer type migrated, especially from Möre and Tröndelag to Shetland and Orkney. In Norway the family, holding cultivated and meadow land by inheritance (called odel land), looked up to its senior male member who had the right to buy back within a limited time into the family any holding within the family territory that a member of the family might have sold and to buy it back at the price at which it had been sold. The odel system was transplanted to Shetland and Orkney and became so definite there that, in the final transfer of these islands to Scotland, when a Dano-Norwegian princess had them as part of her dowry on her marriage to the son of James II of Scotland, it was stipulated that odel should be maintained; its last confirmation by Scotland was in 1587. It is interesting to note in passing that, in the island of Sark in the Channel Isles, the custom of primogeniture in inheritance of the family farm, and the right of men within a stated degree of kinship to buy back into the family, at the price of the first sale, within a year and a day, a farm that has been sold outside it, have persisted to our own time. These customs are mentioned in the scheme under which Helier de Carteret of St. Ouen, Jersey, became lord of the manor in Sark in 1584, but it is very probable that the scheme ir some points accepted and incorporated immemorial custom. Place-names in and around Sark, and the other Channel Islands, indicate the presence of the Norsemen, no doubt in the tenth or even the ninth century ; one may instance the name of Brecqhou, an islet off Sark, Jethou, Lihou, Burhou, etc., *ou* being a Norse term for an islet. The *ey* in Guernsey, Jersey, Alderney is another example.

Place-names for farms, arable fields, meadows, etc., in Shetland and Orkney often end in the suffix *land*. This suffix is very character-istic of south-west Norway, another source of emigrants, and Norwegian research has shown evidence of depopulation of remote districts there in the ninth century.

A further factor here is that Harald Haarfager, who struggled for power over Norway, which he achieved in 872, was concerned, as were so many rulers, to organise his kingdom and to receive dues from the land-owners in respect of their odel land. The more powerful landed families resisted Harald, and some sailed away to the islands off the west of Scotland and in the Irish Sea. The western isles they called Sudreys (southern isles) in contrast with the Nordreys (Orkney and Shetland), and they seem to have settled in Man in the ninth century after a first raid on St. Patrick's Isle (near Peel) in 798. They had raided Iona in 795. The raids on Iona, on St. Patrick's Isle and on Lindisfarne were thus almost contemporary, and were in all cases presages of what was to follow.

The Sudreys and Man had been Christianized by Ninian, Germanus and Columba and a bishopric was organized, probably in the twelfth century, which survives, in its Manx portion, as the diocese of Sodor (i.e. Sudreys)[1] and Man. At first under the Archbishop of Trondhjem, Norway, it was transferred to the province of York, probably after the loss of the Hebrides by the Norsemen in 1266. A feature of Celtic Christianity had been carving in stone, making decorated crosses. These have been specially studied in Man by Kermode. It is highly characteristic that the making of these stone crosses went on under the (Christianized) Norsemen in the Hebrides and Man, so we must think that Christianity more or less maintained itself or revived after their raids. As there are cases of a Norse father giving a Celtic name to his son we understand that the results of inter-marriage of Norse invaders with native girls followed the usual rules. One strongly suspects that such men of mixed descent often became leaders and founders of Scottish clans.

---

[1] The bishopric has for centuries been concerned with the Isle of Man only.

The Norsemen of the Nordreys occupied much of Caithness (Cat-ness ; Brögger thinks the Shetlanders were called Cat-men as contrasted with the Oremen or Boar-men of Orkney) and, seeing the mountains to the south, they gave the name of Sutherland, but neither there nor in the Hebrides nor in Man did they implant the odel system ; these territories were too closely in touch with the growing feudal systems further south. David, king of Scotland, (1124-1153), son of Queen Margaret, of English descent, and a notable organiser, remodelled the dioceses of Scotland and drew Orkney and Shetland into the scheme. He is even credited with having arranged for the canonization in 1135 of Magnus, a Norse Earl of Orkney who had died in 1115, and for the building of the fine cathedral of St. Magnus at Kirkwall in Orkney, in 1137. Orkney especially became increasingly linked with Scotland by inter-marriage and trade, though Sverre, king of Norway at the end of the twelfth century, increased his direct political power over the islands. He separated Shetland from the Nordrey earldom, which had come to be in the hands of Scots (e.g., Gilbert of Angus who married the sister of the last Norse Earl Jon ; the latter died in 1231). Until the middle of the fourteenth century ecclesiastics came and went between Norway and the Nordreys, but afterwards Scots names predominate, especially after the mid-fifteenth century. Brögger draws attention to some very significant facts in connection with the removal of Pope Clement VII to Avignon (1378). France and Scotland alone gave him their support ; Norway, like most other countries, took the Roman side. Orkney's bishop sided with Clement until 1392 when Orkney submitted to Norway and Rome in this matter, but Clement's party continued to influence the Orkney church.

Concerning the migrations to Shetland and Orkney and beyond, some environmental factors must be mentioned. In periods of new opportunity marginal settlements adhering to old habits tend to lose population ; the modern development of the Isle of Man, for instance, has led to the abandonment of old cottages on the hill-fringes of cultivation, and mountain villages in the French and Italian Alps have lost population when the tourist industry has not taken hold. Then generations of cultivation without adequate manuring are likely to bring poverty as a spur to migration (note also p. 139). These factors must be given due weight alongside those of improved boats and the desire to escape from the organization developed under Harald Haarfager.

FIG. 41

The areas of Britain most affected by the spread of the Northmen along
the Minch and the Irish Sea

In spite of the improved boats the crossing was an adventure because of the liability to low-pressure air systems with their west-south-west winds. Such winds were useful, if not too strong, for voyages from Shetland to Norway but not vice-versa in those days of transverse sails needing a following wind. Voyages from Norway to Shetland would therefore be made chiefly in May and perhaps June when cyclonic disturbances are usually weak and short-lived and easterly winds commoner than in the rest of the summer. The return voyages could be made at any time, preferably before the autumn and winter storms were likely to be too frequent. The easterly winds and relatively dry atmosphere over a sea that was still cool in May and June usually gave fairly clear skies, with consequent possibilities of steering by sun and stars, an important help in those days before the mariner's compass was introduced.

Shetland with its hills and valleys was none too fertile and its people looked to the sea as a mainstay ; they must be fisher-farmers ; and the farming meant animals poorly fed and tending to become small. The wood-frame houses of Norway had to give place to stone building because of insufficiency of large trees in that region swept by salt winds. Orkney, too, had to go in for stone building, but there were larger stretches of land for crops, though cattle were important, too. The Orcadians may be called farmer-fishers. Paucity of good trees was probably one factor that sent the islanders prospecting across the Pentland Firth (the Firth or Narrow Water of the Petts or Picts) to Caithness and Sutherland (so-called because south of Orkney and Norway), but commercial opportunities and contacts with the major regions of western civilization also drew the islanders southwards. It is also probable that a number of very severe winters in the fourteenth century impoverished Norway and led to the abandonment of the colony in south-west Greenland. If there be a fair amount of truth in this, one can better understand the shift of allegiance and relation-ships of the islanders from Norway to Scotland. But the rise in power first of the Hanse, secondly of the Danish rulers of the Sound, and thirdly of the rulers of a more or less unified Scotland played a great part in the change.

In the early tenth century Norsemen were attacking the coast of England between Solway and Dee from their bases on the east coast of Ireland ; and, in Cumberland, Westmorland and Lancashire, we again find sculptured Celtic-Norse stone crosses, the great one at

Gosforth being specially famed for the alternative possibilities it offers of interpretation in terms of Christian or of Norse legend. Such syllables as Fell (= Hill), Foss (from Fors, a waterfall), Gate (= street), Thwaite (=a clearing, paddock, etc.), are widely used in place-names in north-west England, and Garthwaite, Haverthwaite, Ickenthwaite, Satterthwaite, illustrate Norse combinations. Raby and Roby, Scholes, Seascale, Buttermere, Greta, Aigburth, Aintree, Arkholme, Anglezark, Rotha and Lazonby are a few other instances of Norse names in this area.

In 795 Norsemen raided near Dublin and made the east coast of Ireland a base of operations from which, for example in the reign of Edward the Elder (tenth century) of Wessex, they at times ruled or besieged York, coming via north-western England. The earlier Norse invaders of Ireland were called Finn Gaill (white foreigners), and in 849 they were attacked by the Dubh Gaill (black foreigners) but the latter were beaten in the end. The black ones are said to have been Danes, the white ones Norwegians.

Pembrokeshire has a number of coastal place-names of Norse origin, which have been studied by B. G. Charles. These include Amroth, Caldey, Cotby, Derbyhaven, Goscar, Fishguard, Skokholm, Gateholm,[1] Gelliwick, Haverfordwest, Lydstep, Milford, Ramsey[1] Island, Skomer. In Gower we have Swansea, Holmes; perhaps Worms is Norse, too. A number in S. Glamorgan were studied by D. R. Paterson. In North Wales we have Great Orme's Head, Bardsey, Priestholm, etc. The importance of Pembrokeshire and South Glamorgan to the Norse traders should be set alongside the interest in the same regions shown by the seafarers who built prehistoric megaliths (ch. 3). It is said that Rhodri Mawr kept the Norse raids in check during his reign, and it seems that some later Welsh princes allied themselves with the Norse Irish of Dublin, or hired mercenaries from among them. In the eleventh century the Norse elements for the most part melted into the local population.

What is so characteristic of the Norsemen, or rather of their hybrid descendants from marriages with native girls, is their power of adaptation to new ways and new skills. In Normandy for example, after raids in the early tenth century, they became great church-builders and the splendid abbeys of Caen and Jumièges and the architectural

---

[1] Holm is Norse and means an isolated piece of land or an islet ; ey is also Norse and means an island. Ou is another suffix for a small island.

gem of Lessay are special witnesses here to the consequences of fusion of the Norsemen into the population. They thus furnish an example, to add to many others, of the fact that, when two outlooks or streams of experience come together, they may produce results far beyond a summation of their respective traditions. A certain amount of objectivity, and with it of original initiative, is apt to emerge from contacts of peoples if hostility is not too bitterly continued. Contacts of diverse traditions are apt to give a measure of liberation from the heavy hand of established and enforced custom and belief.

REFERENCES : see end ch. 8, p. 181.

CHAPTER 8

AN INTRODUCTION
TO CHAPTERS ON MODERN TIMES
IN BRITAIN (1066-1949)

FROM THE days of the struggles with Norse Sea-Rovers onwards we pass into phases for which both documentary and material evidence is more abundant and has been studied from many points of view. Our method of treatment must be adjusted. Even in earlier chapters it has been difficult to keep the threads of the story from getting too tangled ; for later times, the result of an attempt to deal with one period in each chapter would lead to confusion. Several chapters following are therefore treated under various headings, chosen usually because the subject of each chapter—rural settlements, towns, church and castle and so on —gives evidence of outward and visible signs of the mutual adaptation going on between the peoples of Britain and their environments. But, as a prelude to these chapters on special aspects, we must make an attempt at a brief general sketch, knowing full well that no two students would make the same selection of topics to be included.

Among the later Anglo-Saxon kings several had important links with the continent and, under Edgar, Dunstan greatly increased those links in ecclesiastical matters. Whether or not this increase of organization and communications and certain developments of technique would have come to fruition without the Norman Conquest of 1066 is a question that need not be discussed. The Conquest did occur and it was followed by many marked developments.

First we think of communications and wool exports to the industrial cities of Flanders, with London standing out more and more. Bishoprics were newly established at Lincoln, Norwich, Chichester, Exeter, all these mainly ports for continental trade. Towns in general were rising in importance, as was the case in France. The port of Rochester had had a bishop from 600 A.D. It is significant that only one of these new port-bishoprics, Exeter, was west of the Jurassic scarp and that some rising inland towns beyond that scarp such as Chester, Gloucester and Nottingham (Southwell), as well as the port of Bristol did not have bishoprics until much later, save that Bristol had one for a short time. The privileges of the Cinque Ports—Hastings, Romney, Hythe, Dover and Sandwich, to which list Winchelsea and Rye were later added, included the holding of a court of admiralty under a judge who acted in this capacity for the Lord Warden of the Cinque Ports. To the Cinque Ports were affiliated minor harbours ; for example, Folkestone was affiliated to Dover. All this indicated both the increased importance of continental connections and the increase of judicial and administrative organization. The maritime connection with Aquitaine via Bordeaux and Southampton further gave a supply of wine to royalty and nobility, a supply no doubt much valued in those times when water was often a danger to health.

By the twelfth century some town-planning was taken in hand, the founding of Salisbury near the Avon to replace the over-dry Old Sarum on the hill being a notable example. In 1250 the Hanseatic League established Merchants of the Steelyard in London and they greatly developed the city's commerce.

In the matter of organization the great historic monument is the Domesday Survey compiled under William I. The establishment of *Curia Regis,* with officials attending its assembly for lesser matters and also a varying number of tenants-in-chief for major problems, was another important step. The smaller assemblies developed in due course into the Privy Council, and the larger ones were a germ which contributed to the evolution of Parliament. Though feudal lords might be a danger to the king's power, they hardly ranked as sovereigns beside him and there was not the same long struggle as the kings of France had with Toulouse and Champagne, Burgundy and Brittany, and with the kings of England in their capacity as lords of Normandy and Aquitaine.

The institution of money payments as a substitute for service, and the establishment of regional assizes with royal Justices-in-Eyre (travelling to various centres) under Henry II followed by the enquiries under Edward I into the evidence for local custom (*Placita de quo warranto*), as well as the charters of liberties to towns all mark steps in organization that, in Britain, gave sanction to local custom under royal authority. This recognition of local diversity within national unity may be said to have been made more natural by the fact that common law (i.e. law based on custom, *Droit coûtumier*), was a Norman as well as an English tradition.

The Normans in Normandy in the eleventh century became great church-builders, and brought into Britain increased technical skill in the designing of arches and vaults, so that we often speak of the Norman style, whereas continental architects speak of the Romanesque, because the large round arch is usually thought to be an adaptation of Imperial Roman ideas.

About the time of the Norman Conquest, the Roman Catholic Church was establishing the rule of celibacy for priests of parishes (secular clergy) putting them on the same footing in this matter as monks (regular clergy), and it was spreading its organization in more detailed fashion over the countries of western Europe. An increase of secular clergy, drawn in larger measure from the people once celibacy was established,[1] involved the seeping into the Church of popular ideas, and these spread far and wide the worship of the Virgin Mary as a substitute for the cults of the Earth-Mother or Mother Goddess. Dedications to Our Lady multiplied and Lady Chapels were added to many cathedrals, typically at their east ends, where they might help to support a choir and chancel raised to impressive height.

There can be no doubt that church building spread aesthetic opportunity and aroused enthusiasm. A marked feature of the enthusiasm of the last years of the eleventh century, in the midst of an economic revival which had to spread to the countryside to improve food-supplies, was the foundation of the Cistercian Order of monks (1092 A.D.) following that of the Cluniac reform (927 A.D. onwards) of the Benedictine tradition. The Benedictines in Britain often established themselves near a town, the Cluniacs in rural spots, the Cistercians in the remote country. The Cistercian establishments in Wales and north England and their efforts for the development of sheep-and-wool activities are a vital element in the British tradition.

In France the long and difficult struggle between the king and the sovereign nobles led to a close political link between church and king,

---

[1] The inheritance of ecclesiastical positions by sons of previous holders would no longer be effective. The celibate life also meant a sacrifice the privileged classes were not always ready to make.

whereas in England the king's stronger position led rather to clashes; we find Henry II, Edward III, Henry VIII and Elizabeth stiffly resisting ecclesiastical claims. In France, again, the association between king and church included a close link of both with the Sorbonne, as the medieval university of Paris came to be called ; the university attempted to give authoritative decisions on disputed theological questions. In Scotland the two senior Universities (St. Andrews and Glasgow) are associated with the medieval archbishoprics at these centres, but Edinburgh had neither bishopric nor university until later on. In England it is characteristic that neither Canterbury nor York nor London had a medieval university and that neither Oxford nor Cambridge had a medieval bishopric. Centralization has been kept in check amongst us until modern times, when the elaborate technique of administration and the complexity of social legislation are making local diversity more difficult to maintain.

After the Norman Conquest the English language received many additions from Norman French. Beef from *Boeuf*, Mutton from *Mouton*, Pork from *Porc*, are characteristic products of the feasting of the nobles, while ox, sheep, swine are the names used by herdsmen who had to tend the animals rather than feast upon them. Also, as the victors at Senlac were mainly young men seeking fame and fortune, they inter-married with English girls who taught their children the English language enriched by new words learned from the men. In a society thus including two diverse traditions in intimate contact among non-literate folk, we may be sure that inflexions would degenerate in connection with both languages. English does not seem to have been a court language until the reign of Edward I, so it was not likely to become standardised or to maintain the finer details of grammar. It thus had an opportunity to drop inflexions, but also to become involved in complications of pronunciation, some derived from Norman, others from English usage.

Geoffrey of Monmouth wrote in Latin in the twelfth century. Langland and Chaucer wrote in English in the fourteenth, and they further wrote about contemporary English life. English had risen to honour once more. It moreover became important to develop the written version of the common tongue for the use of commerce. Agreements and orders needed to be written, whatever tallies and other devices were, for a while, maintained at the Exchequer and elsewhere. Reading and writing must extend their scope, at least from religion to law and commerce, once guilds and other organizations had established themselves.

Towns grew and, sometimes, were actually planned out, as in the case of Salisbury which replaced Old Sarum. This development was supplemented by the creation of bastide towns (p. 12) in Wales after the Edwardian conquest, but, whereas in an English town persons of Norman and persons of English descent lived side by side, at least to some extent in Wales the Welsh people were for a long time not allowed to live in the bastide towns. In England, too, the town often grew round a castle which needed craftsmen to maintain its equipment of armour, weapons, furnishings and implements, typically made to order rather than bought ready-made from a stall. But goods brought from long distances could not so readily be ordered beforehand, and fairs visited by pedlars and itinerant vendors were held usually just outside a town.

The growth of towns had as a further consequence the growth of workshops making things previously produced in the home, pottery and woollen materials being notable items. Under Edward III (1327-77) Flemish woolworkers were brought over to Norfolk and Suffolk, which thus began their great industrial blossoming, a blossoming that led in the late fifteenth and early sixteenth centuries to the building of large churches, town halls and guild halls with the profits (p. 263 and plate 13, p. 126). Sheep with long-staple wool were reared on the pastures of north Norfolk and Worstead gave its name to a fine cloth. The smelting of iron in the Middle Ages was inevitably a rural industry : wood was needed for the fires and water-power from water dammed up in " hammer-ponds " was needed for hammering the metal. The water power and hard millstone grit of Sheffield, however, brought about a concentration of knife-making there, the grit being sufficiently fine for use in sharpening steel edges. Skilled Flemish workmen, brought in especially in Elizabeth's reign, greatly helped Sheffield's industry, the products of which became more varied. In the twentieth century the development of steel alloys (with chrome, molybdenum, vanadium, tungsten, etc.), has given Sheffield new vigour and led to the use of these specially hard new products for making precision intruments. Precision instruments are now also made in the Manchester, Coventry and other areas.

Parallel with the growth of towns went the clearing of woodland and the growth of villages and of manors, with barns for grain-stores

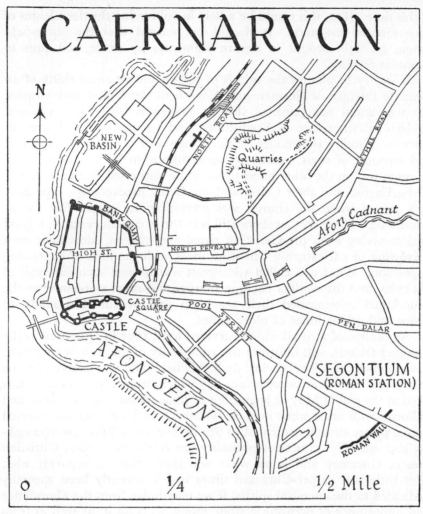

FIG. 42

A bastide town, Caernarvon, founded under Edward I

and mills which relieved women of the drudgery of grinding grain. Water-mills were revived in the twelfth century. Some students think that the mould-board at the side of the ploughshare, to turn the uplifted deep soil down again on to the surface, became more general at this time. If so, this would be a help in cultivating the deep loams of once forested lowlands. It should be realised that the three-field system (p. 246) sought to ensure manuring by cattle and thus to maintain fertility.

If we try to picture the minds of the people we must think of an intimate mixture of Norman and English in the higher social ranks, but we should not think of this as analogous with the occasional modern intermarriage of Englishmen and women of non-European descent. Usually the modern Englishman will consider local beliefs and customs of such women as superstitions to be forgotten. The Norman was on the other hand prone to be impressed by the mysteries of the English and their Celtic and pre-Celtic predecessors, especially in a period when the church was recruiting the simple folk for its priesthood. There was, as there still is in the twentieth century, a good deal surviving from pre-Christian ritual and custom, sometimes even borrowing or caricaturing Christian ideas with the idea of expressing opposition. What was called witchcraft was in part such survivals of old cults, and the conflict became sharper and more systematic as the churchmen systematised their teachings and became less ready to adopt and adapt ideas of older times.

An outline of a ritual which survived until 1837 in Guernsey in the Channel Islands, will illustrate the complexity of the web of tradition. It was called " La Chevauchée de S. Michel " and was supposed to be held every third year on a certain day which, from 1599 onwards, was fixed at the end of May or beginning of June. A procession in specified uniforms with arms, some men on horseback and some on foot, started from a priory church dedicated to St. Michael on a hill-brow overlooking the sea. This church is probably one of the two oldest Christian sites in Guernsey and is on what was then almost a separate islet. This little islet in pre-Christian times had apparently been specially dedicated to the ancestral spirits, if we may judge from the abundance and importance of prehistoric stone monuments on it, as well as from the importance attached to it by early Christian teachers. The church was the priory of S. Michel under the control of the great abbey of Mont S. Michel and had a court with jurisdiction of its own. When the procession left the territory of the priory and entered a royal manor, it was met by the king's representatives and a band of musicians with what appear to have been surplices ; thus it was conducted to receive an offering of bread and wine at the west door of the harbour church

PLATE 19

Robert Atkinson

POLPERRO, a fishermen's and seamen's settlement on an inlet. The houses cluster in the shelter of the hills.
September

PLATE 20

MARKET HOUSE, Shrewsbury (1595) showing mingled mediaeval and renascence features characteristic in

John Markham

of St. Peter (*Ecclesia S. Petri in portu maris*). Leaving the royal manor the members of the procession were given milk, and so they went on from manor to manor. But their route was traditionally set along tracks that passed standing stones or other prehistoric sacred places, and, around these, the footmen of the procession would perform ritual dances. Some of these stones appear to have become boundary stones between manors as so often happened in mediæval times. The footmen were given permission by proclamation to kiss any woman along the route, provided that no woman was to be kissed by more than one of them. These are but a few selected items from a mass of detail, but they show that there are probably regal, manorial, ecclesiastical, megalithic and fertility-cult components in this conglomeration. It was at the foot of one of the great standing-stones that, until modern times, the people of the parish concerned burned the Old Year in effigy (the effigy was called "Bout de l'an", i.e., the end of the vegetation year) in November, apparently originally on what became the festival of All Souls ; the day was later adjusted to 5th November (Guy Fawkes) as in Britain. One district of the island, formerly rich in megaliths, was still recently supposed to be under the guardianship of super-natural animals. Indeed, it may be that the whole island was sacred to ancestral spirits ; and it unfortunately became notorious for witch-craft trials in the sixteenth and seventeenth centuries, probably as a consequence of its having been a stronghold of persistence of megalithic cults. The neighbouring island of Jersey, invaded and largely held by a French nobleman for a while in the fifteenth century, had its attention diverted from these ancient rites by military considerations.

The instance here given illustrates with unusual variety of detail what seems to have been a widespread survival of ancient cults, especially fertility-cults, into and often beyond the Middle Ages. Some British churches still have female fertility figures cut in stone. This shows a state of mind awed by ancient mysteries. This attitude inevit-ably conflicted with the matter-of-fact tendencies of commerce, and the gradual rise of a commercial "middle-class" between aristocracy and peasantry was to lead later on to severe repression of old fancies. But, for a while, the peasantry found scope for dance and song and story in its old traditions. The Roman Church sought to direct these energies, for example by the spread of Christmas and other carols, several of which have come down to us from the fourteenth and fifteenth centuries. The Puritan middle-class later frowned upon the

N

play of fancy in them and in the stained-glass windows and frescoes of the medieval churches.

The development of social and economic life that has been sketched in the preceding pages of this chapter was subject to two grave hindrances. One was world-wide, namely the recurrence of plagues, of which the terrible Black Death (1348-9, 1361-2, 1368-9) is the most famous in the Middle Ages. It caused the abandonment of some village sites and created for a while a sellers' market in labour, and led to monetary inducements for workpeople in some areas. The man-power available was insufficient for the work to be done and many projects were abandoned. Many estates were left in the hands of minors through the deaths of their lords and became partly dis-organised. Wat Tyler and Jack Cade are notable personalities in the long struggle for better conditions of peasant and craftsman life and the attempted change from the serfdom that accompanied feudal organization to a wage-labour system, but labour servitude persisted in many manors.

The other great hindrance was one which particularly affected Britain. This was the frequency with which harvests were damaged by rain, especially in late July and August (the folk-lore statement is " After St. Swithin's Day"). The ocean warms up slowly, but has reached a certain temperature by mid-July, and evaporation from the sea and rainfall on coastlands may increase.

If we think of uncertainty of harvest among our clouded hills and of shortage of man-power following French wars and epidemics, we realise that feudal schemes were doomed and that the old aristocracy was in decay, as the " Wars of the Roses " so abundantly show. The etiquette of feudal nobility in war was at the same time challenged by the archers, who, it is sometimes claimed, came to a considerable extent from the almost non-feudal Welsh tradition. The story of Agincourt with the archers of Henry V striking dismay into the con-ventional feudal nobility of France is the classic illustration here. Still more important was the final defeat of British archers at Formigny (1450) by French cannon, soon to be the destroyers of castles and city walls.

One of the results was the spread of sheep and wool not only as a means of land utilization but also as a basis of industry in East Anglia (especially the material called worsted) and in and around the Cotswolds and Mendips and parts of the Downs, as well as near the

Pennines. Parts of the Pennines had the advantage of soft water; their possibilities of water-power were considerable, especially near Halifax and Bradford; and, much later, their proximity to coal made them outstrip the other English wool centres. In the nineteenth century imported long-staple wool was specially worked up into worsteds at Bradford, Halifax and other places in the west of the West Riding, and Bradford developed the use of alpaca and vicuna wool from South America. Since the mid-eighteenth century[1] Scotland also has developed a woollen industry. It is important to realise that the woollen industry is one of our oldest and one of our strongest in persistence and in quality.

It is well known that the spread of sheep seriously affected many villages. Land used for sheep-grazing needed fewer people working on it, and fewer craftsmen making implements. This led to vagrancy and many disturbances, but it should be remembered at the same time that inheritance had led to the minute subdivision of strips of plough-land so that a household might be dependent on widely scattered fragments, some hardly worth working, some exhausted by failure of the three-field routine (p. 246) for one cause or another. An old system was in decay, peasants might be under-employed and so, in matters of food, under-productive. Under conditions of a self-contained village-group new ideas had difficulty in penetrating and laid their originator open to charges of sorcery or insanity or heresy, all with horrible consequences. The restriction of initiative in thought and custom was severe, and, as usual under such circumstances, an alternative outlet for the human spirit was found in the arts, especially building and the decoration of buildings, as everyone realises who has visited the cathedrals and other monuments of the Middle Ages. In the Middle East after the mid-thirteenth century, Mongolian conquerors in S.W. Asia and Mamelukes in Egypt also restricted initiative in thought, but, further, became unsympathetic to artistic effort.

But even the many atrocities of medieval religious persecution could not stifle the minds of men, and so-called heresies appeared, the most notable leader being Wycliffe (1320-84), who may also be called the father of English prose ; through his influence upon John Hus and others, he became the chief precursor of the religious discussions and reforms that so occupied Europe and Britain in the sixteenth century. He voiced more clearly than anyone else objections

[1] After the troubles of 1745, roads and agricultural developments multiplied in Scotland.

to the exercise of power in England by the Roman Curia, and he made a translation of the scriptures. The stirrings of thought just mentioned were greatly promoted by the discovery of printing and the voyages organised by the influence of Prince Henry of Portugal. Bartolomeo Diaz, Vasco da Gama, the Cabots and, most of all, Columbus are the outstanding discoverers. They stirred British sailors to adventures on the oceans and led to changes in ship-building and increase of maritime commerce, while the revolt against the Roman Curia led the Tudor sovereigns to claim and exercise ecclesiastical authority. The organization of shires in Wales, the supersession of the Hanseatic Merchants in London, the bringing of Flemish workmen to Sheffield and German iron-miners to Cumbria and the Forest of Dean, and the organization of Merchant Adventurers and of Trading Companies, as well as the organization of the Anglican Church, are all indications of a new spirit which receives its crowning illustration in the work of Shakespeare, so far from the medieval theological setting, in the Book of Common Prayer, and in the English versions of the Bible, that due to William Tindale, and the Authorised Version issued under James I.

The spread of carriers' waggons late in the sixteenth century to some extent superseded mule-back porterage. About the same time bridges, sometimes formerly kept in order by religious houses, came to be frequent subjects of dispute when they needed repair. Their improvement to take wheeled traffic became important in due course, but it is characteristic that until much later waggons had to unload at Southwark because they could not cross old London Bridge. The great church of Southwark and its many old inns and places of amusement are a consequence of this difficulty of bridge-crossing.

In the discussions of the sixteenth century, there emerged more definitely than at any time since the death of Socrates the idea that the truth must be sought by free enquiry : in Britain, the new attitude is associated with the names of Francis Bacon, William Harvey, Robert Boyle and Isaac Newton in the seventeenth century. The Civil War of Charles I's reign has often been discussed as almost the last effort of the medieval scheme of King, archbishops, and nobility to keep control ; it has also sometimes been claimed that they sought to protect the peasantry from domination by the squirearchy and the craftsmen from domination by the commercial middle-class. Be this as it may, it is one of the most important facts of British evolution

PLATE IX

ROBERT BURNS, showing features of the dark-haired longheads, a large element in the
British population

PLATE X

CHARLES DARWIN, showing features similar to those of the beaker-making immigrants of about 1900–1800 B.C.

that, at the 1660 Restoration, medieval ideas did not again come forward. Charles II, as is well known, did not want " to go on his travels again " and his brother James' attempt to reintroduce Papal authority was a signal failure. One should mention as a characteristic feature that Charles II gave a charter to the Royal Society of London for the increase of natural knowledge, a directive sign of the new time. A very important concomitant of this was the development of diverse religious groups. This led to the diminution of the atrocities which had darkened the ecclesiastical record of the Middle Ages in most of Europe, and to Voltaire's famous jest about Britain as having " a hundred religions and one sauce". One wonders whether someone did not retort that this was, after all, a better safeguard of the sincere conscience than the scheme of " One religion and a hundred sauces".

In the seventeenth century there were Independents with each local group governing itself, Baptists based upon the idea of adult baptism and Presbyterians with consistories governing churches and groups of churches, and all these profoundly influenced by John Calvin's insistence on the omnipotence of God. Discussions led several local groups in some of these churches in the late eighteenth century to become Unitarian, that is to dissociate themselves from the traditional Trinitarian doctrine. They were often intellectual groups and had to devise means of higher education because Oxford and Cambridge remained subject to theological tests until late in the nineteenth century. The Society of Friends was another group arising in the seventeenth century, and it has tried to promote respect for conscience.

Most seventeenth-century groups outside the Anglican Church were, on the whole, eclectic. In the eighteenth century John Wesley, George Whitefield and their collaborators went out into the wilds of the mining and manufacturing slums, and new religious groups called Methodists came into existence. Their name sprang from the rules of conduct laid down for them.

In the nineteenth century the Anglican Church found new lines of interest and work and, outside it, toleration allowed scope to the Roman Church, while a renewal of the fundamental ideas of Methodism brought into existence the Salvation Army.

The improvement of ship-building diminished bilge-water, which had been a cause of much disease among sailors ; the development of fore-and-aft sails as a supplement to the old cross-sails made it possible to sail nearer the wind and so to make more direct journeys ; while a little more knowledge of nutrition began to cause a diminution of scurvy, the former curse of seamen on ocean voyages. Ocean commerce became more regular and more bulky as raw cotton began to reach this country from the Levant in the seventeenth century. Water-power available on the sharp western slopes of the Pennines, in a damp atmosphere that kept the cotton fibres from snapping too readily, and old-established poverty-stricken spinners and weavers of inferior wool on those slopes (p. 9) all combined with the growth of a port at Liverpool to give rise to the cotton industry in the eighteenth century. How this promoted the invention of machinery and the application of steam-power is too well known to need discussion.

The improvement of ships led to improvement of ship's furniture, especially in mahogany with satin-wood and other inlaid material. House furniture was improved at the same time as settled rule and town life increased, with slowly improving roads, bridges and canals. In London one notes the development of Mayfair and Kensington (with, later, theatres, hotels and restaurants) taking over some functions of the ancient Southwark. The resuscitation of the south bank of the river now beginning (1949) is a very significant fact, suggesting the lessening of class distinctions.

The invention of power-driven machinery and the immense growth of industry drew to the neighbouring towns country-folk, often deprived of their old status and their time-worn privileges as a result of appro-priations following enclosures of the former open fields. And the towns became like what Dr. L. P. Jacks so aptly named " Smokover", a place in which to make money but to be lived in only under some compulsion, often the compulsion of poverty (plate XXIII, p. 270). Trains and especially their electrification and the petrol-bus have greatly increased the tendency to live outside the city. But in all this process it has been nearly forgotten until quite recently that we are basically social beings, we have been as it were atomized or converted into waifs and strays in a crowd. The help the potato gave to the policy of cheap food for cheap people in a " labour pool " has recently been discussed by Salaman (1949).

It has been the aim of this brief review in the eight chapters of Part I of this book to set forth something of the growth of our social tradition, in the belief that the future must build on the past. In so building may we learn from past mistakes made by our forefathers and so many others and realise that unity is more than uniformity, that persecution and ostracism promote insincerity and destroy initiative, that none of us, no sect or party, should presume to claim that it has the whole truth. Milton, speaking for the Liberty of Unlicensed Printing, puts the case for liberty against licensing of printing, an evil of his day as well as of our own in many lands, in his finest prose :—

" There is yet behind of what I purposed to lay open, the incredible loss and detriment that this plot of licensing puts us to, more than if some enemy at sea should stop up all our havens, and ports, and creeks ; it hinders and retards the importation of our richest merchandise, truth."

REFERENCES TO CHAPTERS 5—8 : Bowen (1941), British Museum guides (Britain in Roman Times, Anglo-Saxon Antiquities), Brögger (1929), Chadwick (1907), Charles (1934), Clapham and Power (1941), Collingwood (1930), Collingwood and Myres (1936), Coulton (1925), Crawford (1928, 1940), Darby (1936), Ekwall (1936), Fox (1923, 1926-31, 1934), Gardner (1926), Gomme (1914), Gray (1915), Hammond and Hammond (1919-48), Haverfield (1923, 1924), Hodgkin (1935), Hughes (1907), Kendrick (1930, 1938, 1949), Leeds (1913), Lethbridge (1948), Margary (1948), Meitzen (1895), O'Neil (1945), Ordnance Survey (Roman Britain, Britain in the Dark Ages), Orwin and Orwin (1938), Payne (1947), Pelham (1931), Place-Names Society's Publications, Richmond (1949), Royal Commissions' Reports on ancient and historical monuments, Salaman (1949), Stenton (1927, 1943), Trevelyan (1946), Victoria History of the Counties of England, Wheeler (1927, 1930, 1935), Wheeler and Wheeler (1936), Wooldridge (1936).

CHAPTER 9

THE PEOPLE [1]

IT HAS long been known that the British people show a considerable variety of physical characteristics. Some, especially in South Wales, are dark, slender, and rather short, others, especially near the North Sea and among the Scottish Highlanders of the north and east, are tall and often fair in colouring. The general head-form is rather long, and really broad-headed men are in a small minority in most parts. Our colouring is on the whole darker than that of most Scandinavians, but fairer than that of most Spaniards. While baldness does supervene in a considerable proportion of our males, it is not so common, nor does it appear so early as it is apt to do in Central Europe. In the nineteenth century Dr. John Beddoe published observations of physical traits in Britain that demonstrated his acuteness of observation, but, since his day, comparatively little work has been done on local differences, save in the matter of stature. The present writer, in conjunction with Dr. Elwyn Davies and other friends, has tried to analyse the physical traits found in Welsh-speaking Wales and the Isle of Man, in the belief that, in fringing areas such as these, one may find the successive layers of population somewhat less confused than, for example, in industrial England.

Local differences certainly do occur, and concern the proportions in which men with various physical traits are found ; one must not expect anything approaching absolute contrasts. These differences are to be interpreted usually on the basis of past history, but history must be used with care to avoid certain pitfalls, as will be shown in the pages that follow.

[1] The writer wishes to express his thanks to the Leverhulme Trust for help in the prosecution of researches discussed in this chapter.

Physical traits may be and typically are inherited, so that they may persist for many hundreds of generations, as Mendel's work has shown and has helped us to understand, and as we all know from "family likeness", a topic of conversation around every baby that is born. Particulate inheritance is the general rule, father's nose and mother's eyes or vice versa or both from one or other parent. More and more is it recognised that inheritance is best interpreted on Mendelian lines. In small isolated groups of early times in-breeding was inevitable and characters swamped elsewhere might spread through the little population. Isolation from other groups, further, would lead to differences in accumulation of variations, so we may argue that in the phases of small isolated social units there were

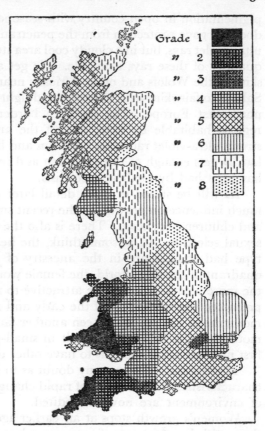

FIG. 43

Tentative map of the distribution of pigmentation (hair- and eye-colour) in the British population

opportunities of differentiation through accumulation and spread of variations without any necessary argument concerning the survival value, or otherwise, of those variations.

But there may also be supplementary natural selection of valuable variations or elimination of persons with deleterious variations. It is likely that this has happened on a large scale in the matter of skin pigmentation. The long argument cannot be given here, but it may be very briefly summarised. An original brown or yellow-brown pigmentation in open country with seasonally strong sunshine and outdoor life gave protection from the penetration of an excess of violet and ultra-violet rays, but in a cloudy cool area stopped too much of the small quantity of these rays available. We get a gradation from very dark skins of the Wolofs and other Africans near the southern border of the Sahara to fair skins with blue eyes and light hair among many people in north-west Europe. The southern border of the Sahara is, among regions habitable by man, one of the areas with longest-continued strong ultra-violet radiation from sun and blue sky. North-west Europe hardly gets enough of this radiation and recourse to artificial sunlight has been had by medical specialists.

As will be stated in more detail later on, environment may have much influence on growth, as the recent supply of vitamins to mothers and children has shown. There is also the question of change through sexual selection. If, as some think, the heavy-browed " Neandertal " type had some share in the ancestry of the men of the north-west quadrant of the Old World, the female would be less heavily built and the more womanly would be attractive to men. This factor may have promoted the weakening of the early and rough features. Age of first motherhood has probably been another factor in the case. Very early motherhood is believed to result in small-grown offspring. Very late first motherhood is thought to have other disadvantages in some cases.

There seems no longer any doubt as to the long persistence of some characteristics. Old theories of rapid change of head-form with change of environment are now discredited.

Women's growth stops at an earlier age than that of men, leaving them with less thickness of bone, an advantage in child-bearing ; but, as a consequence, several physical characteristics are less marked than in men and our figures refer to adult non-senile males. It is desirable to see that a local sample for study is composed of the normal inhabitants of a district, and to ascertain such facts of ancestry as are available, using as constituents of a local sample those who can trace their four grandparents in the district. This means, in many cases, that a great deal of the ancestry is local, for, until modern communications had become really intimately effective, marriages, among ordinary people, took place nearly always between partners living within five miles or so of one another.

It is often unwise to take a modern administrative area as the district to be studied. A belt of high land may have a county boundary nearly along its spine, but the people of that high land have in many instances exported their sons and sometimes their daughters to the edges of the lowland on either side, whereas few lowlanders have settled in the high land unless it has developed some special activity such as mining. In the case of a highland that exports but rarely imports population it is wise to take the whole as a district. A county may include an inland and a maritime area, and the latter may have a history of settlement very different from that of the former. Local knowledge of traditional intercourse, of dialect, business relations and so on give indications for the delimitation of districts for our purposes. Towns usually have a more mixed population than rural districts ; so, for the purpose of a local sample, the latter are usually more valuable.

In Wales the Plynlymon moorland, apart from some lead-mining areas, is a region of economic difficulty ; it has tended to send out a proportion of its young people ; its farmers and shepherds often marry local girls ; a woman accustomed to the more varied resources and equipment of the lowlands might not be ready to face the problems of the highland and, indeed, might not be very successful in the work involved. This highland, considered as including much of North Cardiganshire and West Montgomeryshire, was therefore taken by us as a unit district.

To the south of this district spreads a plateau which has been cut by rivers and is on the whole somewhat lower. It includes south Cardiganshire, most of Carmarthenshire and the north of Pembrokeshire. Maritime relations have some importance here and there, but are, on the whole, secondary. This plateau area of south-west Wales was adopted as another unit district.

To the south-east of Carmarthenshire, lies the very maritime and, at the same time, very distinct Gower peninsula in Glamorganshire. It has much less Welsh speech than the other two areas. It was adopted as a third unit.

In the Plynlymon area the average height (249 cases) was 1684 millimetres (66.2 in.). In the South Wales plateau area (657 cases) the corresponding figure was 1695 millimetres (66.7 in.). In the Gower peninsula (238 cases) it was 1718 millimetres (67.6 in.). In the last case it was found that 82 men with dark hair and eyes averaged 1710 millimetres (67.3 in.) while 156 cases of men with light hair averaged 1723 millimetres (67.8 in.). The two first areas included a certain number of men of stature less than 1600 millimetres (63 in.),

and the Plynlymon sample had none attaining more than 1815 millimetres (71.4 in.). The Gower area on the other hand had very few
as short as 1600 millimetres and some well above 1830 millimetres
(72 inches).

The large proportion of light-haired men in the Gower sample
was noted above. This contrasts with the Plynlymon sample in which
137 men have hair dark and eyes brown as against 71 fair men. Only
distinctly dark and distinctly fair men are included in the numbers
given in this and the two following paragraphs. Expressed in per-
centages, Gower shows the fair men as 190 per cent of the dark
while in Plynlymon the corresponding figure is only 52 per cent.
The plateau of south-west Wales shows approximately the same
proportions in colouring as does the Plynlymon area.

We may thence infer that the Gower area has a special fair and
rather taller element in its population, a fact well-known from general
observation. We may thence go a step farther and draw attention to
the fact that Gower has place-names of Scandinavian derivation, and
that it was used by seafarers of Scandinavian origin as a calling or
sheltering, and probably raiding, station.

The case of Gower is paralleled in the Isle of Man. In the north of
that island a sample of 150 adult men of local ancestry included 40 dark
in hair and eye and 71 fair (fair 175 per cent of dark). In the east centre
of the island an analogous sample of 133 included 65 dark and 44 fair
(fair about 68 per cent of dark). In the south, another analogous sample
of 152 included 47 dark and 68 fair (fair nearly 145 per cent of dark).
The island, populated from megalithic times, has many indications of
prehistoric immigrations, but these are very scanty in the north, a
lowland district formerly largely cut off by marsh. The north, on the
other hand, has boat-burials and place-names which testify to the
presence of Norsemen. In the south, while there are abundant traces
of earlier populations, the entries from the sea at Ronaldsway and
Castletown give evidence of Norse invasion.

One may therefore suppose that we have in Gower and parts of
the Isle of Man special numbers of descendants carrying the characteristics of seafarers of centuries ago, especially as one also finds analogous
features on the coasts of western Normandy and elsewhere.

Fullard in Lancashire found that dark and fair were more or less
evenly distributed in mid-Lancashire west of the Rossendale Hills,
but that fair colouring was far more marked along the through ways

PLATE XI

Portrait by J. S. Sargent
LORD RIBBLESDALE. Tall, sparely built, straight features, long face, a
"Nordic" type

PLATE XII

Robert Adam

from Yorkshire north and south of the Rossendale Hills. Parish Registers showed that there had been very little intermarriage across the Rossendale Hills.

If we look into the question of head-form, we find other interesting divergences. The percentage ratio of breadth to length measured between certain agreed points on the living head is called the *cephalic index*. In most populations in Britain the great majority have a cephalic index somewhere between 74 and 83.

In Gower, for example, in a sample of 299 men, only 14 had cephalic indices below 74 and only 17 indices of 83 and above : i.e., 268 came within the limits. In the plateau region of S.W. Wales (670 cases) 32 had cephalic indices below 74 and 35 had them 83 and above, i.e., 603 came within the limits. In the Plynlymon area (272 cases) 36 cases had cephalic indices below 74, but only 8 had them 83 or above, i.e., 228 came within the limits mentioned in the last paragraph. Plynlymon thus had more of a very long-headed element. i.e., an element with cephalic index below 74 ; the proportion of such men is more than double that obtaining in either the Gower or the plateau of south-west Wales.

Analysing one stage further, we note that, of the 36 men with the very long and narrow heads, only four are fair, 22 have hair and eyes both dark, 10 have dark hair but eyes light. The very long narrow head is therefore, in this locality, correlated strongly with dark colouring.

In the sample from the plateau of south-west Wales we find, again, that of the 32 very long heads, 18 have dark hair and eyes, 9 dark hair and light eyes, and only 5 are fair. Here, therefore, we again get a measure of correlation of very long heads with dark colouring. In Gower we have six of the fourteen very long heads with dark hair and eyes, 3 with dark hair and light eyes and 5 are fair. A small sample (209) from the North Denbighshire moorland showed that the very long heads included 6 with dark hair and eyes and 6 with dark hair and light eyes, but none who are fair. The proportion of very long heads in this sample is somewhat higher than in any others save that from Plynlymon, where it is more than double ; the preponderance of dark colouring is absolute in this case.

Collignon in France found a specially large proportion of men with very long narrow heads in the Dordogne area, Da Costa Ferreira noted the same characters in the province of Tras os Montes, North

Portugal ; Duckworth found the same characteristics in Sardinia. All these may be described as remote and economically difficult situations, likely therefore to have relic populations. In India the very long narrow head is found among jungle peoples of South India and also to some extent among their more advanced neighbours ; i.e., again among relic populations and among the people exported from those populations. It must be mentioned here that very long narrow heads, but with very different characters from those to be discussed below, are numerous in the Punjab. The most remarkable relic population is that of the Australian aborigines. Dr. Hrdlička catalogued 516 aboriginal male Australian skulls. On the skull a breadth 72.5 per cent of the length is about the equivalent of a breadth 74 per cent of the length on the living head, and, of the 516 there were 432 with the cranial index 72.5 or less. They show several details of head-form like those which will be discussed below.

A collection of Easter Island skulls showed 35 within this very narrow and long-headed group.

A collection from Lagoa Santa, E. Brazil, showed 14 skulls within this group, two a very little broader, and only one other, that one being very different and much broader. E. Brazil is a remote fringing area if we consider the Aleutians and the Bering Sea as the main entry of pre-Columbian immigrants into America.

The same facts have been demonstrated by Dr. Broom for Korana people in S. Africa, again a remote fringing region.

The case of the Punjab people is a warning against taking merely the relation of breadth to length of the head, for those long-heads sharply contrast in almost every other feature over against the very long narrow-headed people we are discussing. The type of head under review is usually characterised by strong brow ridges and a deep-set nose-root, by a nose rather broad for the region, by marked (temporal) hollows on each side of the forehead which often recedes, by a (basi-bregmatic) total height of the skull equalling or exceeding its maximum breadth, by the prominence of the median line of the cranium which is sometimes therefore described as gabled, and by the prominence of the cheek-bones laterally (see plate VIII, p. 91). The people of north-west India on the other hand include many with long oval faces, smooth brows and prominent noses which are very narrow.

It is known that, if a type of animal occurs in several unconnected and remote areas, it is probably an ancient type once more generally distributed but exterminated or replaced by modified descendants in several parts of its old province of occurrence. The same idea may be brought forward with reference to these people with very long narrow heads, strong brows and accessory resemblances above mentioned. If so, bearing in mind the Australian aborigines, we are driven to look to the Old Stone Age for possible ancestry of these characters, as Australia has been almost completely isolated ever since.

We have unfortunately only a small number of skulls of *Homo sapiens* preserved from the later Paleolithic, but among them several have the very long narrow head, strong brow ridges and median line, high skull, deep-set nose, broad cheek-bones and marked temporal hollows. Most of these characteristics are functionally associated with strength of some of the muscles working the lower jaw, and are therefore not just a miscellaneous list. Strength of jaw-muscles has declined from the days of early man, so it is not surprising that it is among these relic populations that these characterisitics persist.

A vast number of British citizens shows longheadedness of a less extreme kind, with the contours of head and face far milder, the brow ridges little marked, the facial contour fairly smooth, the stature short to moderate, the hair dark, the eye often brown but sometimes grey. These characters are especially abundant in South Wales, Cornwall and parts of Devon, parts of the Pennines and of the western Highlands, and also, but with fewer brown and more grey eyes, in Ireland. These characters are so widespread in Spain that the possessors have been called the Iberian type. This term was especially used in Britain in the nineteenth century because it is generally agreed (see Chapter 3) that our country received important early immigrants from south-west Europe.

In a sample, analogous with those above-mentioned, taken on the plateau of south-west Wales, 372 out of 670 men had dark hair and dark eyes. Of these 372 only 18 can be classed with the extreme long-heads already discussed, while 207 belong to the group of more moderate long-heads. Of the 670 men in the total sample, 145 had dark hair but light eyes, and, among the 145, 9 could be classed as extreme, and 90 as moderate long-heads.

In north-west Wales out of a total sample of 1766 gathered on the same scheme as before, 559 have both hair and eyes dark while 802 have dark hair and light eyes. The light eye is much more widespread in north than in south Wales. Of the 1361 with dark hair, only 26 can be allocated to the extreme long heads, while 783 are of the more moderate type of long head. 783 among 1361 is about 57.5 per cent, about the same proportion as on the south-west Wales plateau.

If, however, we consider the broad-headed men with dark hair in our sample of 1163 from Caernarvonshire and Merionethshire, we note that they total up to 416 or 35.7 per cent, while on the plateau of south-west Wales they form only 21.3 per cent of the sample. The coasts of Caernarvonshire and Merionethshire thus have a considerable broad-headed dark-haired element. It is not conspicuous in the Isle of Man, it occurs on coastal patches in south Wales and south-west England. Collignon described it for the Breton coast near Paimpol and Binic, and there is a well-known coastal strip with these people in south-west Norway. Beddoe drew attention to these characters among some people of the Long Island (Lewis and Harris) in the Hebrides, and Tocher emphasises them for North Scotland, the Orkneys and Shetlands. The most feasible interpretation of these data is that we are dealing with what may be called deposits from some ancient migrations or commerce, of dates and characters still not ascertained. I may add that a group of broad skulls was found in a grave of the dawn of the Metal Age at Anghelu Ruju on the west coast of Sardinia. A few broad skulls have been found in megalithic tombs (ch. 3), but those tombs yield moderately long heads, sometimes of fairly smooth contour, also some extreme long heads.

What stands out is the importance of the St. George's Channel, Irish Sea, Minch and Pentland Firth as a route of maritime intercourse, in all probability from the dawn of the Metal Age. It remained important at any rate down to the Middle Ages, when trade between Bristol and the Baltic was of some consequence. The discussions in Chapter 2, the latter part of Chapter 3, Chapter 6 and Chapter 7 should be correlated with the statements given here.

In 1923, Dr. J. F. Tocher published a mass of data concerning colouring, stature and head-form in Scotland. His ample tables of measurements have no indices included, so it is difficult to work out the ways in which the different characters are grouped ; but the basic material for a great deal of work is ready for someone who has the patience to do a mass of calculations.

Sampling the tables of measurements in a preliminary way, one finds that the Scottish population is nowhere predominantly dark in colouring, though a dark-haired element may form 40 to 50 per cent of a local sample. It is a little over 50 per cent in a large Aberdeenshire group, and about 50 per cent in a small Argyllshire group, but it falls to 40 per cent in most parts of northern Scotland (Caithness, Sutherland, Ross and Cromarty, and Inverness). In the south-west the percentage falls to about 33 ; but it should be noted that the sample is small, and that Beddoe's small sample taken long ago was rather dark. Red hair is perhaps a little commoner in Argyllshire and the south-west than in Aberdeenshire.

In stature, taking 1750 millimetres (68.9 in.) as a convenient lower limit for tallness so as to include men of 5 ft. 9 in. and over, we find that Caithness and Sutherland have about 42 per cent of the military sample above this height, while the percentage falls to 37 in Ross and Cromarty and to about 27 in Inverness-shire. It is only about 30 in the small sample from south-west Scotland (Wigtownshire and Kirkcud-brightshire). An estimate from Tocher's samples gives an average height of about 1715 millimetres of $67\frac{1}{2}$ inches for Scottish soldiers of 20 years or above. This is a higher value than one gets for most parts of Wales except Gower and south Pembrokeshire, where, as on the east Scottish seaboard, one finds Scandinavian elements in the population.

Tocher's samples appear not to include many extremes in head-form, and, on the whole, the people whose indices are moderately low are apparently a larger proportion than in most parts of Wales. An Aberdeenshire sample on rough calculation showed that about 25 per cent must have the head-breadth well over 80 per cent of the head-length, but this falls to about 17 per cent in north Scotland and to about 7 per cent in Argyllshire and to 9 per cent in South-west Scotland. The samples from Argyllshire and the south-west are rather small. As the samples were of soldiers said to be natives of a given county, it is necessary to use the data with reserve, especially in the indus-trialised areas, where quite a number are likely to be sons of recent immigrants from other counties or from Ireland. The Clyde area seems to include a number of people with short stature.

Reid and Morant added (1928) to Turner's list of skulls from graves in Scotland called "Short Cists" and generally supposed to be of the Bronze Age. Some limb measurements that Turner took suggest that the people concerned were much shorter than the big people of the Round Barrows of England (p. 65). Like the skulls from the Round Barrow of England, however, those from the Short Cists of Scotland are usually short and broad with prominent brow-ridges, and in both areas the

o

burials are often provided with beaker pots. Of 54, the state of preservation of which allowed the requisite measurements, 32 had cranial indices over 80 and 24 of these 32 had indices over 82, i.e., were decidedly broad. These graves are mostly on the east side of Scotland; some in Orkney yielded very long skulls as well as the broad ones more typical for these graves. One solitary grave of this kind from the west of Scotland (Hebrides) had in it a very long skull.

On the south-west, west and north, Scotland has monuments of the megalithic group. From these Turner catalogued sufficient measurements for 19 skulls to show that in all the cranial index was below 80, and in only two did it reach 79. In only two was it below 72.5, the rough limit for extreme long-headedness on the skull, corresponding with 74.0 on the living head, so the great majority is moderately long-headed. This contrast between skulls from east and west coasts is interesting in correlation with what has been said above about modern people. Argyllshire and the south-west have much fewer broad-heads than the east coast counties ; they were apparently little affected by the immigration of broad-heads which makes such a striking contrast with the long-headedness of megalithic and earlier peoples in Scotland. It would be interesting to analyse Tocher's tables of measurements to get an impression of the degree of persistence of the broad-headedness just discussed, especially in Aberdeenshire.

In Neolithic England the full-grown male had a stature averaging about 63 ins.; the Round Barrow burials show taller men, some 69 inches ; the "Anglo-Saxons" averaged about 66 inches ; and such evidence as we have for the sea rovers (Ch. 7) suggests that they were a little taller. Mediæval clothing and armour, generally speaking, would fit average or sub-average men today. There seems to have been, on the whole, an upward trend, which may have been accelerated by better feeding of children in the twentieth century ; though one may ask : Do taller children mean taller adults in most cases ? Sometimes we may be dealing with a hastening rather than an absolute increase of growth. Then there is the widespread observation that emigrants to U.S.A. and the Dominions who were born in Britain seem to be a little taller than the average in Britain. It is generally agreed that the tall fair people emigrate more readily as a rule than the shorter darker men. Tall fair men are often about 68-70 inches, with a few taller (72 inches or more). Shrubsall, about thirty years ago, drew attention to the fact that, London apart, the lands south and east of the Jurassic

scarp (see Ch. 1) have taller men than the lands in England and
Wales that are beyond it to north and west. He thought there was
a tall element, however, in Westmorland, Cumberland and north
Lancashire, a region in which the sea-rovers (Ch. 7) played a
considerable part. He also noted tallness in parts of Merionethshire (a notable fact abundantly verified) and in the hilly area
of Staffordshire. He thought on the whole that rural life conduced
to taller stature, that is to a fuller attainment of height made possible
by the inheritance. There may also have been some positive natural
selection of short dark people in the crowded city populations
of the nineteenth century. The increase of height or hastening of
growth above mentioned makes it possible that the higher statures
Shrubsall noted east and south of the Jurassic scarp are in part due to
better food on the wheat lands.

Parsons in 1920 reviewed the question of colouring in England and
Wales, almost entirely confirming the pioneer work of Beddoe. He
found that rural folk were on the whole more fair and urban people
darker ; and Professor E. G. Bowen has shown that the short dark
people resist urban difficulties rather well, while the taller fair men drift
off, not seldom beyond the seas. South-west England and Wales are
predominantly dark, and the Midlands are on the whole rather dark ;
East Anglia, Lincolnshire and East Yorkshire are much fairer and
so are some port districts on the coasts of Kent and Sussex. North
Lancashire and Cumberland again are notably fair as is most of
Northumberland. The distribution of fair colouring suggests the
contribution that Anglians, Danes, and Norsemen have made to our
population. The data for head-form show that the extreme long
narrow head was very important among early populations (Ch. 2)
and fairly important among the migrants from the south associated
with megalithic cultures (Ch. 3). These last are much narrower-
headed in England than in Scotland. Is this because in England they
found more earlier population and intermarried with it to a greater
extent ? The Round Barrow people of the Early Bronze Age coming
from Middle Europe were broader-headed, but not so much broader
as are the Short Cist people of Scotland (p. 192). Skulls from Early
Iron Age and Anglo-Saxon graves are notably long-headed.

A large number of skulls has been collected from the ambulatory
of the church of St. Leonard's at Hythe; they have been studied by
Parsons and by Stoessiger and Morant. They are mainly broad-headed.

In a catalogue given by the latter authors, of eighty males half have cranial indices over 82, i.e., are decidedly broad-headed, while only a quarter have that index below 80. The lowest cranial index of a male in the catalogue is 75.0, an isolated case, as the next to it is 76.2. Morant and Hoadley have investigated crania excavated at Spitalfields, London, of unknown date but almost certainly before 1600 A.D. Only 2 out of 108 males are extreme long-narrow heads (cranial index below 72.5) while 25 are decidedly broad (cranial index over 82). The broad element already mentioned for Hythe is found here again. The skulls are so different from the Round Barrow and Short Cist crania that they cannot be related. They are, on the other hand, much like many French ones and both Hythe and Spital-fields might well have received a continental immigration. Another, medieval, series of crania from Rothwell, Northants, shows a range of head-form more normal for Britain. These facts are specially interesting because broad-heads are far from being a prominent element in modern English populations. Beddoe and Howe discuss a small sample of about 200 men from the West Riding of Yorkshire. The sample shows an effective range from 73 to 87 in cephalic index (on the living head) with the largest numbers from 76.6 to 80.5 as usual. Four men had narrower heads than those in the effective range. Dark eyes were seen in only a small minority and fair or medium brown hair was commonest. Beddoe, Haddon and Brad-brooke and Parsons have drawn attention to the dark colouring among villagers of the Chiltern Hundreds, in old days a sparsely peopled woodland, apparently for a long time a refuge for pre-Saxon peoples (Ch. 6).

It will be appreciated from the review given in this chapter that we are far from an adequate knowledge of ourselves from the physical-historical point of view. That different physical inheritances persist side by side without barriers to intermarriage seems established beyond doubt. This makes it unlikely that any primarily statistical analysis will separate out the various strains. At the same time the biological observer must be guarded in his inferences, when, as he should, he uses archæological evidence.

It may be permitted to add to this already long chapter a short summary statement. The early post-glacial inhabitants of Britain, probably arriving before we were separate from the continent, were very long- and narrow-headed for the most part, with a few moderate

long-heads ; these two somewhat different balances of growth tendencies seem to persist to the present day. The population (Ch. 2) was
very small and in-bred until the arrival of food-producing and trading
peoples after about 2500 B.C. Immigrants from S.W. Europe and the
Mediterranean came especially to western Britain (Ch. 3) and among
them were many long-headed people, probably with dark hair and
eyes like their predecessors in Britain and their relatives in south-west
Europe. It may be supposed that they were often smoother-boned,
and that the moderately long-head was, or at any rate became, more
general than the extreme long-head. This element in our population is
specially important in the south-west and in Wales, and the Pennines
and parts of western Scotland and the Isle of Man. It may have been
reinforced by movements northwards along the west coast of Europe
in subsquent periods. At some time, or times, in antiquity a broad-
headed dark-haired element was spread here and there along our west
coasts. (p. 67.)

As cultural relations with Denmark and the west Baltic seem
indicated at least as far back as the early part of the second millennium
B.C., we have in Britain types of men akin to those found in the west
Baltic lands, notably tall, fair, with rather thin features, and rather long
heads. They occur in coastal patches in west Britain and are very
generally distributed in east Britain.

Broad-headed people seem to be quite a minor element in our
population. The Round Barrow (England) and Short Cist (Scotland)
immigrants of the dawn of the Metal Age may have left traces of themselves in modern populations of some areas but they have rarely been
clearly identified. It is likely that the exceptional amount of broad-
headedness in Aberdeenshire may be linked with the importance of the
settlement of that region by the Short Cist people. The patches of
broad-headed people of the west coast were mentioned in the previous
paragraph and reference was made above to the problem of the broad-
headed groups of presumably medieval date at Hythe and Spital-
fields. We have noted the abundant occurrence of light eyes even
accompanying very dark hair ; and the fact is that, however "Spanish"
a few British people may look, they are nevertheless not so dark as
most Iberians. Something may be allowed for intermarriage with
more or less blond people immigrating from northern Europe. Something may also be due to lack of stimulus to pigment production in our
cloudy atmosphere. We get a relatively small quantity of violet and

ultra-violet radiation ; and it is the people of regions where that radiation is strongest who are most pigmented. Pigment stops and converts a proportion of this radiation ; we get hardly as much as we need in any case ; it is possible therefore, that the people with only moderate pigment have been at an advantage in Britain.

That the tall, fair element prefers rural life and adventure seems well borne out, and implies the well-known tendency of those people to emigrate from industrialised Britain. In our great centres it is thought that the smaller, darker people have multiplied and are multiplying more rapidly, and this is perhaps especially the case among recent immigrants from Southern Ireland.

Some accessory problems have been omitted from this sketch. Red hair is sometimes just on the edge of the blond condition. Sometimes it is obviously different, and is thought by some to be a result of a cross ; once established it tends to recur and it is somewhat commoner in some parts of Scotland and Wales than in most of England.

A very tall, thin-faced, extremely long-headed type is found here and there and has resemblances with Spanish Castilians, especially those depicted for us by El Greco.

Huguenot, Jewish and other immigrants and refugees have added to the complexity of our population. Some Lanarkshire mining villages have people of east European origin, brought in in the late nineteenth century. Further, Britain, like most other countries, preserves interesting communities, sometimes showing a certain degree of isolation, which may be geographical, as in the case of the Forest of Dean and Romney Marsh, or may be social and occupational, as among gipsies and tinkers.

It is felt that illustrations of well-known men will give more idea of elements in our population than mere types, and a small selection has been made. Lord Ribblesdale (plate XI, p. 186) painted by J. S. Sargent, shows a tall, fair, thin type of country gentleman. Charles Darwin (plate X, p. 179), shown in the days before he grew a long beard, seems to have had some at least of the characters of the round barrow people, though we may not say he was descended from them ; their characters may have been carried by immigrants of some later time. Robert Burns (plate IX, p. 178) seems to illustrate some of the characters of our dark long-heads. These illustrations are given with reserve ; the actual measurements are not known.

There is added to this little series a remarkable photograph of a man carrying the features (extreme long head, strong brows, deep-set nose-root, strong cheek-bones, dark colouring) of the very early inhabitants of Britain (plate VIII, p. 91 and pp. 36-37).

The choral singing and oratory so characteristic in Welsh life, and the interest of the people in education, are well known and are sometimes held to be "racial" characteristics. They may be, but other considerations must be mentioned. Groups which have had meagre equipment have to try to find means of social expression which do not involve the acquisition of costly instruments or organisation, and singing, oratory and at any rate some aspects of education comply with this condition. Moreover, we are here concerned with a people which, since Tudor times, has felt itself somewhat apart from their landed gentry, who have become largely anglicized. So the difficulty of costly equipment has been even greater than appears at first sight. Then we must also take account of the influence of the religious movement of the eighteenth century, which discouraged dancing, drama, and various other social activities, but encouraged singing and oratory. Singing is however a very old interest in Wales, as Giraldus Cambrensis (twelfth century) refers to the Welsh ability to sing in parts. It is noteworthy that choral singing of high quality is also characteristic of people in the West Riding of Yorkshire, where, as in Wales, we are dealing with a population that includes a large element of the dark longheads who form the basis of our British population ; so a possible link with physical characteristics, though not proven, is not ruled out. It would be interesting to know whether high-arched palates are common in these cases ; they are reputed to help resonance.

Singing, oratory and the religious activities associated with the eighteenth century movement in Wales all have a strong emotional component, and all imply interest in matters outside the daily round, the common task. We thus have characteristics widespread amongst the Welsh-speaking people that may be results of environmental factors, with a possibility that racial characteristics may play a part, too.

Oratory and an interest in education are, again, widespread in Scotland, though, for whatever reason, choral singing is not so elaborately organised. Here opportunities of education are of older establishment, the newest of the four Scottish Universities was founded as far back as 1582 at Edinburgh. In both Scotland and Wales the poverty of the country has been a spur to educate young people, who, in the nineteenth and twentieth centuries have emigrated to England, the Dominions and U.S.A.

The quarrying districts of north-west Wales have contributed a good many builders to Merseyside ; the cattle areas of Cardiganshire have a contingent engaged in the milk trade, notably in London ; the sheep and wool region of Teifyside in south Cardiganshire, north-west Carmarthenshire and north-east Pembrokeshire sends men into the drapery business in English cities, and coastal villages and small towns in both Scotland and Wales have produced many ships' officers and, particularly in the case of Scotland, engineers. The importance of both Scottish and Welsh elements in medicine and surgery, and among ministers of religion is well known. While some who emigrate find it difficult to adjust their minds, it is true of a great many that they achieve intellectual and often also economic success. In this result the double perspective plays a part alongside of frugality and industry. The immigrant has in his mind both his home standards and the habits and opportunities of the big city to which he has come. He learns, if he is able enough, to look at each from the point of view of the other; in other words he has gained mental objectivity, which may and often does give critical discriminative ability and a certain plasticity of temperament. The administrative and organising ability so wide-spread among emigrants, especially from east and south Scotland, no doubt owes a good deal to this objectivity, coupled with the tradition of education, and perhaps also with the 350 years of lay participation in church government.

If now we turn to the rural lowlands of south-east England we find a different set of operative factors. It has long been the rule that the wife takes her husband's social position, and cases of women marrying into humbler circumstances than those of their childhood homes are less numerous than those of marrying with what have been considered social equals or superiors. There has been no strict bar to this mainly upward stream among marrying women. At various periods in English history, of which the present day is certainly one, groups hitherto little recognised in the matter of titles and positions of power have come forward. One thinks, in history, of the men who at the Reformation acquired what had been monastic estates, and of Pitt's numerous creations of new peers recruited from among wealthy merchants. This has meant that the grades of the social hierarchy are not as sharply and unalterably marked as in some other countries ; it also of course implies the power of capital. On the whole the rural English lowlander has had a considerable regard for " the gentry ", and the middle classes have tended to adopt conventions from these same gentry. Convention has great power, and with it goes a considerable restraint on violence. English reserve is world-famous and has helped the English sportsman to " play the game ". He may sometimes find himself at some disadvantage in competition with the immigrant from Scotland or Wales, but the characteristic English social life from the middle classes upwards is apt to win the immigrant over to a sufficient extent to prevent his being seriously ostracised as an outsider.

The manufacturing north of England, and to some extent industrial centres further south, has its own social atmosphere. Lancashire has a saying " clogs to clogs in three generations." This implies fairly rapid changes in wealth and social regard of families and carries with it the well-known fact that often a wealthy family keeps for a generation or two traces of the speech and the habits of life of forebears who may have been mill-hands. Plain speaking and often direct thinking and a readiness to take risks are natural accompaniments. The last characteristic has its repercussions in betting and gambling as an alleviation of the dullness of repetitive work in factories.

The urban element in the population of Britain has increased in proportion to the rural from the early eighteenth century onwards (ch. 13), but the effects have become much more conspicuous since traditional wheat-farming declined after the repeal of the Corn Laws (1846) and the flooding-in of American grain (especially after 1870). The decline of agriculture and the lure of the industrial towns have been mutually complementary factors in the process. Side by side with this went large-scale emigration to U.S.A., Canada, Australia, New Zealand and, to some extent, to parts of South Africa. That emigration was in part selective. It took Scots in large numbers to New Zealand and Canada to open up cultivation and railroad enterprise. English folk went off to escape rural poverty ; the crowded quarters of the towns are said to have contributed a smaller proportion of the emigrants, and city-bred people would often be in difficulty when they moved to the great open spaces of the new lands.

The absence of serious invasions for over eight centuries is another factor that has in the long run helped to diminish the authoritarian factors amongst us as well as to promote a good deal of local diversity.

Until recently the centralization of goverment was less marked than it has been, for example, in France.

Another important fact is that, since Elizabeth's reign, there have been several diverse claimants to religious orthodoxy, and this has helped to furnish different forms of religious expression suited to different minds—the " Church and State " attitude of the majority of the aristocracy, the intellectual Dissenting groups of the seventeenth century, the appeal of John Wesley, and later of his disciple William Booth, to the common man, the loyalty of old Romanist families through many difficulties—all have helped to make it possible for people of diverse outlook to carry on side by side, and severe persecution was greatly diminished earlier than in many countries. The several orthodoxies have done a great deal to give British life a stability and a sense of compromise that has been far more difficult to attain in countries of one orthodoxy inclined to persecution or, as that has become an offence to the average mind, to ostracism of deviators.

Our language is often said to suffer from the very irregular relations between spelling and pronunciation, and our American friends are trying to diminish this difficulty a little through spelling modifications, some of which we might adopt with advantage. But those irregular relations are, in considerable measure, the accompaniment of something that makes our language almost uniquely rich, namely its intimate combination of heritages from Anglo-Saxon, from Norman-French, and from the classical sources so specially drawn upon in the seventeenth and eighteenth centuries, when classical styles of architecture were attracting attention. Chaucer's tales and William Tindale's translations of the Scriptures contrast in language with the writings of Dr. Johnson so markedly as to suggest two languages, while in Shakespeare's plays the two are used with almost equal facility and felicity. The wealth of our language in fine shades of expression may have made it less sharply defined than French, but it has helped to build up the literature of the imagination that is a major contribution of Britain to the world. And not only the literature of the imagination claims mention here. It has been a feature of British life that men with leisure have contributed in considerable numbers to science, history, travel-studies, philosophy and government by their writings as well as by their active interest in public affairs. Furthermore, in all these fields of thought there are great contributors to our literature—Darwin and Huxley and Sherrington; Gibbon, Macaulay and Winston Churchill ;

Captain Cook and Doughty, Hobbes and Berkeley, Hume and Mill, Milton, Burke and many another. Their writings are far more than contributions to knowledge in the special fields studied: they have expressed themselves in finely chosen language ; they are literary figures as well as scholars. It has indeed been a great thing for Britain that she is, as it were, between the south and the north, between the Mediterranean and the Northern heritages, partaking of both and effecting combinations of varying proportions, so that variety, ingenuity, initiative and practical compromise are our better features.

Recently, investigation of types of human blood has been brought into relation with the story of our population. In respect of certain constituents blood may be classified under four types, respectively O, A, B, AB. AB is uncommon and has not been related to the population-story. B is widely present in a small percentage of individuals but, apart from noting that this percentage runs a little higher in North Wales, little can be said at present. The vast majority of individuals have blood of type O or type A, the former being especially important in Scotland and in England north of Lancashire and Yorkshire. It seems to be the type characteristic of our ancestral population. Blood of type A occurs in a higher percentage of individuals in the East Riding, the Soke of Peterborough, Cambridgeshire and Norfolk than in most other areas. Now, archaeologically these are regions with Saxon cemeteries of early date as we infer from the occurrence of cremation burials, a practice that ceased rapidly under the influence of the Roman Church. It has long been thought that family boatloads of Anglo Saxons, probably escaping from Slavonic pressure on their old homes near the Baltic, rowed up the Humber and the rivers of the Wash and, having their women with them, founded villages of their own. As blood of type A is very important in the region whence the Anglo Saxons came, we can venture the hypothesis that they brought a lot of this blood type to England and that it maintained itself specially in areas where the immigrant families settled. They were headed off eastwards for a while by the Romano-British kingdom of Elmet lying west of the Yorkshire Ouse, and type A decreases while type O increases west of that river. The same change would occur as young Anglo Saxon men spread, looking for land to cultivate, and marrying British girls. Many other points will arise as these investigations proceed and hypotheses remain quite provisional.

REFERENCES, see end ch. 10, p. 214.

CHAPTER 10

CLOTHES

A
S WITH most human characteristics, one must think of multiple
origins. A hide or fur wrap for carrying a baby or protecting it
from cold or flies is one possibility. Others are disguise, by using some
animal covering to approach a hunted beast unawares; or to represent
an animal in some ceremonial, an ornamental covering with some
social meaning and so on. Women have used a skirt-cover that
protected the womb from the evil eye and yet allowed entry of a
" spirit " to ensure pregnancy. Men might sheath their sex organs to
obviate their rubbing against the thighs in running and to reduce
dangers of sexual excitement at the wrong time. Some naked Bushman-
mothers of South Africa press the baby boy's sex organs upwards and
forwards to obviate the rubbing above mentioned. Clothing in its
evolution has had much influence on sexual excitement, and has led
on to what is called modesty, which has, however, different meanings
for different peoples.

Some Spanish rock paintings that perhaps belong to the Old Stone
Age show what may be furry coverings, and, in the case of women,
skirts of considerable length. The dates of these paintings are, however,
uncertain ; and direct knowledge of Old Stone Age clothing is almost
nil. Small awls and needles of Magdalenian (late Palaeolithic) Age
suggest tailoring.

From the First Dynasty in Egypt and from (ca 3400 B.C.) broadly
the same period in Mesopotamia we have evidence of woven material,
chiefly linen or bast. Evidently tough fibres were sought and no doubt
cultivated, spun and woven. For the full development of weaving a
whole series of inventions was needed but, as they occurred far from
Britain, we need not follow them out here. The earlier series of Swiss

202

lake-dwellings show that the idea of woven clothing had reached Switzerland by the later centuries of the third millennium B.C. The chief evidence is from spindle-whorls and weights to keep the thread taut in weaving. Wool fibres had probably come into use in the period of the early Swiss lake-dwellings, but it was only in the Bronze Age that domesticated sheep became really important in Europe. Nettle fibre was apparently used in early Britain, and the related ramie has long been used in China. At least from the Bronze Age onwards woollen clothing seems to have been more important than linen in Europe north of the Mediterranean ; sheep increased greatly in that period.

All this is understandable considering the climate. Probably the earliest clothing was mainly skins. No doubt early wool had a good deal of hair (kemp) in it. It is only under quite exceptional circumstances that prehistoric clothing is preserved in Europe and we have no British evidence, but, where spindle-whorls and weaver's thread weights occur, clothing was surely woven.

All that is known about forms of clothing of Neolithic people in Europe is from clay figurines in a few places in east-central Europe. From the Bronze Age we have Danish burials in what later became bogland and these in a few cases have preserved the clothes A man had an outer cloak which was a kind of shawl with a fringe, a coat or

FIG. 44

Woman's dress, Danish Bronze Age. In other cases the skirt was longer

shirt-like garment reaching down to the knees and hanging from shoulder straps, and a cap and shoes. Around the waist was a band fastened by a bronze double button. Strabo gives a fairly similar description of the clothing of men of the " Kassiterides ".[1] A woman wore a cloak like that of the man, or what we should now call a pull-over a pleated skirt (as in the diagram or longer), and a waist girdle with a large bronze ornament. The edges of some of the garments

[1] The Kassiterides or Tin Islands have been variously identified as islands off the north-est coasts of Spain, or the south coast of Brittany, or as the Scilly Isles.

were sewn in blanket-stitch. There is no indication, for either the man or the woman, of washable underclothing. The clothes enumerated suggest protection against cold. Pin fastening was known, and before the end of the Bronze Age a two-piece metal pin, forerunner of the Iron Age bronze safety-pin (fibula), made in two pieces afterwards linked up, had come into use. One frequently finds pins near female skeletons and

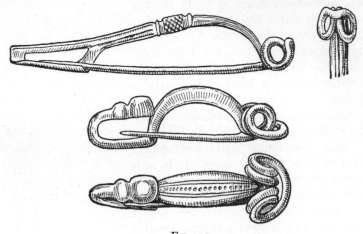

FIG. 45
British fibulae of the pre-Roman Iron Age

this suggests that the women put up their hair in some way. In south-east Europe, probably Danubia or perhaps north Italy, the bronze safety-pin, made in one piece, was developed and it spread far and wide. As these pins more or less survive even cremated burial, and as fashion in safety-pins varied from region to region and from time to time, they are especially valuable as guides to dating and to cultural relations between regions, especially from the beginning of the Iron Age. Buttons are not identifiable with certainty until the Bronze Age, when we get the double button passed through slits in the material, somewhat analogous with later cuff-links. Irish gold was much sought for ornaments, and lunulæ (crescents) of thin gold plate worn on the breast have been found in numbers in Ireland, also one at Llanllyfni, Caernarvonshire, two in Cornwall, as well as a few in western France, Luxembourg, Hanover and Denmark. Torcs or neck ornaments, arm-rings and other objects of Irish gold were also worn, as were beads of amber, jet, callaïs (p. 60) and other substances including faience.

Representations of men and women on urns of the Early Iron Age give a little information for that period. The women decorated themselves with earrings, ornamental collars and tassels, and both sexes wore tunics, with a girdle at least in the case of the men. The tunic was fastened at the neck. In south and central Europe the chieftain apparently had breeches and a woollen mantle, the latter light for summer and of heavy wool for winter. Women's arm-rings suggest that the arms were bare. No doubt ideas of clothing spread west and north-west from the Mediterranean world in the last centuries B.C. Tattooing and woad-staining had been practised in western Europe and skin and fur were used. Roman descriptions tell of woollen clothes in chequer patterns with red colourings conspicuous. Apparently druids wore blue robes and astrologers green ones. Fighting men might have a closely felted garment that, according to Pliny, a sword could hardly penetrate. In Roman days in Britain Roman fashions competed with native ones, and the toga or mantle was widespread. Boots had hob-nails.

For the post-Roman centuries we have hints from illustrations in manuscripts. The English invaders loved ornament as an offset to the squalor of the time, and the Sutton Hoo treasure (p. 134) hints at delicate workmanship, probably by Celtic, perhaps Irish, craftsmen. Most of the jewellery of those centuries is of a more barbaric splendour, later toned down by Christianity ; bells were worn as charms to drive off evil spirits. Both sexes wore a tunic. Among ordinary men the tunic reached to the knee, was slit at the side, and had the upper arm loose-sleeved but the fore-arm closely wrapped. The neck was open in front, more or less like that of a modern shirt. A full-length tunic for a man may have been a mark of age, rank, or priesthood. The legs, unless bare, might have hose cross-gartered with leather. Leather shoes appear to have had wooden soles. A cloak over the tunic was fastened on the shoulder by a brooch, and had a hood. Separate head-coverings were rare. The tunic was held by a waist-belt. Under the tunic a shirt and breeches might be worn, the latter sometimes fastened by a buckle below the knee, sometimes continuing down to the ankle and then fitting closely on the shins. Iron-work had become sufficiently general by this time for some fighting men to have rings of iron around their bodies ; these rings were fastened together with fibre, foreshadowing medieval armour. Women wore a long tunic covering the feet, and over it often a shorter one, to the knees, with long sleeves ; the tunics were held by a girdle from which hung various objects that the wearer needed. A woman usually had a linen undergarment if possible. Her mantle and hood might more or less parallel that of a man.

In the post-Roman time Christian missionaries spread over Europe. The tunic, then in widespread use, was worn by them and became the white priestly alb, eventually the surplice of some regions. The mantle or cloak became the chasuble, with a hood; from these garments are derived the gown and hood of academic ceremony. The early preacher's walking-stick came to be prized as a personal memento, later a relic encased in metal, whence the bishop's pastoral staff. But it should be noted that, in Pharaonic Egypt, the King had a shepherd's crook as a symbol of his protectorship of the good, as well as a flail for chastisement of evil-doers. The missionary gathered people to hear him by tinkling a bell, probably a simple cowbell, or a bell hitherto used to ward off evil spirits.

FIG. 46
Anglo-Saxon Costume

This, again, encased in ornamental metal, became the bell used in the celebration of the Mass. Fear, especially of evil spirits, was accompanied by trivial protective devices and, no doubt, stories of the stupidity of such spirits. One recalls that in 1940-43, when Nazi success was dreaded, stories were invented to make people laugh at Hitler.

Among the old-fashioned folk of the north-west of Britain, the early shawl mentioned above (p. 203) seems to have become a long shawl-like wrap woven in rectangular patterns and called a plaid. For ease of movement of the arms a jacket or coat was substituted for the upper part and the lower part of the plaid survived as the kilt, which acquired patterning, basically a recognition-mark. A leather pouch hung from the waist-belt of the kilt has become the ornamental sporran. It is characteristic of a people which has so strenuously and so long maintained an organization of clans based on kinship that the tartan patterns were standardised for each clan (plate 10, p. 63).

During the Middle Ages for a time, with more definite growth of professions and social grades, the tunic was to some extent used as a class-mark. It was long for professional men who became differentiated from the priesthood, but a long tunic was out of place for agricultural or craft work of many kinds. For such work the tunic was shortened into a jacket or cotte that at first might reach down to mid-thigh and was held by a girdle round the waist or, later, on the hips. Long close-fitting hose from waist to ankle often cross-gartered on the shins, were called by the French and Normans *chausses*. At the end of the Middle Ages they were divided into stockings (*bas de chausses*) and breeches or trunk hose (*haut de chausses*). This is how stockings have come to be called *bas*

FIG. 47
Fourteenth-Century Costume

in modern French. The woman's outer tunic was called a *bliaut* and was later modified into a surcoat. The under tunic became known as the *cotte* (coat), and was divided into bodice and petti-coat (*petit cotte*). With these elaborations of the tunic, the cloak became largely a luxury item, sometimes extravagantly bejewelled. Gold and silver thread were woven into the material of the nobleman's cloak and it was often adorned with fur, a fashion derived from Hanseatic trade. The elaboration of armour as the smith's skill improved led on to widespread use of the ancient type of chain-mail

P

which gave more flexibility, but the introduction of gunpowder made armour useless and military pride then elaborated uniforms. A definite and separate cap or hat, sometimes with a brim, came into general use for men, and a *couvre chef* (coverchief or kerchief) was worn by women. But women's headgear went through many fashions, some of them, such as the steeple-hat with a kerchief draped on it, being very extravagant. Silk added itself to the general luxury and display in fourteenth-century Britain. It was introduced into Italy from Saracen Sicily and Constantinople and spread thence via France.

It is probable that washable linen underclothing was in use to some extent from the thirteenth, or, at any rate, the fourteenth century. Accompanying this came the use of rags for paper-making. Parchment for manuscripts had been difficult to obtain, and rag-paper was therefore specially valuable, and became even more important when printing developed in the fifteenth century.

FIG. 48
Fifteenth-Century Costume

Until late in the sixteenth century soap, of doubtful quality, was made by mixing wood-ash solution with grease from domestic animals ; it was a home product, often none too clean. Then the whale fisheries brought in blubber on a large scale and it could be cleaned. Soap of better quality became available for the wealthy. As a consequence we find white ruffs and other finery coming into fashion as everyone knows from paintings of Queen Elizabeth and many others, and from some of our traditional snap-cards. Franz Hals painted a man, who was probably a *nouveau-riche*, with a ruff which was more or less the mark of an aristocrat ; the artist with characteristic mischief makes the subject look a trifle uncomfortable in his unaccustomed splendour. Lord Conway, in his essay on *The Domain of Art*, expressed the opinion that the new finery was an important factor in the development of portrait painting ; it undoubtedly had a good deal to do with the development of white starched headdress among nuns, and among women in Brittany and elsewhere. It is thought that white washable underclothing became more elaborate about this time, especially as weaving of linen from the fifteenth, and of cotton from the seventeenth century onwards was expanding as a specialised activity. Men had hats with broad brims and sometimes a tall crown (steeple hat), especially used by those who cut their hair short, i.e., by those who became "Roundheads" rather than "Cavaliers".

FIG. 49
Elizabethan costume

It is interesting to notice here that, while among men the wearing of one's hair long and curled was obviously a dangerous mark of distinction under the Commonwealth (1649-60), the Restoration revived the custom of long hair in modified form by the acceptance of the French habit of wigs. It has been thought that reasons of cleanliness helped this change from natural long hair to wigs, but there are stories to the contrary. One should note the persistence of wigs and robes in the legal profession, even among women barristers both in Europe and in intertropical lands.

For general wear the coat and waistcoat established themselves from France to Britain with the advent of King Charles II. Men's knee-breeches and stockings for the shins became general and the breeches were fastened at the knees by buckles as of old. The rise of industrialism and of a new type of propertied men in the nineteenth century sometimes promoted copying, by plutocrats' sons, of the ways and clothes of the older gentry, but the flowered waistcoats, buckled breeches and patterned hose were not suitable in the smoky atmosphere of the industrial town. One could probably trace the descent of the long frock-coat of the nineteenth century from a man's tunic or cotte, and one could infer that, by cutting away the lower part in front, one gets the morning coat which the nineteenth century considered rather less formal. More cutting away gave the "tails" variety of evening dress with its old-fashioned display of starched shirt-front, collar and cuffs, and sometimes a very high stiff collar. Economy and convenience have led to the evolution of the lounge suit and dinner jacket, the coat being short in both.

FIG. 50
Cavalier costume (17th Century)

The aristocratic garb of one generation tends to become a service garb of a later time. The frock coat has almost completed this transition and some think the " tails " variety of evening dress is going the same way.

What may be called the natural evolution of clothing is thus firstly the result of progress in use of material and correlated method of treatment. Speculatively we assign first place, in time, to skins. Then, with the more definitely settled habitats of early cultivators, we find evidence of treatment of plants for extraction of fibres to be felted or spun and woven, in the first case probably including hair from animals. The increase of sheep and consequent supply of wool marks the next

PLATE XIII

John Murkham

PREACHER'S HOUSE, Ludlow. Timber-frame house of the West Midlands style, showing elaborate pattern

PLATE XIV

step, in the Bronze Age, in the latter part of which double buttons as well as safety and other pins were being used as fasteners. The long pin was also often used as a stylus for writing on wax. Something of the nature of silk (dimaks or damask from Damascus) was used at Cos in classical times and the introduction of improved iron implements made fine work in wood for looms, etc., more generally available. These facts, added to craft-specialisation and increase of maritime commerce, promoted elaboration of luxury in clothing. The tunic spread as a garment to western Europe. There followed the organization of silk-worm-breeding at or from Constantinople about the time of the Emperor Justinian (sixth century A.D.), based on the bringing of moths' eggs from China in a hollow bamboo cane, but silk was rare in the west until manufacture of silk cloth spread to North Italy after the introduction of the silkworm in the twelfth century. In Chaucer's day silk was luxury material in Britain. In the late fifteenth century its manufacture spread to France and, on a small scale, to England. Embroidery seems to have spread into Britain about this time. In our country religious refugees from Romanist persecution of the late six-

FIG. 51
Roundhead costume (17th Century)

teenth century in the Low Countries and France established the silk industry on a larger scale, and the refugees after the Revocation of the Edict of Nantes (1685) were even more important in this respect, as in several other social and industrial matters. The development of urban life and commerce in eighteenth-century Britain spread the luxury use of silk. In the late nineteenth century Japanese silk, raw and woven, came into commerce and so did that of the oak-eggar moth (Shantung silk) originally from the province of that name in North China. The introduction of wood-fibre for textiles and the development of the rayon industry by Samuel Courtauld at Rochdale, a pioneering centre in so many ways, are an industrial romance of the twentieth century.

Flax remained subordinate to wool as clothing material in the cool climate of northern and western Europe. Its cultivation as an industrial crop in Flanders, where the waters of the Scheldt were suitable for retting (dissociation of the fibres), developed late in the Middle Ages, chiefly outside the old towns of the woollen trade where guild restrictions hampered new developments. The linen manufacture made washable bed-linen and underclothing more abundant. Flax-growing expanded in north-eastern Ireland in the eighteenth century as part of the general British development promoted by religious refugees, but flax was increasingly rivalled and, in some matters, displaced by cotton—cheaper, more easily flexible, washable and colourable. But the custom of starched linen for ruffs at first and later for collars, cuffs and shirtfronts had a great vogue that lasted until the Second World War.

FIG. 52

Eighteenth-Century costume

Fur for decoration is linked, in north-western Europe, with Hanseatic trade and was characteristically taken up by civic authorities (the Hanseatic league was a civic organisation). Silk on the other hand, from Italy and France, was aristocratic, ecclesiastical and professional, as is implied by the phrase "taking silk" used for appointment as King's Counsel. In some University robes fur is an element in the garb of a graduate holding an initial degree, while silk and fine red cloth become more conspicuous among the holders of higher degrees. The persistence of the hood from monkish days in British Universities and its disappearance in French Universities are characteristic of both countries, the continuity of form in spite of change of ideas in the one, the strong tendency to express change of ideas in the other.

Colouring of woven materials and of various fibres has had a long and complex evolution intimately related to the evolution of communications. The dyeing of textiles by vegetable colouring matter, sometimes grown in a home-garden, may be followed out, but only madder and saffron will be mentioned here. The proud use of purple comes down to us from the days of Tyre and its extraction of the dye from the marine snail *Purpura*. The scarlet robe of the university doctorate is linked with medieval Florentine manufacture of high-grade cloth dyed scarlet and sold far and wide.

From other points of view the evolution of clothing is interesting, especially as expressing or reflecting social conditions. The influence of classical Europe encouraging western barbarians to wear the tunic, the refinement of woollen clothing as the export of wool to be worked up in Flanders developed from about the eleventh century, the improvement of beauty and design, especially in women's clothing as the worship of the Virgin Mary spread in the twelfth and thirteenth centuries, the display and even extravagance of the fourteenth century paralleled to a large extent in the elaboration of Gothic architecture, the rise of absolute monarchy with organised luxury in bejewelled clothing and bright colours in the sixteenth century, the Puritan revolt on the one hand and the starched linen already mentioned on the other for the seventeenth century, the renewal of luxurious and extravagant display in the " Age of Reason " (eighteenth century), all follow, or sometimes lead, in society's changes. The nineteenth century spread of trousers for men, and in the twentieth century for women in some occupations and sports, and the decline of special clothes for men (evening tail-coats, frock coats, even morning coats), the parallel decline of the cocked hat, the tall silk hat, even the hard bowler hat, have all tended in modern times to diminish the outward and visible signs of social stratification. With this levelling of differences, there have died out many local specialities of costume, so that today the British farm labourer is clad much as is the townsman; nearly all men who wear hats at all wear the soft felt or cloth cap, an occupational contrast ; old local variants have gone. In several districts changes in men's dress have followed changes in woman's dress. The adaptation of the patterned tie to the suit and to the occasion is a modern feature of men's costume.

The diminution of what have been called prudish ideas has had remarkable effects upon the bathing costumes of women, who "paddled" in early Victorian days wearing heavy pleated serge skirts. In pre-industrial days women might be hard-worked in domestic affairs or might be ladies of leisure, and dress differed accordingly, the leisured women being often stiffly corseted with waist reduced as much as possible. Apparently all women wore a number of petticoats, and skirts were supposed to hide their legs entirely. The amount of exposure of neck and shoulders and breasts varied from time to time.

In the nineteenth century, factory-work for women increased enormously, and we find the shawl becoming the typical covering of the factory woman's head. At the end of that century women came into office work and other non-domestic activities. Stiff corsets and long skirts and multiplicity of petticoats all became inconvenient, and the war of 1914-18 was followed by a great change in women's dress and life. In the late nineteenth century *Punch* had a picture of "mixed tennis" with a caption stressing the drawbacks of the ankle skirt and tight waist. More recently another picture, also in *Punch*, showed the woman player in "shorts" asking the man why he tried to play clad in long flannel trousers.

REFERENCES TO CHAPTERS 9 AND 10 : Beddoe (1885), Beddoe and Rowe (1907), Boas (1911, 1940), Bowen (1933), Bradbrooke and Parsons (1922), Broom (1923), Collignon (1894), Conway (1911), Coon (1939), Da Costa Ferreira (1913), Davies and Fleure (1936), Duckworth (1911), Fleure (1920), Fleure and James (1916), Fullard (1938), Haddon and Huxley (1935), Hiler (1929), Hodgkin (1935), Hrdlička (1928), Keith (1948), Kelly and Schwabe (1925), "Kleidung" (1926), Morant (1926, 1939), Morant and Hoadley (1931), Morant and Samson (1936), Parsons (1920), Reid and Morant (1928), Ripley (1900), Shrubsall (1924), Stoessiger and Morant (1932), Tocher (1924), Turner (1915), Victoria and Albert Museum (1924).

CHAPTER II

DWELLINGS

THE EARLIEST conjectural evidence of constructed dwellings is from the drawings in south French and north Spanish caves occupied in the latter part of the Old Stone Age. What look like drawings of tents supported on poles may represent summer habitations of people who returned to cave-shelters for winter. We know of hut-bases of Neolithic or very early post-Neolithic phases and, in western Europe, they tend to be round or oval. They were probably constructions of branches and mud, sometimes on a stone basis, sometimes with a stone floor. In somewhat later times, the full Bronze Age and the early Iron Age, probably with better timber work, we find the rectangular building more in evidence. Piggott has recently reinterpreted the complex plan of post-holes at Overton Hill (the Sanctuary) near Avebury as indicating successive constructions around an original sacred circular building (pp. 52-53 and fig. 15), presumably, in its first phase, of late Neolithic date. Gorsey Bigbury (p. 63) and Skara Brae (p. 82) have also been mentioned. Lethbridge thinks hut-walls of stone developed as additions inside and outside a tent. Since so many huts are double-walled this is quite possible.

The Romans brought in more advanced ideas of building in dressed stone and burnt brick and of heating and of decoration with tiles. The villas or large rural establishments often show great elaboration in the parts occupied by the owner. The Roman constructions contrast dramatically with the hut-bases of British villages more or less touched by Roman civilization. With the collapse of the Roman power, construction in dressed stone and burnt brick ceased for a time, wood and earth, with rough stone, being our more natural materials. Dressed stone later began to be used again for churches. Concerning

215

the larger establishments of post-Roman times our knowledge is meagre but increasing. Bersu has recently examined circular enclosures of considerable size in the Isle of Man, and he interprets them as remains of dwellings with a roof supported by concentric circles of posts. Another site excavated in 1934-36 at Glendarragh, Braaid, Isle of Man showed in outline, in unmortared stone, foundations of the side-walls of what was a long subrectangular building ; the lines of the walls almost suggest a boat-form. The walls at their east ends have monumental standing stones. Nearby was a circle, of considerable size, of stones, probably the outline of a circular dwelling of the type later described by Bersu ; but the soil, tested at several points within the circle, was too disturbed for detection of post-holes. Such buildings, if one may give them that name, are difficult to date, but most probably belong to some date within the period 400-1000 A.D. To the later part of that period belong the raths of Ireland which Bersu and Estyn Evans are investigating. A rath site may have a diameter of as much as 100 feet, and the area was covered by a roof supported by concentric circles of posts. The roof was probably of turf or thatch on a wooden frame. The hearth was central, and no doubt there was a smoke-hole in the roof. The roof may have been removed periodically and used as a rather doubtful manure, valued for its soot-content and decaying turf or thatch. Raths have not been adequately identified in Britain though they are spoken of in Pembrokeshire ; and it is possible that, by the tenth century, to which many Irish ones belong, building of other types had come back into British life. The rath and the other large dwellings just noticed must have been establishments of groups, perhaps of relatives, perhaps of a chief with his family or families, servitors and slaves.

For Britain, we have some indications from the Welsh laws of Hywel Dda (tenth century) and a few other sources. A King's Hall seems to have been an oblong structure resting mainly on six wooden uprights, of which two were placed at one end, with the door between them, and two at the other end. The central couple had the open hearth between them and divided the hall into an upper section for the king and leading officials, and a lower section for the people of lower status. Some halls had side-aisles in which people slept at night ; and some writers think halls were often circular, with people sleeping feet towards a central hearth. It seems probable that there were often aisles as just mentioned, and that halls, broadly of this kind, were a feature of

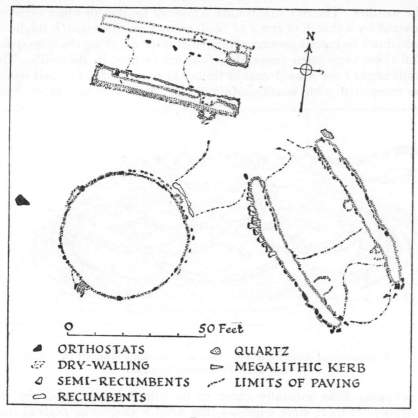

FIG. 53

Plan of Glendarragh, Braaid, Isle of Man. On the right are foundation-walls of a boat-shaped hall or house, with more rectilinear foundation-walls of another hall or house to the north, and circular foundation-walls to the west. A large standing-stone is placed still farther to the west.

post-Roman, and possibly also of earlier times, in north-west Europe. The central part or nave of the hall was often a rod (later standardised at 16½ feet) wide, each aisle being half a rod across. At each end of the building the two posts were crossed at the top, or might be curved around until they thus crossed. They would in this way give a V at each gable-end, and the ridge-pole would rest in the Vs, with the roof framework sloping down on each side, if possible reaching a little beyond the wall-top so as to give eaves protecting the wall to some extent from the weather. The roof might have a layer of heather or other material covered by a thatch of straw or reed, or by turf. The thatch might be held down by special timbers arranged at intervals along the ridge-pole, and there were often ropes also, fastened to pegs in the walls. The walls might have a good deal of timber in woodland areas, and would be completed with wattle-and-daub, i.e., branches and mud. Mud

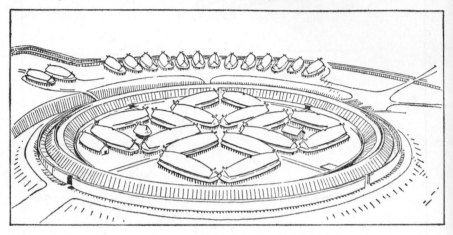

FIG. 54

Reconstructed diagram of boat-shaped habitations grouped in a fortified area; Trelleburg, Denmark

containing lime naturally came to be considered valuable for this purpose. If there were windows (the word is said to be derived from wind-eye) they would be open spaces in the walls, usually on the sheltered side of the hall ; and they might be stuffed at night with straw, wattle, wood or a stretched skin.

Lethbridge has shown, from reliquaries and from the Bayeux tapestry, that the ridge-pole might have a figure of a protective dragon at one or both ends. It seems that a few houses in East Anglia still have the gable-ridge rising at its end.

The central hearth would have a guardian of the fire charged to keep it alive and to cover it at night to keep it quiet (curfew comes from *couvre-feu*). A smoke-hole above the hearth let some of the smoke escape and helped ventilation ; the guardian of the fire was often also the doorkeeper. The hall had accessory buildings for animals, stores and other purposes, arranged in a palisaded enclosure with gateway

PLATE XV

Aerofilms, Ltd.

a. MOTTE AND BAILEY earthwork of Norman times, Berkhampstead Castle. The motte (mound) had a wooden building on it; the bailey was enclosed by a palisade and may also have had wooden buildings on it

F. J. North

b. THE "ROMAN" STEPS, Ardudwy, Merionethshire. Probably a mediaeval stepway going through a pass in the Rhinog mountains

PLATE XVI

Robert Atkinson

A FISHERMAN'S LANE, Looe, Cornwall. Narrow lanes with close-set houses are very characteristic of fishing villages

entrance at a bridge across a protective ditch. There was need to guard against both wolves and human enemies. The hall itself, and perhaps some stores, might be in an inner enclosure. Apparently these fairly large establishments, of a hall and accessory buildings, were often isolated from other habitations in a clearing in the woods, as we have seen (p. 150). Early English days were a great period of woodland

FIG. 55

Diagram of a boat-shaped house; Trelleborg, Denmark

cutting. It is noteworthy that in recent centuries the squire's residence in a village has often been called "*the Hall*". The style of building of the wooden halls of Early English centuries was carried on later in the designs of barns.

The hut or house, in our climate primarily for shelter of both man and beast, for warmth from a fire which it would not be easy to keep alive in the open air, and for storage, might be built durably in stone (plate 12, p. 79), but would often have stone merely for wall-bases and would be built, for the rest, in wattle-and-daub on a wooden frame. This was perhaps, on the whole, in the interests of health, as the hut would become foul and verminous, especially if it housed animals as well as people, as was most often the case. Discarded huts may have become storage places, or refuse depositories, or may have been used for burials, while a burial in a hut may, conversely, have led to its being discarded.

Graham says this type of dwelling was very widespread in rural Scotland until 1750 or later, and no doubt it lingered in south Britain as well. A tenant leaving such a house took away any beams or rafters he had inserted, so the new tenant came into what was almost a ruin. In the north of Scotland, crofters would make a hut of this kind, exploit the land near it until it was exhausted, and then squat somewhere else, leaving a ruin behind. Graham hints here and there that conditions in and about 1700 were worse than they had been some generations earlier. In 1750-1800 enclosures for potatoes and turnips, tree-planting, marsh drainage and better seeds led to better houses, chiefly of mortared stone.

Mention has already been made of Skara Brae (p. 82) in Orkney, where very early habitations were examined by Gordon Childe. There slate slabs were the typical materials, and beds were against the (double) walls and under a canopy, so that they in a sense foreshadowed the later alcove-beds (*lits-clos*) of Brittany and other regions, where they may be protected by doors with airholes for a little ventilation. It is interesting that Thomas Jefferson in planning his mansion at Monticello (Charlottesville, Virginia, U.S.A.) used a variant of this idea of the alcove bed.

E. T. Leeds has examined what remains of an early post-Roman English village at Sutton Courtenay, near Oxford, but in Berkshire. The base of a hut was dug out of the gravel and was about two feet below the level outside. Post-holes were found which showed that the roof was held up by posts. Probably a ridge-pole stretched from end to end and the walls may have been of mud-with-straw. In the best preserved example, a family seems to have had three of these one-roomed constructions, one being supposed to be a kitchen from its accumulation of potsherds and refuse. The supposed living room had a circular hearth. A room added to it had a burial of a middle-aged man only slightly covered. Lethbridge has found somewhat similar huts at the Car Dyke, Cambridgeshire, where the people apparently threw or pushed into a water-trough pebbles heated in a fire and so got hot water, a very ancient and widespread scheme. The conditions found at Sutton Courtenay and at Car Dyke indicate low standards of hygiene ; and yet the former site yielded an elaborate brooch and the latter an ivory armlet and a silver dirk.

Peate in *The Welsh House* and Estyn Evans in *Irish Heritage* both discuss the small rural dwelling. One type is the oval or circular house of unmortared stone which may have been roofed by stone corbelling or, like many black-houses in the Hebrides, may have had a cover of branches and turf (plate XII, p. 187). It should be remembered that sometimes people of the dawn of the Age of Metal were skilled enough to make good corbelled roofs (New Grange near Drogheda and Maes Howe in Orkney) to their tombs or, as suggested in ch. III, spirit-stores. The house for the living may have been modelled on that for the spirits of the dead awaiting re-birth, or *vice versa*, always with the proviso that the dwelling's replaceable roofing of branches and turf impregnated with soot was considered an agricultural asset; but the tomb would preferably have a more durable roof, a stone-corbel in a few cases in which there were skilled men available. In Wales many hut-bases, some round, or oval, some more or less rectangular, are seen to have been built of unmortared stone. They are popularly called *Cytiau'r Gwyddelod* (Huts of the Goidels—i.e., of the non-Welsh). Here again a network of bush-branches plastered with mud and covered with turf was probably the superstructure. After a time the turf, grown continuous from the hut-side to the surrounding soil, would give the impression of the doorway as a hole in the ground ; and there are Welsh folk-tales of wanderers lost on a moorland who hear fairy music from below the ground. The "fairies" of the tales are often the early peoples of the moorlands, as seen, or not seen, by the later (in some tales the Iron Age) peoples intruding along the valleys.

As late as the early nineteenth century, squatters on the open moor-lands and rough grazings, at any rate in Wales, were, by custom, allowed to stay if they put up a house between sunset and sunrise and had smoke from a fire emerging from a chimney or "hole in the roof" by morning. Some of these houses were circular or oval huts of turf blocks or earth blocks with straw and a roof of wattle covered with turf or thatch all made ready beforehand ; they have sometimes been nicknamed ink-bottle huts. But the old circular hut has practically gone out of use as a human habitation in Britain save here and there in the Hebrides. Its old accessory function of sheltering the beasts in addition to the people, has led to its survival in a few places for use as a pigsty, and Peate has collected a number of examples of this, some completely corbelled, but without hearth or smoke-hole.

The rectangular dwelling, like the round one, may be partly of stone, but of course will not have a stone roof. If stone is available, at least the lower parts of the walls, and sometimes the whole of the weather-wall (on the west or south-west side), may be of stone. This may be in large blocks of crystalline or other hard rock or in slabs where layered grits or schists or other rocks are available. If stone was not available, earth blocks were shaped, and straws were put in to help keep the block together, or sometimes turves were used. In some cases a wooden framework, foreshadowing the " timber-frame "

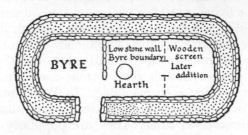

Fig. 56

Plan and diagram of a " Black House " in the Hebrides

of the Middle Ages, was filled in with wattle-and-daub. If the gable end of the rectangular hut was not of stone, it might have posts like those discussed for the hall (p. 216), or, sometimes, a tree-trunk (preferably oak) of Y form was employed, each arm of the Y supporting one side of the roof. Some have survived in use in remote areas until recently. In the Chalk lands it is probable that flints were sometimes used in early as in later times for house-building.

The rectangular dwelling typically had doorways near the middle of the long sides, front and back, opposite one another. On the one side of the passage between the doorways would be the dwelling for the people, on the other that for the beasts, and the beasts might be

PLATE 21

P. L. Emery

CWMPARC VALLEY. The South Wales coalfield has parallel deep narrow valleys beneath which coal is dug. River, rail, road and ribbons of houses run along them. July

PLATE 22

John Markham

MORAY PLACE, Edinburgh. A fine example of Georgian planning erected *c.* 1822 from designs by Gillespie Graham

brought in at the front
doorway for milking and
driven out through the
back doorway afterwards.
What has been called the
doorway must not be held
to imply a hinged door
as we know it. A wattle
shield, a length of skin,
pieces of wood braced
together could be alternatives; and in the north of
England the phrase "Put
t'wood i' t'oil" (*put the wood
in the hole*) is sometimes still
used for "Shut the door".

The floor on the human
side might be raised above
the floor on the animal
side, though the effects of
this might not be very
great, as dung was allowed
to accumulate sometimes
for a whole winter! Some-
times the long side of a
rectangular hut was along
a slope, with the human
side towards the upper and
the animal side towards
the lower end. Sometimes
a well or spring was within
the house, with a stream
of water flowing through.
The hearth might be
central, and if so, the
proximity of the doorways
might lead to, at any rate,

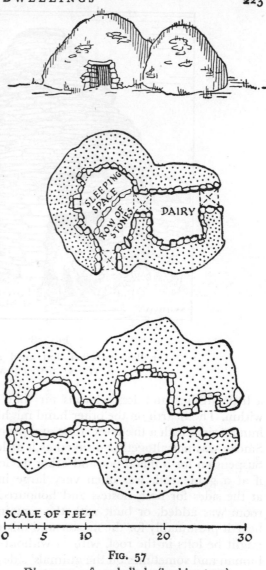

SCALE OF FEET

0   5   10   20   30

FIG. 57

Diagrams of corbelled (beehive-type)
huts; Outer Hebrides

the lower half of the door being closed by wood, for sheltering the fire,
as well as for resting one's arms as one looked out on to the field and got

Q

FIG. 58

Circular corbelled hut used as a pig-sty;
S. Wales. (After Peate)

a little fresher and less odorous air than was likely to be available within. The hearth on the other hand might be at the gable-end on the human side, with a fire-back stone and probably a hearth-stone as well. Smoke was not altogether disliked as it at least mitigated stable-smells. Suspension for a metal pot and other devices are known. The hearth, if at a gable end, was often very large in a great alcove with seats at the sides for host, hostess and honoured guests. Sometimes a bed-room was added, or built with the remainder, beyond the gable-end hearth presumably for the master and mistress of the household. There might be lofts in the roof, with or without windows, sometimes on the human and sometimes on the animals' side or on both, and they would be reached by a ladder on the loft floor, pulled down when people wanted to climb up. Sometimes the loft might be divided medially so that the sexes might sleep separately. If the hearth was central, the ends of the roof might be " hipped ", i.e. the roof might be shaped with

a triangle sloping down to a vertical wall at each end, and the lateral
flanks of the gable adjusted accordingly. Increase in numbers of cattle
and horses meant the prolongation of the animals' side of the dwelling ;
and, when we find a gable entrance at the animals' end and stalls on
either side of a median walk, we are well on the way towards the modern
stable. The animals' side of the dwelling might be partly shut off from
the human side by furniture
—for example, the back of a
dresser, or of an alcove bed.
The cover of the alcove bed
supported by posts might be
at the same time the floor
of a storage space. Probably
the pigs were the first farm
animals to be housed quite
separately ; the hens were
until recently sometimes ad-
mitted on the human side.

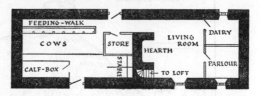

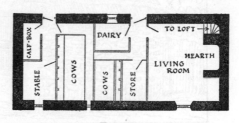

FIG. 59

Plans of " Long Houses," Wales. (After
Peate)

   Needless to say there are
many variants into which
such a short statement as
this cannot enter far. The
evolution during the Middle
Ages of some sort of chimney
improving the draught of the
fire, the substitution of a partial and ultimately a complete partition between human and animal sides and the conversion of the partition into
a stone wall, the making of separate doorways for men and animals, the
conversion of the roof-loft above the stable into a barn or store, the
development of windows in the roof-loft or just beneath the eaves of
the human dwelling are all improvements that make the transition
towards the more modern farmhouse with outbuildings set around
three sides of a rectangle. It is probable that several of these ameliora-
tions came to us from the Low Countries. Sometimes the manure-heap
may still have a place of honour in the centre of the rectangular
courtyard, a slightly more hygienic scheme than that of the old-time
accumulation of dung in the stable-part of the dwelling.
   It is significant that our words *carpenter* and *mason* come to us from
French or Low Latin. Carpenter is *charpentier* in modern and *carpentier*

in old French and is an old-established and widespread French sur-
name. This suggests that improvements in these crafts occurred with
the spread of French and Norman influences to Britain in and after
the eleventh century.

FIG. 60
Welsh cottage, timber-framed, with stone for the more
exposed wall

In Normandy there is splendid freestone, so called because it can
be cut in any direction and shaped exactly to make stone lintels and
posts. Freestone was brought to Britain, especially to south-eastern
England, for the surrounds of church windows and doorways, capitals
of pillars and so on, as Pelham has shown ; and it was also used in
castles built by Norman rulers and, when they weakened, by unruly
barons. But it did not greatly affect dwellings, though masons helped
to replace the old wooden and thatched constructions by stone and
tiled ones less liable to fire. Normandy also has good timber for house-
frames and the timber-frame house no doubt owes something to
French and Norman models, but is also to some extent a carpenter's
improvement on the old scheme of timber posts and wattle-and-daub.
    In south-eastern England with its chalk-ridges and clay vales there

was little real building-stone. Some flint might be used, a little chalk, of a variety called clunch, was hard enough to be of value, and is found near Cambridge, and in Surrey and elsewhere, in the Lower Chalk, and a few quarries in the Greensand, etc., have had local importance. But, broadly the eastern region was in the main dependent on wood for housebuilding. The common or pedunculate oak *Quercus robur* (the species with stalked or pedunculate acorns) flourishes in this part of Britain, and westwards through the Midlands. The timber-frame house is therefore widely characteristic and is specially well built and designed in parts of the east and south-east. As one goes west one finds the cottage built with rougher timbers less exactly arranged, and, often, the larger building with the timber elaborately patterned, a patterning sometimes indeed overdone. Lack of stone in some areas as well as lack of skill in stone-dressing and in mortaring, among village folk at least, made the timber-frame house an acceptable building scheme where good oak timbers of the pedunculate oak were available. The timber-frame house is traditional over wide areas, mostly in England. In those areas it is the dominant style for the traditional cottage and small rural house.

These areas are

(a) Kent, Surrey, Sussex and Hampshire.

(b) East Anglia, with extensions into Lincolnshire and East Yorkshire where it is less general.

(c) Herefordshire, Salop, Warwickshire and Worcestershire, South Staffordshire, parts of Cheshire and West Lancashire.

The timber-frame has been filled in in various ways. " Wattle-and-daub", i.e., pieces of branches, etc., and clay, may be the primary method. Cattle-hairs or other devices might be used to keep the clay from cracking too quickly, and, where, as in chalk areas (parts of *a* and *b* above), lime was available, the clay would be mixed with chalk (often one part of clay to three of chalk) and would give a more durable material. A further device with remarkable developments in East Anglia and Kent was the plastering of the surface, covering sometimes timber-frame and all. If the timbers were covered with plaster the surface of the wood was generally studded with nails to give the plaster a better hold. In the seventeenth century bricknogging, that is, the filling in of the framework with brick, became more common, and this eventually made the timber-frame unnecessary, a national advantage at the time as oak for ships was becoming scarce.

Plaster is a very ancient material for obtaining a relatively smooth surface of light colour, and it was used in mediæval churches and in mansions, in the latter case especially for the upper parts of walls above the wainscot. With the general development of handicraft in Tudor times, plaster ceilings became a feature at any rate of large houses, and there are many examples of elaborate moulding of ornament in plaster ceilings and house frontages from Tudor and Stuart times onwards. One at the Feathers Hotel, Ludlow, is very widely known. The decorative plasterers of Kent and East Anglia called themselves Pargetters. It thus has happened that a number of timber-frame houses had their frontages plastered over (see plate 15, p. 142). Many a frescoed church interior was replastered, to hide medieval paintings, after the Reformation. The plaster ceiling and plastered interior walls spread in the course of time to simpler houses, with, still later, wallpaper or distemper to take the place of the older colourwork of the mansions, and of their Arras tapestries. Roughcasting or the dashing of small pebbles against a plaster surface came into use as another means of dealing with the surface of the spaces between the timbers of a timber-frame house.

In the sixteenth century the seizure of monastic lands and royal grants of these to private owners made a class of *nouveaux riches* who travelled and brought into England ideas of Renaissance France and Italy which they sometimes imposed on English craftsmen. In Tudor and some early Stuart buildings we thus get at times a mixture of heterogeneous notions, some only half-digested and therefore clumsily expressed. One must, however, also allow for the fact that domestic architecture developed rather early in Britain. It was only after the lifework of Inigo Jones (died 1652), who had much experience of Italy, that the classical tradition really became assimilated by British builders. Another circumstance greatly helped here ; it was that the Puritan regime came to an end in 1659-60 and the reaction burst forth in every direction, starting experiments in building, furnishing, upholstering and decorative metal-work. The genius of Sir Christopher Wren was supplemented by a widespread desire for elaboration. We thence get progress towards the varied outbursts of skill that made eighteenth and very early nineteenth century work so remarkable. The Romantic revival and the renewed enthusiasm for Gothic that accompanied religious changes in the nineteenth century hampered that craft tradition of initiative, which was also faced with the influence of machinery and mass-production for groups of *nouveaux riches* who had made money out of factories and eastern trade.

Sometimes flint was used in a timber-frame house, in a district near chalk-with-flints, for filling in the framework, and it was often inter-mingled with brick for decorative effect. The bricks were sometimes set herring-bone fashion. In the south-east of England the more exposed walls of a cottage might be covered with tiles, hanging from nails, and in Lakeland and Cornwall and parts of Wales weather-exposed walls of cottages have often been covered with slates, similarly hung. These are valued protection against south-westerly gales and their heavy rain. In these western rainy areas the fact that the cottage wall was often of cob (clay, sometimes without lime, though collection of shells for lime is a long-established custom) made this protection desirable even though the cob might be " trodden " or stamped as hard as possible by the builders. In the east of Britain, from the end of the seventeenth century onwards, pantiles began to come into use under Dutch influence for roofing ; but before that time straw or, where possible, reed thatch was in general rural use (plate 14, p. 127), with heath as an inferior substitute in a few areas. The underside of the thatch was liable to catch fire if the outer part might almost refuse to burn. Boarding or some other internal protection was therefore a great advantage. Thatched roofs were often fastened by ropes, which rot in a few seasons. In the north, stone slates were widely used for roofing, and, partly in relation with their weight and the danger of their falling, the roofs are traditionally low-pitched.

The cottages in region (c) above, broadly the West Midlands, have the timber-frame coarser with the posts farther apart and larger. Often the gable ends had specially large oak beams that might be curved with an overlap at the top, forming a X on which the ridge-pole of the roof would rest as already mentioned. In some cases a Y-shaped trunk was fitted into the gable, each arm of the Y helping to support one flank of the roof-frame. A medial division of the cottage gave added support to the roof-frame and made possible division of front and back rooms, while a front-to-back partition had allowed the sleeping-place to be separate from the living place, and often another room, a larder, was added as equipment developed. A lean-to shed may be built on behind. The oak posts of the frame have been, traditionally, used inverted. This placing of the broader root-end

FIG. 61

Timber-framed cottage with wall-base of stone; Leek Wootton

at the top gave a larger foundation for the roof frame ; it was also widely believed that inversion let the sap run out more freely from the wood and that this made it last better.

The pieces of the timber-frame were traditionally fixed to one another by tenon and mortise (peg and hole), a scheme which is evidently a very ancient one for we find it adapted for working in stone in the case of the great sarsen stone-posts and lintels at Stonehenge (p. 58). The timber-frame scheme allowed the beams supporting an upper storey to project beyond the posts framing the lower storey. This projection of the upper rooms is typical for many areas and is to be interpreted partly by the fact that this protected the lower storey from rain-drip ; it also gave a little shelter to pedestrians. The gable end of the house in towns was often on the street, thus reducing frontage, and a gutter between continuous house-roofs could collect water from both sides and spout it on to the street ; no wonder therefore that the lower part of the house needed shelter, as also did the pedestrians using the footpath or side-walk. Ludlow and Shrewsbury are famous for timber-frame houses (see plate XIII, p. 210), and the Holborn frontage of Staple Inn, London, is a familiar instance.

The old country cottage rarely faced southwards, as the south wind was supposed to be unhealthy, but wiser counsels appear to have come in in the seventeenth century. A large nineteenth century girls' school, in northern England, in a smoky city, however, still showed avoidance of south lights for its classrooms. Often enough the cottage had no dug-in foundations, but it might have some stone, if available, at the base of its walls. The floor was typically earth, sometimes hardened, almost polished black, by mixing in bullock's blood, and it was sometimes patterned by placing animal bones in it ; or it might be covered with rushes to keep down the dust. Needless to say accumulations of all sorts of organic matter in and on the floor made it nitrogenous and there long were men whose business it was to dig out floors in order to extract saltpetre. The hearth was large, for burning great logs, and might have a slab of stone at its back, and a bake-stone in front, while a metal pot, hung or standing on three feet, was a valued item of equipment and inheritance. Sometimes a pot-oven was made outside the cottage in a dug-out ; such ovens are well known in parts of East Central Europe. Built in stone or cob, or, later, brick, ovens came to be features of the rural cottage. A log pillow and straw pallet made a bed.

If one goes up the Severn valley one finds timber-frame buildings as far up as Llanidloes, and up the tributary Carno valley beyond Pontdolgoch, where, near the hamlet of Carno, there is an example with the weather corner (S.W.) in masonry. Westwards beyond these points the pedunculate oak rarely thrives, and the sessile oak (*Quercus sessiliflora*) becomes typical on the stony hillsides. In correlation with this the timber-frame house becomes rare, though one or two examples occur for special reasons.

Again, in the Pennines and the West Riding of Yorkshire, grits (e.g. Millstone Grit) provide stone that can be dressed to make regular walls ; while, in the higher parts of this region, the pedunculate oak does not grow. Around Builth in Central Wales volcanic rocks provide suitable stone, and the timber-frame house is correspondingly rare, though it approaches this neighbourhood both from the east, up the Wye, and from the north up the Severn. Cornwall and Devon may have granite-block cottages, or buildings of cob, sometimes with slate covering on the weather sides. Buchan and other Scottish localities with granite and sandstones, and often few pedunculate oaks, have more stone cottages ; and other Scottish regions may have cob, or, in the Hebrides, as already stated, unmortared stone.

In England itself the Oolite Belt across from Dorset via the Cotswolds and Northampton to Lincoln Edge and north-east Yorkshire has workable building stone of good quality, and the typical building surviving is of stone. The beauty of the Cotswolds stone house is famous and the villages of the Cotswolds rival the beauty of the old-world parts of Kent (plates 17 and 18, pp. 158 and 159). The older stone houses of the Cotswolds are nearly all dateable to the late sixteenth and early seventeenth century, i.e. to the prosperity of the wool-trade, which before the Reformation expressed itself in the building of great churches of Perpendicular Gothic, and, after that change, led to rising standards of life expressed in housing and craftmanship in general. The great wool churches of England occur especially in Norfolk, the Cotswolds and Somerset, but the prosperity-wave was fairly widespread and Perpendicular Gothic is almost too abundant in England.

It seems that, in the late twelfth century, the danger of fire in towns of thatched timber-frame cottages led to the production of tiles ; and burnt bricks may have been imported from the Low Countries in the thirteenth century for building in the east, at Little Coggeshall, Essex, and a few other places. Burnt brick had been known to the Romans and Roman bricks occur in later walls at Dover Castle, Canterbury, Colchester, St. Albans and elsewhere, but this craft lapsed from the fifth to perhaps the eleventh century in western Europe. It had an early revival in the stoneless Low Countries, which were, on the whole, prosperous almost throughout the Middle Ages. In Britain stones and tiles were used in towns where possible in the thirteenth century, and in the fourteenth century we hear of brick-works at Hull and Beverley.

In view of the frequent difficulty of getting stone that could be easily and suitably dressed, it is perhaps a little surprising that brick does not seem to have made very rapid progress in fourteenth-century Britain for house-building. Probably the Hundred Years' War, the

Black Death, Peasant Revolts, and prolonged and recurrent troubles between the Hanseatic League and the kings of England held back a development which was specially characteristic of Hanse Towns, the Low Countries and Denmark. We know that, about 1425 or rather later, Caister near Yarmouth was built of brick. Hurstmonceaux, Sussex, another brick castle, dates from near the middle of the century and so does Tattershall Castle, Lincolnshire. About 1474-75 peace with the Hanse was restored ; and economic and social life was

FIG. 62

Welsh house based on the " long-house " type; Ty'n Dolan, Cardiganshire

developing, after the wars of the Roses, towards the more organised conditions of the Tudor regime (see plate XIX, p. 250). Brick-building became widespread, sometimes with stone still used for framing windows, arched gateways and corners of walls of important buildings, as, for example, at Lambeth Palace, London. Sometimes bricks of different colours might make a pattern. Bricks also came to be moulded into many shapes, for example, to imitate the cluster-pillar of stone of a medieval arch. Hampton Court is one of the finest achievements of Tudor brick-work (1520) in Britain. The great demand for building material after the fire of London (1666) stimulated the brick-making industry at a time when Italian ideas were being assimilated in Britain.

When stone-masonry became more important in house-building at the end of the twelfth and in the thirteenth century, and the hearth came to be placed typically against a gable-end of the house, a simple round upward chimney passage was lined with stone and provided with a cap under which were lateral openings. This superseded the smoke-hole. In the fifteenth and sixteenth centuries, especially as brick came into more general use and more attention was given to comfort, a mansion would have fireplaces in its various rooms and brick-built flues leading up to chimneys that, especially if in brick, might rise a considerable height above the roof for better draught and might be arranged in rows or clusters. The bricks might be arranged in patterns and the tops might have decorative forms. The flue was usually less wide than in the older, clumsier stone chimneys, and it might be in a curve, or even bent, so there was less fear that rain might come all the way down and put out the fire. Early brickwork is seen at its best in Kent, which also has many fine examples of hipped roofs (p. 224). Sometimes tiles were used as covering for walls as well as for roofing.

The chimney-piece above the hearth began probably as a protective hood over the fire projected into the room, but in the sixteenth and seventeenth centuries it was elaborated with many types of decoration in mansions, and with simpler pillars and mantelpieces (note the derivation from *manteau* or hood) in more ordinary dwellings. Chimney-pieces would hardly have been appropriate for the very large hearths, made to burn the enormous logs of the early Middle Ages. The use of coal fuel (sea coal from Newcastle in the case of London) made smaller fireplaces more practicable. Coal was available by the time of the social revival after the Wars of the Roses, and in more general use after Tudor times.

In the eighteenth century the agrarian revolution introduced root-crops and consequent widespread supersession of stubble pasture. The new four-course (Norfolk) rotation was carried out on compact farms of enclosed fields, in place of the three-course (wheat, spring corn or beans, fallow) practised on open fields in which peasants held strips. This loosened out the old clustered village of the wheat areas, and led to the building of farmhouses on the now compacted farms. In many areas these were built of brick. The same century saw a development of town life with country gentry coming into the county town for the winter to dine and dance and marry off their daughters. Queen Anne and Georgian architecture in brick became a feature of many towns and there are particularly fine examples at Shrewsbury near the Quarry Gardens, where the houses have a broad frontage, not a gable end, on the street.

Towards the end of the eighteenth century, the fashion spread of covering brick with plaster, or cement, surfaced with white sand. When a stone-like effect was produced it was called stucco. Somewhat later, here and there, a brown cement came into use for frontages, and, later still, yellow brick added what was only too often a further dis-figurement. The improvement of brick colours, of rough-cast work and other processes has been attempted in the twentieth century, which has also seen the introduction of ferro-concrete, of made-up blocks of cement and gravel and many other experiments, including that of the pre-fabricated house of 1945 onwards.

In the nineteenth century sea traffic spread the use of Welsh and other slates for roofing, those of Bethesda, Llanberis, Penygroes and Blaenau Ffestiniog, all in north-west Wales, being specially famous. They were formed in mountain-building by extreme pressure on ancient fine-grained shale rocks, pressure exerted when the rocks of what is now the mountain system of Caernarvonshire were up-folded many million years ago. Slates have very naturally displaced thatch in many districts, but tiles also have to some extent given place to them. Tiles, improved primarily in the Low Countries, came to be shaped in an S-curve, so that each series of tiles from ridge-pole to eaves had a continuous groove for leading down the rain. These tiles, called pantiles, introduced into Britain in the late seventeenth century, remain very characteristic in many parts of east and south Britain and may be bedded on and pointed with mortar. The view as the mail-boat approaches St. Peter Port, Guernsey, with its steep hillsides, is made still more picturesque by red tile roofs on one of the hills in an oldish part of the town, Quartier Beauregard. The importance of cultural influences from the Low Countries in the late seventeenth century is clear when we think of improved earthenware and china, of the pantiles just mentioned, of the draining of our fens (plate 5, p. 50), of the root-crops and of their consequences, including the growth of parks around mansions and of landscape painting.

Along with the present distribution of pantiles goes to a certain extent a distribution of what is called the step-gable, another Low Country (and Hanseatic) feature, natural where brick was the building material. Steps were easier to make in brick than was a continuous oblique edge which would need careful chipping of the bricks. Step-gables may be seen here and there in eastern Britain from Kent to Scotland.

The interesting old town of Stirling may be specially mentioned here for its good examples of the step-gable. There is also an old mansion in Stirling that might have been imported ready-made from Normandy, an indication of the historic Franco-Scottish link. The hill of Stirling is crowned by the castle, which has the church closely associated with it (cf. Durham, Lancaster, etc.). The Scottish baronial style, still used in some recent buildings, has round *tourelles* following French models. These tourelles are rarely seen in England ; they usually contained the staircase.

It would be possible to prolong this chapter indefinitely by enlarging on the contents of the dwellings and the utensils of the people but for such studies, the reader must look to the works of specialists. Here only a few general points can be mentioned.

The first is that, apart from smith's work, the early post-Roman household strove to make as much as possible of what it needed. Wood was used for bowls, spoons, dishes, churns and many other things. Where bog-oak and bog-fir were available, they were much valued for their durable character. Oak and ash were favourite woods when accessible, also alder for soles of shoes, and yew for bows. Oak chests to hold meal, oak dressers to hold earthenware and a variety of implements without occupying much floor-space, oak cupboards for clothes and linen as equipment increased ; these are all features of old houses. The oak may be decoratively carved in the richer houses, or may be more simply panelled, with either gothic outlines or rectangles. There is a certain amount of regional tradition in the style of these furnishings and experts can often say, broadly, where an old piece of furniture was made.

When oaks were being cut down to build ships, and scarcity was feared, in late Stuart times, oak furniture-making seems to have diminished and attention was given to walnut, which again was not very abundant and sometimes not very satisfactory. In the early eighteenth century better ships and more maritime commerce began to bring to Britain hard woods from hot countries, notably mahogany from Honduras, and a certain amount of sandalwood, satinwood and other timbers valued for decorative inlay. Mahogany being so hard and so close-grained permitted fine and exact cutting, and was a great resource for the furnishings of ships' officers' cabins, in which space is inevitably so limited. The great development of the cabinet-makers' art in the eighteenth century is known to all. Sometimes it was associated with building and fitting of wooden ships, sometimes it was independent of this connection. The three most widely-known English cabinet-makers of the eighteenth century, Chippendale, Hepplewhite and Sheraton, worked in London and, apart from Sheraton's later extravagances of design, maintained a high level of taste and workmanship, which disappeared as the Industrial Revolution proceeded and made quantity-production and display for tasteless plutocrats and their imitators the dominant feature of the situation. A collection of Chippendale's furniture made to order for the Feoffees' room at Chetham's Hospital, Manchester, has remained there ever since, save for war-time removal to greater safety. Often enough it is difficult to distinguish between the work of Chippendale and that of imitators, so probably a good deal that goes under his name has only an indirect link with him.

It is true of mankind in general that a temperature of 62° to 74° or 75° Fahrenheit is the most acceptable and that a clear atmosphere and occasional cool spells, provided artificial warmth is available at need, are a help to vigour of body and mind. *Homo sapiens* probably went through important early stages of his evolution under conditions of this kind, on grass-lands some of which in late Pleistocene times in north Africa and south-west Asia became desert. Northward migration in Europe involved facing cold which was only partially met by clothing. Probably the small hut with heat from rudimentary lamps or fires was a help in this direction, but it cramped equipment and social life in other ways. The Romans with their engineering skill heated their villas and were thereby able to organise life more elaborately ; but the halls of early English and, no doubt, Celtic nobles, with their smoke-holes and draughts were deficient in many ways. The air was smoky, privacy was difficult, sanitation was almost impossible. Such housing conditions must have been a serious hindrance to cultural development, especially as wooden buildings were liable to both fire and decay. This partly accounts for the lateness of growth of civilization in north-west Europe and Britain, though agricultural problems of our region (p. 87) were also factors of delay. In the early Middle Ages, especially in and after the eleventh century, changes began to multiply. The manor might have a solar, or retiring room especially for the women, and mills relieved some of the humbler women of the drudgery of grinding grain, while, in the towns, the specialised making of pots, soon improved by glazing, helped their kitchen work in many ways. Glazing of pots reached western Europe through Islamic Spain from Persia, which followed Chinese ideas in this matter. The development of chimneys and the stronger timber-frame houses with separated rooms that could be warmed from gable-end fireplaces under mantelpieces brought a great step forward in general equipment as well as in protection of women ; and, along with this, we notice the rise of chivalry among the wealthier people and their household staffs. Roof-tiles made the dwellings drier and a little less liable to fire, and the development of brick chimneys and of double brick walls further diminished damp and helped to keep the internal atmosphere clearer as well as to ventilate the rooms. The development of glass for windows, in churches about the eleventh century, in good houses a century or two later, added both efficiency and comfort.

An increase of social order, with occasional lapses it is true, promoted the desire for comfort and winter warmth, and this desire expressed itself in more elaborate house-building in Tudor times; it was an important aspect of the development of a more civilised life. We must not, however, forget that the invention of printing, or its spread to Europe from China, was another mighty factor of change at this time. In medieval times literacy had been associated in most men's minds with the monastic clergy, towards whom the knights very often had feelings of mixed fear and contempt. The Tudor sovereigns and their entourage sought to patronise learning and Henry VIII and Elizabeth were themselves highly educated. It is widely true of the evolution of the pattern of life that concurrent changes interweave their results in ways that are so complex as to be beyond efficient analysis.

REFERENCES, see end ch. 12, p. 159.

PLATE 23

Robert Atkinson

VICTORIAN HOUSE (1887), showing the love of display in the period of the first industrial revolution. A meaningless tower is a frequent feature

PLATE 24

John Markham

a. LLANRHYCHWIN CHURCH, North Wales. In moorland Britain a village church is often a simple rectangle with gabled roof and a small belfry. July

John Markham

b. CRAIGWEN CHAPEL, Caernarvonshire, showing two doors, originally one for men and one for women. September

CHAPTER 12

VILLAGES AND HAMLETS

VILLAGES IN southern and eastern England are often of mellow beauty, hallowed by centuries of associations, yet too often desperately poor, with dwellings all roses outside, all thorns within. A medieval church may be set among the elms of its churchyard with a yew once used for bows. The church itself may still be a monument of the Romanesque or Norman style (chiefly eleventh and twelfth centuries), as in the case of the fine church of Melbourne, Derbyshire. More often, however, it will have been enlarged when thrust and counterthrust of walls was more fully appreciated and larger windows became possible without interfering with a stone vault. It was especially as wealth increased in the latter part of the fifteenth century that enlargement of churches and particularly of windows became widespread ; and the perpendicular tracery of the windows is highly characteristic. Naturally these enlargements are specially found in the areas that became famous for wool and the wool trade—Norfolk, parts of the Cotswolds, Somerset, and the Newbury region of Berkshire, to name only samples (plate 28, p. 303). The village churches of old England are on the whole a finer feature of the landscape than those of many parts of France.

A dwelling here and there may antedate Tudor times, but many are Elizabethan or Stuart, with a squire's mansion and a rectory both probably remodelled in the eighteenth century when the privileged classes were gaining wealth from cattle on enclosed park lands with supplementary food from root-crops. The house of the squire may still have a picture by Old Crome or Morland or one of the other artists called in to paint the setting of the mansion or its animals ; more often the pictures of this type have found their way to salerooms or public collections, though family portraits may remain.

The rectory also speaks of social change. The village parson of Elizabethan days was often almost an upper servant of the great family, very distinct from the higher clergy. As time went on the squire came to look upon the living as a possible career for a younger son, especially if he happened not to be adapted to a military life. With marriage of the clergy there thus arose a rural stock which, in spite of many failings, has produced ability in remarkable profusion. A factor here no doubt is the need for combining relatively plain living and high thinking. The married clergy of rural England have in this way been a source of national strength beyond anything contributed by the celibate secular rural clergy of many European lands. Disraeli gave as a reason for supporting the Anglican church that it put a gentleman in each parish.

In our day the maintenance of rectory and hall, to give the squire's mansion its traditional name, have become too heavy a burden on reduced values of incomes from rural land, and for housewives who find domestic help so hard to come by. For a while in the nineteenth century the landed gentry gave their daughters to the sons of *nouveaux riches* from industry, and these tried to assimilate themselves to the old tradition, sometimes with patronage replacing the old paternalism. It has long been a saying in Manchester that a man may progress from Hulme or Cheetham Hill to Didsbury, Didsbury to Alderley Edge, Alderley Edge to a title and a country seat in the south. Of late, however, the rural mansions have been increasingly taken over for public purposes as training colleges, hospitals and boarding schools, or loaded on to the shoulders of the National Trust.

The cottages of the village may nestle near the squire's park gates and the church ; and the roads along which they stand bend around these major features. In some cases the squire has moved the village farther away from his private domain. Only here and there does one still find the windmill or the watermill, used of old for grinding the grain to the great profit of the medieval lord of the manor. It is probable that windmills came into use in the Middle Ages and spread more widely late in that period ; one of the earliest drawings of a windmill is in the Luttrell Psalter (fourteenth century). Watermills are a more ancient device, known in Roman Britain.

The village chapel or chapels, too apt to be in the Gothic revival style of the second half of the nineteenth century, may occasionally have a simple dignity based on adaptation of the scheme of a barn of the

Georgian (eighteenth century) agrarian revolution. If so, it may have two doors side by side recalling the custom that the sexes sat or stood apart in worship (plate 24b, p. 239); this rule is sometimes, rather doubtfully, said to be connected with improvements of congregational singing, but it needs little imagination to realise how a lad and lass sitting together might contrive to amuse one another quietly during an interminable sermon.

The school too often suggests the bad old principle that education of " the people " should be kept to a minimum, and that the teacher should be an upper servant to the rector ; but, in parts of the north of England and Wales, as well as most notably in Scotland, the school-master or schoolmistress has sometimes won high regard as leader, counsellor and friend.

The shop may have sold all manner of things in the days before travelling sale-vans and, especially, ration books. Before the spread of radio it was often a news centre, and it often continues to be a gossip club ; the women go less to the inn than do their men. The post office may be in the shop or may have gained the dignity of a separate personality, perhaps with the distribution of newspapers and magazines as a subsidiary feature, women's magazines having multiplied enormously in the last 50 years.

The inn may have a tell-tale name such as Wheatsheaf, Hop-Pole, Waggon and Horses, or, if it be on an old pilgrim route, Lamb and Flag. Or it may pay homage to a Lion, Red or White, Black or even Blue, never named Yellow or Brown ! Or it may acknowledge some historic event or person, Nelson or Trafalgar, Wellington or Waterloo ; one does not find Cromwell commemorated in this way. Or, again, it may offer its homage to the local aristocrat and be the Howard Arms. It often happens that the name is older than the building which may have been reconstructed by some brewery company as a " Tied House".

A smithy was an ancient feature, placed on the outskirts of the village in the hope that its sparks would not fire the thatch. But it has now been replaced by a garage with petrol pumps and servicing of cars, and, in some cases, a bus station. A railway station may have been added in the expansive Victorian period.

Our word-picture still needs a note about gardens, naturally better in the south and east and typically poor in stock-raising areas. Protective hedgerows, with flowering briar and bramble, and sometimes gorse, may be tree-crowned with oak and elm and ash and beech, and conquering sycamore. The old Physick Garden had horehound and rue, catmint and pellitory, hyssop and camomile, unless the latter grew wild on rough grazing land nearby. The sweet herbs, for kitchen use, included rosemary and sage, sweet basil and marjoram and there were other flavouring plants such as parsley, thyme and fennel. Old-established garden flowers include heartsease and forget-me-not, primrose and violet and periwinkle, columbine, lily and rose, and there are many later introductions. Polyanthus and sweet william have later become notable elements of the cottage garden.

Of the village before early English times we know but little, though groups of hut-foundations have already been mentioned (ch. 11). The early English seem to have come up our eastern rivers and to have been attracted by the meadow grass for their cattle. The brow of a river terrace above the water-meadow may have the cottages, with their arable land occupying most of that terrace. In the case of a very small stream easily crossed, the village may work the meadow and terrace of the far bank ; this may have resulted in the building of a hamlet on that far bank. If the arable grades upwards into rough or good pasture, the village lands may extend upwards too, for example on some chalk slopes. Dr. Alice Garnett has been showing that in some deep valleys the village and its arable avoid the bottom and are fixed on the hillside above, at a level high enough to avoid serious winter inversion of temperature (cold often lasting night and day more severe in the valley bottom than up the hillside) which may last from the old All Souls' Day (now November 13th) to some date in February, sometimes said to be the birds' wedding day or St. Valentine's Day. At the same time, the village does not often risk a very high site because, Dr. Garnett thinks, of exposure to high winds and cloud cap above a certain level. Miss Sylvester has pointed out the occurrence of hill villages where there is fairly level upland above steep valleys, and, in a considerable number of cases, the hill-villagers seem to have been men more interested in stock farming than in crops. Estyn Evans, Mogey and McCourt, working in northern Ireland, draw attention to the clachan type of settlement, traditionally families in groups of four with some communal arable system, the four quarterlands forming what is there known as a townland. The clachan has been inhabited in most cases by a much inter-related group, and it may have been at one time almost a family-settlement, using the term family in its broader sense for a group having a large

PLATE XVII

Aerofilms, Ltd.

OXFORD, aerial view. St. Aldate's, Carfax (with St. Martin's tower), the Cornmarket, St. Giles' Fairground, the Woodstock and Banbury roads can be followed S–N. The High Street with alignments of churches and colleges runs W–E

PLATE XVIII

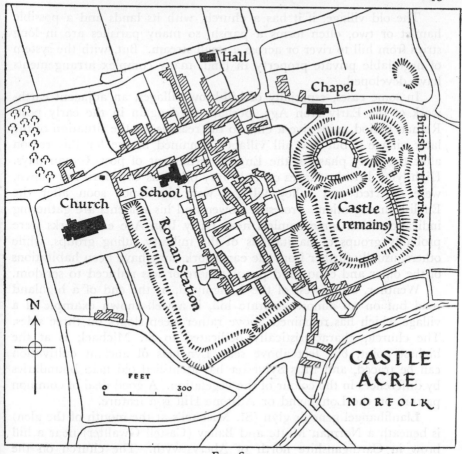

FIG. 63

Castleacre, Norfolk. A village with Roman basic plan and a Medieval fortification

element of common descent, somewhat like a small clan. There is little doubt that a number of small clusters of houses around the rough pastures of the moorlands of south-western England have analogies with these Irish clachans, as Mogey points out. One wonders whether the villages of south-east England with names ending in *ing* after a patronymic also had at first some analogy with the Irish clachan. In addition, quite a number of clusters on high ground, near rough pasture, are " squatter settlements ".

The old village, if it has a church, with its lands and a possible hamlet or two, often forms a parish, so many parishes are in long strips from hill to river or across a small stream. But, with the system of negotiable private property in land, many complex arrangements have developed.

In some cases, especially of hill-brow villages, an adjacent earthwork of the Early Iron Age, perhaps used again in the early post-Roman period, may give a clue to the reasons for the situation of the later village ; but few hill villages remained in use for this reason after the early phase of the English settlement of post-Roman days. High-lying British villages on Salisbury plain, as Crawford has shown, were deserted and valley villages were developed soon after the English immigration. Professor Bowen and his students are gathering indications that some hamlets near Early Iron Age earthworks were probably groups of habitations of the military ruling groups, while others, usually further from the earthwork, may have been habitations of the older and conquered peoples more or less reduced to serfdom.

Wentnor, south-west of the Longmynd, at the end of a highland road but on an almost separate hill, is a well-known example of a village which has remained above rather steep slopes on three sides. The church, characteristically dedicated to St. Michael, is at the highest point, 867 feet above sea. Lynchets of ancient cultivation can be traced, and Miss Sylvester has identified old field boundaries by differences in the colour of the vegetation. A good deal of common pasture on the Longmynd or Adstone Hill is a feature.

Llanfihangel geneu'r glyn (St. Michael's at the mouth of the glen) is beneath a Norman Motte and Bailey (Castell Gwallter) near a hill brow in Cardiganshire north of Aberystwyth. The church on the hillside has the glen's little stream flowing past the churchyard gates, now under an iron grid. Folk-lore alleges that ghosts do not cross running water, but we cannot say that this is, or is not, the reason for the arrangement just mentioned. Just below the churchyard several old houses stand along what has been a footpath or bridle path of the hillside. The main road on the valley bottom, and later the railway station, have drawn house-building towards them in modern times. Car and bus developments in this century have attracted new residents who have built houses on the main road, and, typically, follow professions in Aberystwyth. This little village thus illustrates several points in the evolution of settlement and especially the valleyward shift.

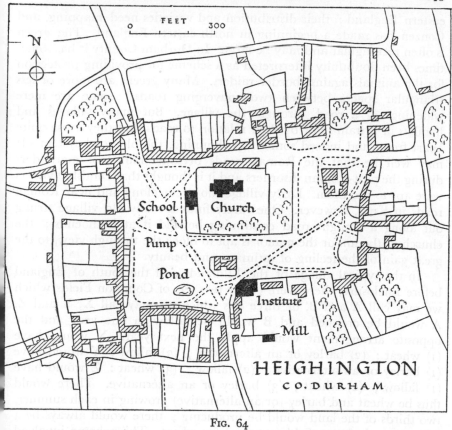

FIG. 64

Heighington, Durham.   A village set around a more-or-less rectangular
green; the church and school are on the green

Whereas, in north-west Germany between Weser and Elbe, the
traditional village is a quite irregular cluster there known as a
Haufendorf " heap-village ",   and footpaths wind in and out among the
houses, this scheme is rare in Britain, though it was the usual arrangement in some prehistoric villages.   East of the Elbe a belt of land,
apparently largely colonised from west of the river, has *Rundlingen*
or Round Villages with a central open space, and the houses may have
little plots of land of their own in addition to their shares in common
fields.   In Britain we have many villages with central open spaces
or greens in east Scotland, Durham and parts of Yorkshire and

eastern England ; their distribution and varieties need mapping, and
Conzen has made a beginning in north-eastern England. The green
is often rectangular and may be large. In Durham County it has sometimes been doubtfully interpreted as a scheme for providing protection
for the animals against border raiders. Many greens are more or less
triangular spaces between two converging roads ; some are mere
widenings of a road through the village. But many villages and
hamlets in Britain show by their relation to roads that they arose quite
apart from, and indeed sometimes shunning, the old road system. It
may well be that the Roman roads became haunts of marauders
during the post-Roman disorders and it is thought that Danish invaders
were apt to use them. Early villages do occur along and near Roman
roads in Kent, however. One rarely finds a really old village strung
out along a straight road continuing beyond it at both ends ; the
church or the inn or the manor is apt to block the through view, to the
great gain of the feeling of intimacy and beauty.

In the typical village of the Midlands and the south of England
before Enclosure, there were either two sets of Common Fields which
we may call A and B, or three sets which we may call X, Y and Z.
A would be cropped and B would be fallow in one year and the
opposite arrangement would apply the next year. X would have
(1) wheat ; (2) barley or an alternative ; (3) fallow : Y would have
(1) barley or an alternative ; (2) fallow ; (3) wheat : Z would have
(1) fallow ; (2) wheat ; (3) barley or an alternative. There would
thus be wheat and barley (or an alternative) growing in each summer,
two thirds of the land would be producing ; there would always be a
fallow year before a field was used for wheat. This scheme involved
a large measure of uniformity and checked initiative, and the enclosure
schemes broke it down, earlier in Britain than in several continental
countries, where it lasted past the middle of the nineteenth
century.

It has already been said that few houses still standing in villages
antedate the sixteenth century and many belong to the seventeenth
or later still. The enclosure of common lands, the decay of the manor,
and the handing of monastery lands to lay proprietors, the new
squirearchy owning property instead of having merely feudal rights,
brought about many changes. The squire's park has already been
mentioned, and, especially after root-crops spread in the eighteenth
century, the erstwhile common fields were laid out in enclosed block

farms. The farmer tended to build a house on his farm, especially as brick was coming into general use at that time (p. 233). Scattered farmhouses thus came into existence around the original cluster and the distribution of population was loosened out, but it is quite probable

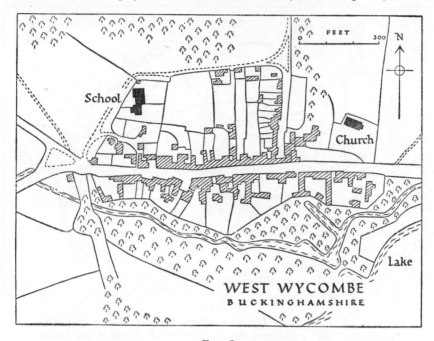

FIG. 65

West Wycombe. A street-village; the dwellings are set along both sides of a through-road

that some dispersal of houses may be much older. Peake suggested that Danes and Vikings in East Anglia (855 A.D. onwards) may have had some dispersed settlements.

As forest was cleared, all sorts of special local arrangements arose. The village in a forest clearing was often smaller than that in open country, it might often be described as a hamlet. Sometimes it seems to have had an Infield cultivated every year, and manured by folding animals on it when it was not under crop. The rest of the clearing might be an Outfield, and, in this, a patch or patches might be cultivated for a season or two at fairly long intervals. A three field system (X. Y. Z. above), with strips allocated to the households might, however, be gradually established by taking in more land ; it gave a larger food supply but demanded organization and control. With such organisation the village in a clearing could increase in size.

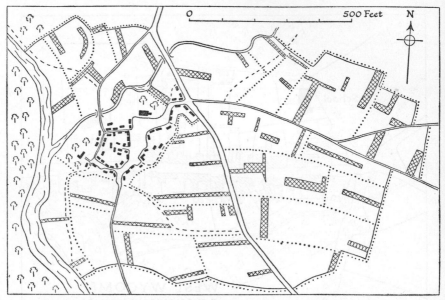

FIG. 66

Diagram of an irregular German village between Wesar and Elbe (Haufendorf) with communal fields.   The strip holdings of one household are cross-hatched

An Infield and Outfield scheme has already been mentioned in connection with parts of Scotland, so it is by no means exclusively connected with forest clearings of early English or subsequent date. It has been thought by some investigators to have been a widespread scheme of very early cultivation at any rate in north-west Europe, but this is inevitably speculative.

It is advisable to recapitulate here the broad outline of the change in the relation between the people and the land that was an accompaniment of Enclosures, especially of those in the eighteenth and nineteenth centuries. Under the feudal regime the lord of the manor was not quite what we should call an owner. He had many rights and privileges, but his tenants also had rights however much these might at times be disregarded. The little man might pasture cattle on the common grazing land and swine in the oakwood ; he might cut wood in the forest, he had his land-strips in the open fields, and so on. The idea that each household in the manor had these rights, or sources of food, could be maintained so long as the population did not increase much or move much. It has been guessed that, in order to maintain population in the Middle Ages, each adult woman must have borne, on an average, six children. No wonder then that population increased only slowly, and that ravages of disease such as the Black Death caused serious temporary declines in numbers.

The lord's special connection with defence helped to emphasise his rights over any woodland surrounding the arable of the manor, and he sometimes came to be looked upon as the grantor of the privilege of pasturing swine among the oaks and of cutting wood. Charcoal burners, wicker-workers, clog-makers and others must seek his permission to use the woodland products. At every step he was moving towards ownership ; and the change was accelerated when it became desirable, from his point of view, to guard the diminishing wild life of the forest in which he wished to hunt.

The introduction of root-crops ripening in autumn meant enclosing land for these crops to keep it from the beasts, which, by custom, previously wandered over the stubble fields after the cereal harvest. The lord's permission had to be obtained for such enclosures in some cases, and, moreover, the more such enclosures developed the less stubble area there was left for the cottager's cow. The man with enclosable land, and the lord, by now often called the squire, profited in this way. The lord or squire came nearer still to becoming the owner while the cottager came nearer to being merely a tenant.

Arthur Young in the eighteenth century was able to demonstrate the inefficiency of the old system of communal cultivation and the value of the four-course rotation, including root-crops as a regular feature. This was supposed to presage large increases of food supply to the general advantage. The same type of argument was used when, in the mid-nineteenth century, chemical manures came into use, and it was too optimistically stated that large areas of British moorland, ten million acres it was said, would be brought into grain cultivation. The result of all this was the loss by the cottager of his small but traditional rights, and the complete conversion of what had long ago been lordship into full ownership. Many cottagers were forced by these circumstances to move into the poor quarters of adjacent towns, and those who remained came, in several districts, under the evil Speenhamland system. This was devised in the late eighteenth century by landowners of Speenhamland, Berkshire, to mitigate distress. It provided that poor relief should be given to make up deficiencies in wages earned, if these fell below a settled minimum. In practice it meant a subsidy to agricultural employers from the rates ; many employed only those men who had got poor relief, and they thus reduced their wages bills.

The nett result of all this change was that vastly improved methods of agriculture, followed by great improvements in stock raising, brought depression to a multitude of cottagers ; the descendants of old-time peasants became underpaid wage-labourers living largely on potatoes and liable to fluctuation of employment, also usually needing poor-relief. The New Lands, in North America and the Southern Hemisphere, greatly profited from the consequent emigration ; and politicians in Britain urged humble folk to be thrifty and save the few pounds then needed to take them to the Lands of Opportunity.

The old social bonds of the village were almost dissolved, individualist ambition was fostered, indeed preached, as the cure of all ills. Naturally it too often happened that the people of character and initiative emigrated to the New Lands, that the poor quarters of the growing towns became filled with restless folk of less capacity, and that not seldom a below-average residue grew up in the village cottages. There followed the serious neglect of agriculture in Britain when cheap grain could be imported from outside from Norh American Argentina, Australia and elsewhere. It is only quite recently that real thought on the part of legislators and ministries has been applied to the rehabilitation of food production in our countryside, and of village social life as an essential concomitant.

Studies of evolution of settlement in Wales have been progressing in recent years and, though views are still rather tentative, it will be useful to add a short summary here. Whether Infield and Outfield were in use in early times we cannot as yet say. The tenth-century laws of Hywel Dda and the twelfth-century writings of Giraldus Cambrensis picture for us people without towns or villages leading a life in very small groups on the edges, often the upper edges, of the woods. Peate speaks of the Tyddyn as the nucleus of the Welsh national life ; it was a smallish family-holding of four or eight erwau

PLATE XIX

Travel Association

COMPTON WYNYATES, Warwickshire. Built largely during the second half of the fifteenth century, it was once fortified. Here Charles I lodged during the Civil Wars

PLATE XX

Jarrold, Norwich

COURTYARD of the Strangers' Hall, Norwich. A mediaeval house of superior character

(erw, in the singular, varies and is often about 0.89 acres). The holder of the Tyddyn associated himself with others similarly placed in the neighbourhood who were his kinsfolk, three generations back in the male line being often known and acknowledged. The group was called the Gwely (=Bed), which itself was considered a part of a larger group. There was in early times much unoccupied land to be cleared, and new Gwelyau had to be formed generation after generation ; a man within the Gwely would claim a Tyddyn when he married. Emrys Jones has pointed out that the making of a new Tyddyn for a newly married man became in course of time the squatter homestead-making described in an earlier chapter (p. 221) and important in the early nineteenth century when cultivation was rashly extended to poor lands. The establishment of the right of the first born in Tudor times promoted squatting because it left the younger sons to seek a livelihood elsewhere or otherwise. The squatter settlements of the early nineteenth century, often on high land with poor soil and much rain, have in many cases been deserted in the later part of the century when agriculture was in recession and there was industrial employment in the towns. Sometimes the kinsfolk might live near one another as a group, and it seems that the group might be called a Tref, (c.f. Clachan p. 242) a name which came to be associated sometimes with a group of houses, the settlement unit being a *Treflan* if it included a church. But Bowen and Emrys Jones do not think the church had much influence in determining grouping of houses in west Wales. The latter writer draws attention to the existence also, of rather haphazard groupings of houses, in several cases around a mill, or a place which had had a mill. Such a group might be a settlement of serfs, probably originally of the older moorland stocks discussed on pp. 66-68, under the lordship of Celtic conquerors of the Iron Age (p. 244) or of subsequent overlords. When associated with a Treflan it was called a Pentref, and it appears that quite a number of these are traceable on the ground or in place names. The Treflan and Pentref may be on the valley floor, or on the lower parts of its sides. The Tyddyn belongs mainly to the upper hill sides. These names and ideas are not results of legal definition, but rather rural practical names the meaning of which varies a good deal. The practice of taking the cattle up to moorland or mountain-side pastures in summer not only helped to ensure the nimble character of the traditional Welsh black cattle, but gave rise to the rough mountain or moorland summer shelter called hafotty (hafod = summer pasture). This was contrasted with the winter home of the men who were sent up with the cattle, and the names hendre, hendref, were associated with this. They have come to be linked sometimes with the substantial farmhouse of an owner rather than the irregular gatherings of cottages of serving men.

It should be understood that upland Wales, well to the west of the border, was, until towards the end of the seventeenth century, mainly concerned with cattle ; it had few three-field systems except in the Anglicised parts of South Wales, and few towns or villages or manors with any general systematic organisation, but it often had a system of co-aration with patches (quillets) belonging to each household. It was the head of the Gwely or of the larger grouping (Cwmmwd, Cantref) who dominated so far as his personality made this possible. On the English border sheep and wool became important in the Middle Ages and weakened attempts at manorial organisation adapted to control of a rotation of crops. The taking of the wool to lowland centres helped development of towns of the Anglo-Welsh border. The provision of the wool for the Lord Chancellor's Woolsack in the House of Lords by Leominster is a memorial of this phase. After the late seventeenth century, sheep increased greatly in Wales, and cattle later came to be fed in winter on root-crops. The hafod or summer pasture area has sometimes become the upland farm owning the sheep and sending them " on tack " to the lowlands for the winter. Courts Leet have concerned themselves with registration of sheep marks (cuts in the ears and other marks) and questions relating to stray animals, " sheep on tack " and so on, all connected with the seasonal movements of a large flock often belonging to several owners.

In the eastern lowlands of Scotland one finds villages set around greens and along roads as well as fishing villages on the coast. Elsewhere in Scotland, according to Graham, the agricultural conditions have altered very radically since about 1750, after which turnips and potatoes spread as food-crops for man and beast, and tree planting for shelter became an enthusiasm, almost a mania. Before that, the Run Rig (=Ridge) system prevailed over large areas. A field might be occupied by four or more persons, and the Rig might be auctioned, or re-allocated by a chief, year by year. The occupiers had to agree to work together, and laggards made " punctuality the thief of time ". A rig was 20 to 40 feet wide and only the top was ploughed. The rest, and the hollow between two ridges was a balk (baulk) with briars and many weeds and often pools. Cattle were turned in as soon as the harvest was gathered. The occupiers of a farm, perhaps 15 to 20 families, lived in a cluster of cottages near the farm. The thatch of the cottages might be removed and used to feed the soil, which, however, often needed lime to correct acidity and drainage to make crops possible, as well as to reduce the then prevalence of ague and of water-snails carrying parasites affecting sheep. A farmer-owner would probably have farm hands living with him or in a cottage or two quite near ; and his house would be little better than a cottage but would probably have two or three rooms. In the Highlands a chieftain having almost sovereign rights would have his clansmen gathered in cottage clusters near him ; his status would depend on the size of the clan and its prowess in wars and raids. The chieftain would receive dues in cattle, eggs and meal from his clansmen, and so could be expansively hospitable ; but he could not sell the produce, largely because of lack of any means of transport to a market, often because there was no market. There was thus no money for improvements and little desire for change.

After 1750, roads were developed and brought possibilities of movement of sheep and wool ; while the chieftains after the '45 were deprived of their old partial sovereignty and of opportunities for raiding and clan-war. So they became less interested in the numbers and the strength for war of the clansmen, and more interested in having land for sheep and wool. Clansmen might be turned out or encouraged to emigrate, and many did so to their great advantage but often to Scotland's loss ; others left the glens and grew potatoes on damp coastlands. Money given to chiefs in compensation for the loss of their old legal powers came in useful for land improvement ; and money brought back home by Scots, chiefly lowlanders, who had done well in foreign parts, including London and India, was also applied to the land. Apparently all this made a revolutionary change in the plan of settlement in Scotland which, from being a " backward " country, became a leader in agricultural development so far as the Lothians and some other counties were concerned, but began the long depopulation process in many parts of the Highlands. The relation of the new wealth in the late eighteenth century to the spacious planning of the New Town at Edinburgh should be mentioned (see plate 22, p. 223, plate XXVI, p. 275 and fig. 69, p. 278).

The fishermen's village has some special characteristics, particularly in western Britain. It has often been built in huddled fashion in shelter from storms ; and estuaries are naturally favoured sites (see plate 19, p. 174). The fisherfolk may or may not also cultivate. If they do not cultivate, their houses are often close-set in fishermen's lanes, very narrow and leading out to the water, which sometimes may come up, or, rather, before more recent changes, came up the lane between the houses (plate XVI, p. 219). The division of labour between the sexes typically gives the women much work in dealing with and perhaps selling the catch brought in by the men, for whom they have also knitted " jerseys " and "guernseys."[1] The cleaning and salting and hawking of fish (whence the name fish-wife) are activities that do not attract those who have been brought up in other surroundings. It thence follows that the men of fishing villages have far more often married women from fisher-families than from purely agricultural ones. Indeed one comes across indications of some degree of objection to marriage of a farmer's daughter with a fisherman. It has sometimes been suggested that the fisher-groups are settlers from the sea distinct of old from their farming neighbours. A few folk-tales about the strange ways of such folk (e.g. tales of the men of Aberdaron in Caer-narvonshire) may give a little support to ideas of this kind, but it is probable that the economic considerations mentioned just above account for a good deal.

There are many clusters of houses in modern Britain which do not come into the groups hitherto considered. Some are rows of miners' houses, often of lamentable quality in bad situations from the point of view of hygiene, placed near pit-heads in the days before transport facilities had developed on modern lines. The mining valleys of South Wales have long lines of such houses with groups of shops here and there, but little of the amenities of either a good village or a good town (plate 21, p. 222). Much the same kind of criticism may be made of the house-clusters for workers on other coalfields and near a good many industrial establishments. On the other hand, some indus-trial undertakings have tackled the problem with a measure of success; Bournville near Birmingham and Port Sunlight near the Mersey are the two most widely known examples, and at Bournville the firm of Cadbury is entirely separate, financially and so far as policy is concerned, from the trust which manages the property (plate XXIV, p. 271).

Discussion fifty years ago was carried on briskly between scholars

---

[1] These names owe their origin to the fact that in Elizabethan-Stuart times wool was sent by Britain to the Channel Islands to be knitted up by the women and old men.

PLATE XXI

John Markham

An Adam Room, Lion Hotel, Shrewsbury. The Adam brothers were notable architects (1728–92)

PLATE XXII

Liverpool Daily Post and Echo Ltd.

RODNEY STREET, Liverpool. A street with typical late Georgian buildings

who thought the early English village an association of equals which later came to be under a lord, and other specialists who thought there was some kind of lordship from the beginning. The trend of opinion more recently seems to have favoured the latter view, though the lordship of early days was no doubt less elaborately devised and carried out than in the Middle Ages, and a universal system cannot be claimed to have existed at any period. It is probable that the working of a three-field system, with everyone's strips in each field cultivated according to a general scheme, promoted the idea of an authority to restrain the greedy and spur the laggards. There are records of the order, from the lord of the manor, or through long-established custom, to ring the church bell at a certain time on a fixed day as a sign that the village cattle might be turned into the arable fields after harvest to eat the growth coming up amongst the stubble. A laggard might lose an unreaped crop. In the seventeenth century in Alderney a strip owner might not enclose a part of his strip to grow parsnips unless he had the special permission of the lord of the manor. This indicates how the idea of root-crops militated against the old system, and how the old system cramped enterprise. The root-crops stay in the ground until autumn ; the old system pre-supposed stubble pasture and manuring of the land by the dung of the cattle from the end of the grain harvest onwards until the cold became too sharp.

Communal control enforced the rule of custom and penalised initiative, and it is quite probable that its long continuance in Germany has had a share in making so much of the population of that country inclined to welcome orders from above. There is a striking modern contrast between the German people and those of the Scandinavian lands and parts of Holland in which the system was weaker or absent. The contrast between these latter lands and Britain in the matter of the urban proletariat is also very marked. Holland and the Scandinavian lands have profited in this matter from the fact that their industrial development has come so largely with the use of electrical power and the internal combustion engine.

One might write a long chapter on the evidence place-names can give concerning the natural history of settlement, but we have already mentioned this subject in Chapter 6, (pp. 130-31), and, for fuller study, we must refer readers rather to such works as those of the English Place Names Society, while the old book (1882) by Isaac Taylor entitled *Words and Places* is most stimulating ; it should be read with

s

Sir Allen Mawer's *Chief Elements in English Place Names* (1924) as a check, because of adjustments made necessary by the progress of research since Taylor's time, research in connection with which the names of Ekwall and Stenton stand out. The study is full of complexities as names become modified by popular usage and their derivation becomes confused. An instance is the name of Barmouth, formerly Abermawddach where Aber means Mouth and Mawddach is a river-name. Yet Aber has become Bar and Mawddach has become Mouth.

Beorg, primarily a hill, and Burh, a fortified place are between them responsible for many place names that include the words Burgh, Borough, Brough, Borrow, Barrow, Bury, Berry, Ber, even sometimes Bear though in several cases names with Ber, Bear, Byr, Bur, Bar have other derivations. Ber or Bar may be a derivative from Aber as we have just seen. Byr and Byre mean in some cases a separate farm or tenancy. Wick, on the coast, is a sea rover's name for a creek or haven ; Wick, inland, is often an early English name for a settlement. And either may be modified into Wich. Isaac Taylor thought the salt-towns such as Northwich, Middlewich, Droitwich, etc. got their suffixes from the fact that salt was often made in early times from evaporation of salt water in creeks, etc., and that the name got transferred to places that brought into use salt deposits.

Places good for Butter, Milk, Cheese, Fats, etc., may have tell-tale names such as Botterley, Bitterley, Birley, Cheswick, Chiswick, Keswick (a Scandinavian variant), Smerden (Smear is related to Scandinavian words for Butter) and so on.

Mor often means a place that was once waste but More may mean Great in Gaelic-Celtic areas (Glenmore=Great Glen), and Mor in Welsh means Sea. Great in Welsh is Mawr (or Fawr in the feminine gender). Moss a peaty area, Mire a former swamp, Saur an area of poor acid soil (Sowerby), Stroud an overgrown area of marsh, Heath comes into Hatfield, Hadley, etc., Chart an overgrown common, Hese land covered with brushwood (Heysham, Heston), Bent land covered with the bent grass (Chowbent), Bush land (Bushey), Breck either uncultivated land or land that has been taken into cultivation for a short time from the uncultivated waste—all these and others help to describe former conditions of the land.

Into the varied forms that imply a clearing in the woods for whatever purpose, or an enclosure for cattle, or pigs, or other purposes, or an enclosure in marsh land or elsewhere, we must not enter. Many of these clearings and enclosures may be relatively late, and local variations of the words used are numerous. Alsop, Bacup, owe their last syllable to a root which means clearing in a marsh (in northern England), Bere, Beer, Bear, in south-west England often but not always mean pasture for pigs; typically in a clearing. Holt in south England means woodland. Leigh and its variants, especially in Hampshire, Cheshire, Staffordshire and Derbyshire may mean clearing, and often originally meant woodland, but it is mixed up with various forms meaning pasture, e.g., Summerlease in Cornwall, Leasowe (Cheshire).

As an example of the complications against which one has to guard it may be explained that Field or Feld, widely used in connection with unenclosed land, has been altered into Ville on occasion in the west country.

Wal in place names often seems to go back to clusters of habitations of Welsh in Early English times, Walworth, Walton, and other variants could be listed.

Ceorl, Charl, with the Scandinavian form Karl, meaning originally a peasant holder and later often a serf, is much used in place-names— Charlton, Chorlton, Chorley, etc., Carlton or Carleton, etc. These suggest clusters of houses inhabited by churls.

Kniht and Knight mean servant of a military superior, above the rank of the common soldier, and give us many place names such as Knighton.

The syllables Tun (and Ton), Ham, Ing, Thorp, Worth, Wic, By, and others are in some senses the most interesting and informative elements in our English place-names. Ing, Ham, Ton, and some others have been mentioned in Chapter 6, (pp. 130-31). Pitfalls in place-names study are illustrated by the fact that while Kingston refers to the King's Ton, Wroxton refers to Wrocc's Stan or Stone, and it is thought that the same interpretation applies to a number of names of Norse origin ending in Ston in Pembrokeshire. Thorp was another name for a settlement and is ascribed by some to the Danes and Norsemen, chiefly in eastern England, north of the area in which " Ham " is a common suffix, but occurring in Norfolk ; its absence from Cambridgeshire and Middlesex is noteworthy in this connection and it seems gradually to have come to be associated with a small settlement, as was Worth with its variants Worthy and Wardine. By as a prefix may mean *near*, but as a suffix it usually denotes a settlement made or enlarged by the Danes, a detail to which reference is made later in this chapter.

Danish invasions and Norwegian seamen played a great part in ninth-century Britain. The invaders on the east coast were mainly Danes, those on the west included Norwegians and were often called Vikings but there is also the traditional name of Black Danes for some of them. On the east side the suffix By, omnipresent in Denmark but almost unknown south of Slesvig-Holstein, is abundant in Lincolnshire and of some importance in Leicestershire but thins out to the south and south-west. Toft occurs in settlement names in areas occupied by the Danes. Their main bases for penetration seem to have been the Norfolk, Lincolnshire and Yorkshire coasts, with apparently less advance through the marsh and fen country to Cambridgeshire and the south-east Midlands so far as settlement was concerned. In many parts the Danes were mainly an aristocracy, and their rural settlers seem to have been men well above servile status. The Danes had coastal stations here and there along most of the south-east and the east. Their penetration into Yorkshire seems to have paid special attention to the route through south-west Durham to the Eden valley, important from prehistoric times (p. 51).

By occurs as a suffix in two regions on the west, namely Dumfries-shire and the Wirral and this brings up the idea of the " Black Danes " above mentioned. The Wirral in olden time was almost isolated from the rest of Cheshire, which is poor in possible Danish names. Thwaite (a field) has already been instanced as an important element in names due to Norwegian conquerors and is abundant in Cumberland along with other Norwegian elements in place names such as Beck, Fell, Force, Garth. Force is a notable instance of the spread of a Norwegian name south-eastwards into south-west Durham, a counter-spread to the opposite extension of Danish names just mentioned. Ekwall has identified Gaelic Celtic (Irish) place-names near the Cumbrian coast, and the medieval relations of Furness Abbey with Ireland are well known. The early English already, like ourselves, used Ford to mean a river crossing, and there are many relevant instances. The seamen of the west, on the other hand, used it for a water-passage into a harbour, so we have Waterford and Wexford on the Irish side and Haverford and Milford on the Welsh side. Pembrokeshire, apart from the Preseli hills, abounds in Norse names, and both it and Gower were much used by Vikings. Ey and A as suffixes meaning island are characteristic in Atlantic Britain as evidence of the Norwegians— Orkney, Sudrey, Nordrey, Ronaldsha, etc., but A also ends river names (Greta, Rotha).

REFERENCES TO CHAPTERS 11 AND 12. Angus (1949), Bersu (see Kinvig), Bloch (1931), Bowen (1941), Childe (1931), Clapham and Power (1941), Conzen (1949), Coulton (1925), Crawford (1928), Garnett (unpublished), Graham (1937), Ekwall (1936), Evans (1942), Evans, Mogey and McCourt (see Evans, and Mogey), Fleure and Dunlop (1942), Fussell (1949), Hammond and Hammond (1919-48), E. Jones (1945), Kinvig (1944), Kissling (1943), Leeds (1913), Lethbridge (1948), Mawer (1924), Meitzen (1895), Mogey (1947), Norlund (1948), Oliver (1929), Orwin and Orwin (1938), Peake (1922), Peate (1940), Pelham (1931), Place-Names Society's Publications, Pulbrook[1] (n.d.), Richardson and Everlein[1] (n.d.), Sharp (1946), Stenton (1927, 1943), Sylvester (1948), Taylor 1882), Wickham (1933)[1].

[1] Illustrated books published by B. T. Batsford.

CHAPTER 13

TOWNS

A VOTE FOR choosing the most charming of the small towns of England would bring strong support for Ludlow, King's Lynn, Cotswold townlets and little Lavenham. Among larger towns Bath, Lincoln, Norwich, Shrewsbury, Chester and York would have strong claims, and some others would have been included here before the devastations of 1940-1945. Among the great cities of Britain Edinburgh surely stands out, while Liverpool has some great buildings and Rodney Street (plate XXII, p. 255) and Abercromby Square to balance the mean quarters and slums in which she is matched by most of what Dr. Jacks calls our Smokovers. Bristol has fine monuments and surroundings, with a considerable medieval, renascence and subsequent heritage from its commercial history. But, broadly speaking, the lack of beauty in our cities shows how deficient they are as modes of social expression. London's unique series of fine buildings of the last nine centuries is, yet, deprived of many possibilities by the ungoverned modern sprawl. A few cities of quite special character stand, in a sense, apart, and one may name here Oxford (plate XVII, p. 242) and Cambridge, and perhaps also the little village-city of St. David's (plate XVIII, p. 243) at a focus of ways from a number of alternative landings marked by ancient chapels (St. Non, St. Patrick, St. Justinian).

Towns may have begun in Britain in Iron Age B or Iron Age C (p. 95), the possibilities including what afterwards became Colchester, Verulamium, Winchester and perhaps London. Reference has been made (p. 115) to towns in Roman Britain. Before the breakdown of the Imperial Roman system in Gaul there were Christian bishops in several towns. Britain had a few. In Gaul, however, the bishops continued through the subsequent centuries ; amongst us they did

260

not. The Romano-British towns were almost obliterated save for the Newport Gate at Lincoln, the recovered amphitheatre at Caerleon, the plan of the centre of Chester, and the Multangular Tower and other traces in the walls of York.

The early English, like the Franks in France, were rurally minded. The Franks were largely military and married native girls, the early English came in considerable proportion as families hoping to settle and cultivate. The Franks quickly got into touch with cities and their bishops, the early English lacked this contact for about 150 years. The towns of Britain therefore belong mainly to periods well after the withdrawal of Roman power when specialisation of labour and consequent exchange were developing once more. Danish invaders, apparently interested in lines of communication, promoted town-life to some extent, but the great impetus came with, and following, the Norman conquerors. Our town development was therefore in some measure an extension of what was taking place in France (including Normandy where the erstwhile Norse raiders had become builders of castles and churches).

A few of our towns such as those mentioned above and Canterbury were in existence during, and, as we have seen, probably before the arrival of the early English. Others, for the most part, grew in the later Saxon times. Oxford, which will be discussed below, and Cambridge and Thetford have artificial fortress mounds of pre-Norman date and they are at what were, or still are, important nodes of communications. The special early importance of the site of Cambridge has been mentioned on pp. 131 and 135.

Oxford illustrates so many features of our early town-development that we may give a few points (plate XVII, p. 242). The north-south road (now Banbury Road), St. Giles, Cornmarket, Carfax and St. Aldates (which last was formerly Fish Street leading to the Grand Pont over the main stream of the Thames) crossed at Carfax (derived from *Quadrifurcus*) the east-west road of which the High Street of Oxford and the High Street of Osney are portions. These two High Streets are connected by the curve of Paradise Street and Castle Street around what was the bailey of the castle that succeeded the mound as the defence of the cross-roads and that had the water-mill fed by a branch stream. The High Street of Osney ends at the churchyard of the church of St. Thomas à Becket, beyond which once stood the famous Abbey of St. Mary, Osney. It is probable that Osney was primarily Ouseney,

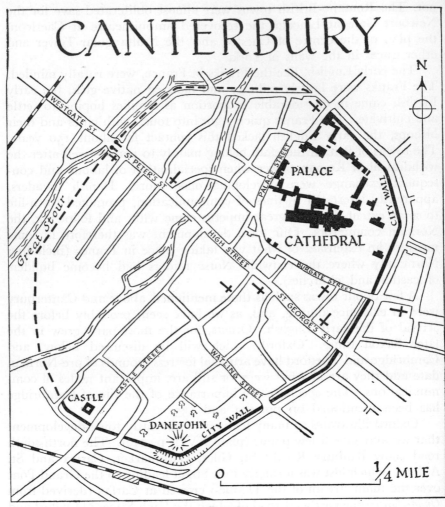

FIG. 67

Canterbury.   A city based on a Roman plan with a Medieval abbey-
cathedral in its own close, away from the city-centre

the island in the river. The crossing of the rivers Thames and Cherwell
and of the former river's branch streams gave a connection between
Mercia and Wessex.

The city wall stood at a short distance from Carfax in every direction, enclosing the little city with its cornmarket inside the northern entry and a church of St. Martin (a typical early dedication) at the cross roads. A strange ancient figure associated with pre-Christian fertility ritual is preserved among the stones of the tower of St. Martin's ; the church itself has been destroyed. The site is evidently of very ancient importance ; and a royal palace, north-east of what is now Worcester College added to the city's prestige in the twelfth century. Outside the north wall we have the road-broadening called St. Giles, the historic fair ground, which explains the dedication, Giles being the patron of pedlars. When sheep fairs developed and the Cistercians gave a special attention to wool, the monastery of this order was built fronting St. Giles. In 1555 it became St. John's College. To the east of St. Giles is what is now Broad Street but was the Horse Fair. From the Horse Fair a small postern gate in the town wall (some say it was Twirlgate, others say Thurl refers to a hole, c.f. tril in Nostril) led into " The Turl " one of the old lanes going to the High Street. S. Frideswide's Abbey outside the wall, on the south, became in the sixteenth century Ædes Christi and is thence known to its members as " The House ", while to the general public it is Christ Church. The lower parts of the meadows south of Christ Church were once marsh-land, but were dried and raised by tipping there what was excavated when making foundations for the great buildings of the city. Most of the remainder of Oxford's story concerns the University, but the nineteenth century saw the location of railways at a certain distance west of the city because of local opposition, and the twentieth century has seen the immense growth of machinery and automobile making, under Morris Ltd., at Cowley. Oxford has become an agglomerate of about 100,000 people, with industry rivalling the university and the tourist traffic as another vital factor of the city's life.

Lavenham in Suffolk is a little medieval town hardly touched by modern life and now inhabited by only 1,400 people. It was not a walled city, but rather a medieval industrial centre which became very prosperous as the woollen industry of East Anglia grew in the late fifteenth and the sixteenth century. A Hall of the Guild of Corpus Christi (plate 13, p. 186), a Wool Hall and the Church of St. Peter and St. Paul in the outskirts (plate 28, p. 303), all dating from the early sixteenth century (with portions of the church chancel from the late fourteenth century), are the best known features along with the street frontages and the market place. The little old town is, in fact, an historic monument.

We are too apt to think of the early town as analogous with the often congested old quarter of a modern town, but this is an error. The townsfolk in the early Middle Ages needed to produce a good deal of their own food, and the houses seem to have had long strips of land attached to serve this purpose ; in fact some writers have suggested that the early town in Anglo-Saxon and Norman times had something of the character of a garden city. If we allow some value to this analogy, we must be careful not to think of the dwellings and streets of those days as appropriate to what we should call garden cities.

The land of a household in the town was often a long narrow strip reaching back from a narrow frontage on the street, a scheme which made the builder put the gable-end on the street and the roof-ridge at right angles to it. Gable-ends might sometimes follow one another in a continuous series along the street, an arrangement which promoted warmth and mutual support, but greatly increased the danger of fire, especially so long as thatch was used for roofs. About the year 1200 it seems that tiles came into use for roofing in several places and reduced fire-risks a little. Already a little before this oak ceilings for churches were being replaced by stone vaults, with the same intent. If gables succeeded one another in continuous series, gutters between them collected the rain and spouted it down on the street, which, without surfacing, became a muddy mess. Access to the household's land behind the house or to the stable-yard and barn behind an inn was often by a covered entry, i.e., part of the house extended over the entry. The house door might be on the street, more often in the entry, sometimes even at the back in a courtyard. These positions of the door are still fairly common in the cases of old posting inns.

In outlying or for any reason more spacious areas, or in the case of houses of wealthy families, sometimes urban or burgage holdings of rural magnates, the house front might be broad. In this case it was often provided with an entry, frequently but not always central, into a rectangular courtyard the sides of which were parts of the house. The old mansion that became the Stranger's Hall at Norwich (plate XX, p. 251) is a very famous instance of this, and the Golden Cross Inn at Oxford may also be mentioned here. Inns had to have courtyards with stables for coach-horses. The early Halls[1] of Oxford were probably

---

[1] Halls in Oxford were houses arranged for students' residence. Some began as houses of wealthy Jews who, fearing attack, built solidly in stone. One had the significant name of Chimney Hall, in token of the then rarity of that luxury.

somewhat analogous, and the courtyard idea with a covered entry apparently influenced William of Wykeham in his planning of the New College quadrangle.

Sometimes the ground floor of the narrow house-front was a shop, typically at first a workshop. The front ground floor of a broader-fronted house or hall might have a series of shops. We must not think of shops stored with goods for chance sale to any great extent ; they were often workshops working to order. Exposure for chance sale was rather a feature of markets and fairs. The town if incorporated with a charter was typically given the right to hold a market on a certain day of the week, sometimes two days, as in the case of the Tuesday market and the former Saturday market at King's Lynn ; it would also have the right to hold an annual fair. This fair fixed itself usually just outside the town and to it came itinerant pedlars, sometimes from a long distance. St. Giles at Oxford and Stourbridge at Cambridge are notable cases.

The dates of fairs were usually described in terms of festivals of the church, largely because these festivals marked so many of the crucial dates of the climatic and agricultural calendar. In a number of cases Benedictine and other monks established themselves near fair grounds, just outside the towns ; they were specially interested in agriculture as well as in the towns. The abbey that has become the church of the Holy Cross at Shrewsbury is a good instance of this, and several are just outside old towns, e.g., at St. Albans.

It is a widespread feature of our cathedrals that they stand in closes entered by a gateway, and in this respect they contrast with the typical French cathedrals which stand on what is, or at any rate was, the central market place. What has just been said about cathedrals applies very widely also to town churches ; only occasionally do they dominate the town's central market-place, as St. Margaret's dominated the Saturday market at King's Lynn, a market that has now ceased.

Looking at our towns as indicators of our social evolution we may realise the meanings of a number of features if we imagine ourselves coming towards and into the town by motor-bus. While still a little way outside we come upon what would like to consider itself a village but is now largely a dormitory for the more prosperous men of the town. It probably shows a contrast in modern houses between those built respectively before and after the domestic service difficulty became almost too acute to retain its place as a subject of conversation.

The larger house built in the expectation of domestic help may have trees as a screen of privacy, the smaller houses built for family housework may be one-storeyed, and, if so, usually have small bushes rather than trees outlining their gardens. The dormitory ex-village is usually inhabited by those whose experience is wide enough to give some at

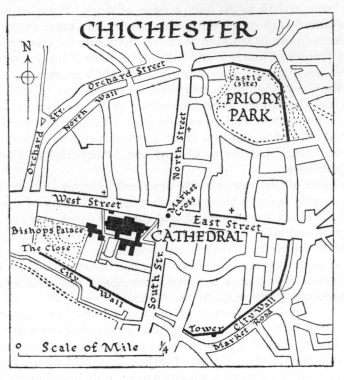

FIG. 68

Chichester. A city on a Roman plan with a Medieval
cathedral at the city-centre but in an enclosure of its own

least of them an historical sense, and there is beneath all this the half-conscious feeling that the industrial revolutions have cut our old roots of social life. When we realise how much historic background means in our national life with our unwritten constitution and our centuries of continuity of ceremonial, we do not wonder that the families now using the ex-village hanker after historic roots, especially as they are apt to have social aspirations. These attitudes have often expressed themselves in the building of modern timber-frame houses, not always in the genuine traditional style, or sometimes in dignified copies of the eighteenth-century town houses of the wealthy. The modern houses are likely to be on a tree-lined avenue with grass verges and, often, open greens at corners. An old squire's house may have become a residential hotel or a golf club headquarters, and it is likely to look as *depaysée* as the medieval church of the old-time village, which, if personified, would have a puzzled look at its present congregation, so different from the " rude forefathers of the hamlet " for whom it was built in the days when a village three miles from a town was " right in the country ".

The ex-village has often been disappointed in its hopes of keeping a houseless zone between itself and the town ; ribbon development is strong in its appeal to the profit-motive, and is convenient as a help to accessibility. If the ribbon is continuous, some of it may show twentieth-century houses built under the influence of bus-services. If it is not, and the town is not a large one, then, as we approach it, we find mostly Victorian dwellings, detached and in gardens at first (plate 23, p. 238), but further in we find them more often semi-detached with gardens correspondingly reduced. At a cross-roads will be a cluster of shops and probably a bank branch and a service-station for petrol. With this, we shall very probably enter the next zone of small houses in continuous rows with little garden patches, and with names such as Mon Plaisir, St. Heliers (or some other honey-moon spot) over the door. Another group of shops for immediate household needs and a public authority school will be likely to accompany streets of gardenless brick houses of the bleak age, as the Hammonds have called the period 1810-50. These are the result of a combination of the idea of warmth through contiguity and of the desire for profit from land in private ownership.

Towards the inner part of the zone of little houses the eye catches here and there one of different style, a survival from the Georgian period, probably once occupied by a professional man, but even in its decadence suggesting a dignity that the first industrial revolution destroyed and replaced by a heightened desire for display. Along some of the streets the continuous series of houses that once had small gardens have often had the ground floors converted into shops built out forwards to cover the gardens and give a shop-front right on the street. These curious streets with the shops projecting from houses are a most characteristic feature of the nineteenth century in Britain. In the zone of small gardenless houses one finds mission halls and chapels and here and there a rather forlorn church usually of the nineteenth-century Gothic revival, sometimes, however, an eighteenth-century structure with more meaning. Towards the town centre there may be some chapels of the Georgian period, perhaps including one appertaining to an old Presbyterian congregation the originators of which gathered around one of the ministers ejected following the Act of Uniformity of 1661. Several groups of this character became Unitarian in doctrine towards the end of the eighteenth century. Another religious organization that in several places has an old building, often with a little open space or burial-ground attached, is the Society of Friends (plate 16b, p. 143). These religious groups were able to build meeting houses in towns after the Revolution of 1688, but long found difficulty in obtaining the right to conduct their own funeral services in the churchyard. Chapels near the town centre, built in the days when business folk lived above and behind their shops, now have very small congregations ; the business folk have moved to the town fringe or to the dormitory villages beyond, and have often become members of the State Church as they moved out.

The town centre may retain with pride an Elizabethan timber frame house, the ground floor of which may have been altered into a modern shop. Near the Welsh border, there is a market-house in the square ; it is raised on arches that frame an open-access shelter for market-folk (plate 20, p. 175). A study of the distribution and dates of these market-houses, once inhabited by officers who had the oversight of the market, could be interesting. There may be Assembly Rooms, sometimes attached to an eighteenth-century town hall, sometimes independent ; and these rooms are usually a testimony to the social life of the more leisured folk before the Industrial Revolution and the migration to the remoter suburbs. As Belloc has it :

> " They called in a horse and carriage,
> They danced at the County Ball,
> They married and gave in marriage
> And the flood destroyed them all ".

The fact is that, after the 1688 revolution, town life began to grow quickly, country landowners acquired or built town houses and spent part of the winters in them, a very understandable scheme for those who could get away from the isolation of the country in the days before the roads were improved and highway robbery and murder were put down.

The town centre will often have a few modern public buildings in the Georgian style and it may have hotels that are genuine antiques or modern copies of old styles. It is interesting to try to estimate at what size the town begins to have a centre that is almost without inhabitants at night—a night-dead heart. Towns with more than 50,000 people often show this feature and it becomes a general rule in towns with 100,000 or more. Factors in this are the size of businesses and the value of the sites. In towns of over 50,000 the shop will often have showrooms and stores upstairs, or upstair suites of rooms are let as offices for solicitors, insurance agencies and other matters. The size of town that is invaded by chain-stores is another interesting question. A quite small town (say of 10,000 people or less) in a stock-raising area may nevertheless be a district-focus, and chain-stores will establish themselves there. The chain-store is a much more general feature of the British than of the French town. A number of cinemas are usually found, some occupying what were once down-town chapels.

Bus services have grown enormously of late years and have altered the life of both villages and towns. There is likely to be a bus centre on or near a market place, and one may compare the recent departure of buses every ten minutes from Luton to Watford via Harpenden and St. Albans, half emptying and refilling at each of these intermediate towns, with the much more limited facilities of the days of dependence on local trains. As so often happens, the railways did not adequately foresee the value of bus services as a supplement to their own schemes. so that bus and train stations are often unrelated.

The town typically has represented in it the five leading banking companies, occupying positions that rival those of the inns for conspicuousness, and a town of even moderate size may also have branch offices of the banks near its fringe. Insurance offices are as widespread as banks, but a special building for an Insurance Company is not so general as one for a bank ; it is usually found only in rather large towns. In the old-established wheat lands of eastern England there is often a Cornmarket Hall, usually little used at present and probably taken over by a seed merchant. The Carnegie United Kingdom Trust a generation or two ago helped to spread lending and reference libraries in our towns, even in some small ones, and occasionally a lecture hall has been built at the library by a local authority with vision. But, generally speaking, it is our misfortune that so much of the growth of our towns has taken place on land which became private property through the Enclosure of Commons. That growth moreover took place in the hurry of the first industrial revolution, when the ideal of " toil, thrift, triumph " was held up so often for popular admiration.

In dealing with the villages it was a melancholy duty to mention the metamorphosis of a peasantry, especially in the eighteenth and early nineteenth centuries, into landless and almost hopeless wage-labourers. Many escaped to the towns and gave immense opportunities to town landowners to enrich themselves by building crowded houses (see plate XXIII, p. 270), often back-to-back, in dark alleys and courts. The heritages of the slums on the one hand and of certain large accumulations of private wealth on the other have both been very costly to the nation. Only in 1909 did back-to-back houses become illegal.

The improvement of the more crowded quarters of our towns has involved long struggles and only fractional achievements. Open spaces and playgrounds have increased since the days when, under Puritan administrators in the mid-nineteenth century, alcohol, sex and betting were almost the only lines of relaxation left, one cannot quite say allowed, to wage-labourers. Some disused churchyards have been cleared and made into playgrounds, and some school playgrounds are fairly good, but far too little had been done before 1945-46 to maintain a green zone with open spaces within easy distance of the centre. Market garden soil has too often been built over. And it is only here and there that citizens are banded together to make their town beautiful, yet this beauty would be a sign of healthy civic life. Our towns, and especially our larger cities, lag behind several of those on the continent, which expanded chiefly under the influence of the second industrial revolution, gathering around oil and electric power. One thinks of Copenhagen and Zürich in this connection.

Schools are still, too often, on busy roads instead of being sited within a group of residential streets well away from through traffic. The schools are sometimes opened in the evenings for adult education groups, the members of which have to sit in children's desks in a building without amenities for adult students, who might meet in a remodelled public library and learn to use reference books, especially

PLATE XXIII

Aerofilms, Ltd.

WAGE-LABOURERS' QUARTER in a nineteenth-century industrial town in the North of England. The one-family house is typical

PLATE XXIV

Bournville Village Trust

PART OF THE BOURNVILLE VILLAGE TRUST ESTATE, near Birmingham. The Bournville Estate was founded in 1895 by the late George Cadbury and his work has been carried on by the Bournville Village Trust which he also founded. Mr. Cadbury laid down in the Trust Deed that dwellings should occupy about a fourth part of their own sites, and before being transferred to the tenant or purchaser gardens were laid out and fruit trees planted. This Estate is a separate organisation and residence in it is not confined to the employees of Messrs. Cadbury Brothers Ltd.

if that library had coffee rooms to help it to fulfil its function as a centre for discussion. Local collections of pictures are too often gifts of deplorable character, and we still usually lack an attractive local museum that can set out in models, well-chosen exhibits, maps, pictures and crisp explanations, the evolution of the town as a local illustration of the general human story, with our changing adaptations to environment and adaptations of environment to our ideas. It could gather material to demonstrate the evolution of the local industry, as has been done at Halifax, Yorkshire.

In former centuries most towns, except some ports, were dependent in the main on local supplies of food, and their craft-work supplied local needs in the country around. Modern conditions have altered this profoundly. Trains and lorries bring food from ports many miles away, and even milk is by no means always local in origin. Few things are made by the local town for its rural orbit, more are brought from special manufacturing centres and distributed through retail stores in the hands of large companies, which in some cases are almost monopolists. Instead of the old horse-and-cart relations we have new ones dependent on motor-car and bus, sometimes on the train service. Householders who can manage it live on the farthest fringes or in dormitory villages. They need a car park and a lunch bar, but are only too apt to shake off responsibility for the character and amenities of the town in which they work. A leading citizen of Manchester recently said that, whereas our grandparents lived above their offices in Portland Street, we live above our incomes in Alderley Edge. People in the surrounding villages look to the cinemas of the town for evening amusement and use the bus services for the purpose. Delivery and sale vans serve the district from the town, even with meat, bread and cakes.

It is especially characteristic of Britain that we have large clusters of population which have swallowed what were once separate units of citizenship. Patrick Geddes invented for them the apt if unbeautiful name of conurbations, but, as he added, the name was all the more apt because they are generally unbeautiful themselves. Manchester, Salford, Stretford, are no longer distinguishable from one another on the ground, or distinct from various ex-villages they have either swallowed completely or at least converted into slight swellings on their far-reaching tentacles. Boston in U.S.A. is another even more marked case ; its census population within the administrative limits

T

is 771,000, but the population of the effective cluster is 2,500,000. Paris, and still more London, shows this on an immense scale ; the population within the administrative limits of Paris is 2,725,000, that of the effective cluster is estimated at over 4,500,000, the little *département* of Seine having nearly five million. The historic City of London has a very small resident population, the London County Council has about 4,500,000 under its care, the effective cluster reaches nearly twice this total.

More or less engulfed villages and even towns are thus a marked feature of our large cities and the old centre of the engulfed unit may often be traced through survival, perhaps of a fragment of an old central common or green or square, sometimes with an old parish church or inn quite near. Nineteenth-century churches often show little regard for the old centre so far as their siting is concerned.

The heavy price of liberty without vigilance has been paid by many of our cities in their relations with railways. The fairly large city usually has two, three or more main passenger stations inadequately linked, making traffic in the streets heavier than it need be ; it also has immense goods stations not always placed to the city's best advantage because they were made when any huddled housing near their work was thought good enough for families of wage-labourers, and streets and little yards were the children's only playgrounds and sunshine and fresh air were for the rich.

Reference has been made to the break in our social record which was made by the first industrial revolution. Masses of victims of the enclosure movements, managed with so little care for the poor, escaped into the hurriedly growing cities, a crowd rather than a community. In that crowd the social tendencies began to work especially in and through the noncomformist, largely methodist, chapels, until these became too much associated with dress displays on Sundays and with the influence of repressive employers who were often, at the same time, leading men in church and chapel. An alternative outlet for the social tendencies, over and above the public-house, was the Friendly Society, the Oddfellows being most notable here. These friendly societies, and soon the trade-unions, helped to train the wage-earners for their citizenship responsibilities and are a characteristic British feature, illustrating British methods of proceeding by voluntary association, at least until the experimental phase of a movement is well advanced.

Reference has also been made to the lack of open spaces for the townsfolk in the days of the first industrial revolution. Whereas, in the matter of friendly societies and trades unions, the mass of the people could put forth leaders to act for them, efforts for open spaces were dependent on landowners or municipal authorities. Too many of those in power had the idea that food, work, sex and sleep were the only four human needs, and many a devout minister condemned play as taking time from work that might lead to success in this world and the next. John Wesley's sympathy for the poor too often took this unattractive form. But the social tendencies worked in spite of greed and repression ; and, from the middle of the nineteenth century, our cities began to have open spaces, spaces that are still woefully inadequate in the poor quarters, or among the docks and railyards. Those who know Denmark will realise the contrast between most of our dock areas on the one hand and the Lange Linie between the harbours at Copenhagen on the other.

The improvement of our cities has been much hampered in many cases by the small amount of publicly-owned land and the compensation payable for the immense increases in site-values in the hands of private owners on locations needed for public use. The preservation of more or less of a green belt around our cities from invasion by the notorious ribbons of houses has had only relatively small successes until the last year or two. There seems to have been too little preparation by experts, and of the public mind as well, for civic betterment, which is now pursuing its difficult advance under the Ministry of Town and Country Planning in a period of public impoverishment.

Our small towns are or have been in most cases market centres and shopping foci for a rural area, sometimes with a small factory or " works " of one or other trade, and, in districts geologically appropriate, with brick and tile making. Many of these little towns are, for various reasons, inclined to lose population. Somewhat larger towns in the regions of good crop-farming, have engineering works, making or keeping in order farming equipment and doing other work. As a consequence the implement-making or machine industry is developed in many towns on a moderate scale, though its major developments are concentrated at a few great centres. Some of the towns in this general class are also administrative centres for counties and have buildings connected with administration, insurance and other offices, as well as the head-location of a cross-country omnibus company. In some cases a county town is also a cathedral town, with a close for resident clergy, perhaps a theological college or a training college for teachers as well. A Museum, Art Gallery and Reference Library sometimes exist, too often in a stunted and stinted condition ; they greatly need a closer link with adolescent and adult education. Several of these old towns are characterised on the one hand by almshouses and by trusts for the benefit of the poor, and on the other by " poor quarters " of specially unfortunate types.

Towns in the next larger grade often have some special activity, usually an industry represented by more than one or two firms. Several of these are products of the first (i.e. the coal-and-steam) industrial revolution and show the results of hurry in expansion, of Puritan disregard for amenities and of neglect of the workers by the masters in the nineteenth and even sometimes in the twentieth century. Some town-ribbons in the South Welsh valleys illustrate these defects in a degree enhanced by the fact that so many of the past or present owners have drifted away from any personal proximity to the industry. The narrowness of the valleys in the South Wales coalfield accentuates the ribbon difficulty and makes the development of worthy civic centres more difficult (see plate 21, p. 222). But the towns of this type, largely dependent on one activity, be it coal as in the Rhondda, ordinary cotton spinning as at Oldham, cotton weaving at Blackburn, have also suffered severely from trade fluctuations which have in the past faced them with huge payments in times of widespread unemployment. Merthyr Tydfil, originally an iron-mining and working settlement, badly built, has been a special sufferer in this way. The reactions on civic life have often been most unfortunate, as problems have been set to local authorities which it was quite beyond their strength to solve. Recent and prospective arrangements to diminish contrasts in local rating should help such towns ; it is hoped that they may not undermine local initiative, which has been one of the healthiest features of British tradition.

Where a town has surmounted a crisis which was due to the definitive decline of an old leading industry, the results have often been most interesting from the human point of view. Such a decline has usually been spread over at least a few years during which some firms concerned have found various alternative activities. The nett result has been the development of a number of diverse industries, sometimes with an incidental linkage. Norwich, for example, lost its

PLATE XXV

The Times

MODERN FACTORIES along the Great West Road. The industrialisation of the approaches to London has been a marked feature of the years between the two World Wars

PLATE XXVI

Aerofilms, Ltd.

EDINBURGH, aerial view showing on the right the Castle and the old High Street. In the centre is the drained loch, now gardens. On the left is the planned extension set out at the end of the eighteenth century on either side of George Street. Princes Street faces the gardens. Calton Hill is seen beyond Princes Street

old woollen industry. It would be beyond the scope of this chapter to recount various attempts, some temporarily successful in a measure, to keep the workers employed in making other products. The preparation and especially the packing of mustard originally grown near the city led on to the preparation or making of other goods needing packing and, as is typical of an old Quaker and Unitarian centre, we find starch, chocolate and tobacco have added themselves, and boots and shoes as well. The development of mechanised farming and army work has helped engineering here. The city has thus a number of industries, and there is some hope that they may not all slump together, apart from national calamity. Bristol, larger in the twentieth century than ever before, illustrates in remarkable fashion the sprouting of new shoots of activity to replace older trunks that have lost their vegetative power. But Bristol belongs in many ways to a sub-metropolitan class of cities, though classifications are of only very limited value in such matters. These sub-metroplitan cities tend in any case to accumulate a number of industries whether or no they once depended more on one activity. Manchester, the merchanting city of the cotton industry, has special activities arising from the curious evolution of the industry with the processes of spinning, weaving, dyeing and printing often done in different towns at quite a distance from one another. Manchester does not do much in connection with these manufacturing processes, but its district supplies machinery, and Manchester has a vast engineering industry, part of which owes its location to the fact that the Ship Canal and Trafford Park, near the canal, were laid out for industry just when electrical engineering was going ahead. Chemical Industries, some supplying materials for dyeing cotton cloth, are another activity. Printing and paper industries are accessory to those previously mentioned, and clothing and others might be added. The imported-produce market, thanks to the Ship Canal, has had a wide range of business spreading over much of northern England. We must add to this for sub-metropolitan cities in general the possession of theatres in addition to cinemas, usually of a concert hall, often of a professional orchestra if the city has over half a million people, of a University and a Hospital system with a wide range of specialists, of Libraries and Art Collections of aesthetic value, and usually of a cathedral which in some cases is an adapted parish or collegiate church. Leeds is an interesting case in this connection ; its church is not a cathedral, the adjacent bishop's seat is at Ripon, but a long series of promotions shows that the Vicar of Leeds is considered an important person in the Church. A sub-metropolitan city often strives to maintain a " learned society ", perhaps, as at Manchester, more than one, if possible with publica-tion of a Journal of Proceedings and Transactions. The city may have retained the headship of some banking company or companies not completely absorbed into the " the big five " and it may be the headquarters of one or more insurance companies.

Both Bristol and Liverpool rank as sub-metropolitan, but they are also ports which must next be noticed in the same general way.

The old-time port tended to be a good distance up on an estuary partly for protection against attack, partly to increase the region to be supplied from it, largely to be near the lowest bridge which spanned the river or inlet and helped communication on both sides. This has made necessary in some cases the creation of an outport to cope with modern boats of deep draught—Bristol has Avonmouth, Cardiff has Barry, London has Tilbury, but Liverpool and Southampton have managed without this aid. Glasgow has grown into such a huge centre that it combines, in a sense, port and outport. Newcastle has Tynemouth, etc. At first growing for the purpose of coping with what may be called straight importation and exportation, passenger traffic and the building and repairing of ships, the port city has now to deal with the processing of goods imported,—sugar-refining, flour-milling, even ore-smelting in some cases. It has also lent itself to, and en-couraged in its neighbourhood, manufactures based on goods imported. Hull in Elizabethan days imported whale oil and this greatly improved the quality of soap, and better soap led to brighter raiment, starched white ruffs, portrait painting and much else (p. 208). Merseyside in modern times with Warrington and Port Sunlight specialising in soap and other cleansers and the whole estuary full of industry illustrates this point as does Glasgow. In both cases shipbuilding is a feature, and modern shipbuilding is a conglomeration of industries rather than a single one. The special importance of marine insurance has helped a great port like Liverpool to become the headquarters of insurance companies.

In the first years of the twentieth century rapid communication by steamship developed on an international scale ; and Southampton, in closer touch with France, and on the way to the Low Countries, Hamburg and Bremen, was developing as a passenger port at the expense of Liverpool. Now that really rapid travel is by air, and international links are so restricted, the same factors are not operating with as much force. The substitution of oil for coal together with the cessation of the need for a large group of stokers gave additional free space for cargo on ships, and the cargo-liner developed, especially in the period 1919-39 ; so, for a time at least, cargoes seemed to be tending to go to Southampton for export, but Liverpool and London and Glasgow retained their leadership in goods traffic ; the so-called tramp-steamer is after all a very great factor in trade, as Mr. Masefield's poem rightly emphasises.

Our two truly metropolitan cities are Edinburgh and London with their special collections of national monuments, and of buildings connected with national administration and royal ceremony. Each has been the subject of many books, and it would take too much space to enlarge on the fascinating topic of these strikingly contrasted cities as expressions of social life. Edinburgh is very notably characterised by its distinct, yet contiguous elements derived from different periods (plate XXVI, p. 275) ; the castle begun in the early Middle Ages, St. Giles' Church in what was the outer or strangers' quarter, a short distance from the castle and its little gathering of houses, Holyrood with its one-time house of the Augustinians, transformed later into a royal palace, the Canongate, naturally near the Holyrood, decayed into the worst of the slums of High Street and the Royal Mile, the fine streets and squares of the end of the eighteenth and the early nineteenth century (plate 22, p. 223) planned around George Street which, however, has yielded primacy to Princes Street fronting the gardens on the drained loch and, unfortunately, the scar that the railway has made. The story is set forth on the ground with many more details.

Of London's unique interest a little has already been said (p. 19) and it would not be profitable to expand here to any extent. Medieval, Renascence, Georgian, and Modern are hardly as strikingly separate in regions on the ground as they are in Edinburgh, and London suffered more from the worse aspects of the first industrial revolution, at which time London-river was functioning very actively as an entrepot dock-area. Its river, "liquid history" as John Burns lovingly said, is in utter need of redemption from decayed commercial efforts of past generations clinging still, because of inevitable inertia, to places they were allowed to disfigure as the river ceased to be a highway for

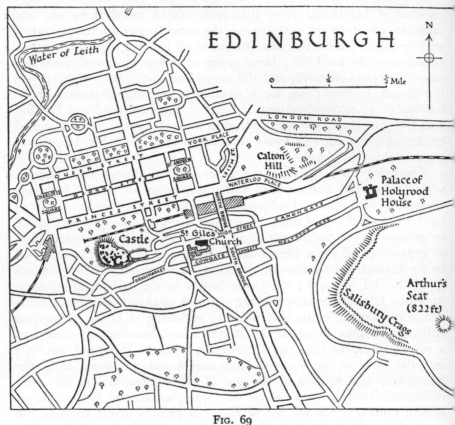

FIG. 69

Edinburgh. The Medieval city is mainly along the High Street and its extensions reaching from the castle to Holyrood. It began around the castle, with St. Giles' Church in the Strangers' quarter. In the late 18th and early 19th centuries a new town was added, with George Street as its centre. Princes Street later became more important

Londoners. A great park in, shall we say, Limehouse, a riverside avenue with appropriate public buildings (that shall not be all black and dead in the evenings) continuing at least from County Hall, Westminster, to Southwark Cathedral, these and other betterment plans are not mere aesthetic fancies ; they are serious needs for the public expression of social values to accompany family housing on a less penurious scale. Yet there is no city that tells the story of the long

struggle for betterment of social life with such continuity of record
in streets and buildings and activities as does London. Even its
untidy patches need study before treatment, and treatment on the
basis of function rather than of façade. Its better growth has been
along the gravel terraces of the Thames, especially the Middle or
Taplow Terrace, with consequent emphasis on east and west roads
(see plate XXV, p. 274). Extension on to the London clay areas
north of Euston Road gave cheap sites for railway use, but often bad
drainage for houses. A London Trust to which gifts, especially of
decayed riverside sites, could be handed for redemption and social
betterment, could be of great value if the trustees could be on guard
against the mere ostentation which so harmfully affected Berlin and
through it the life and thought of the German people.

The idea of Precincts has been much discussed in connection with
Town Planning and could be applied in ways that would encourage
the sense of community on the smaller scale within a great city. But
here again, care and balance of ideas are very important. It would
be easy to distort the valuable idea of Precincts in such a way as to
lead to the creation of different kinds of professional and other groups
encouraged to live and think apart from the wider community ; segre-
gation of occupational groups can be a serious danger to social
solidarity.

REFERENCES : see end of chapter 15, p. 313.

CHAPTER 14

CHURCH AND CASTLE

A BRIEF REVIEW

I N THE realm of building of church and castle we may be described
as islands off the coast of France, though we also owe some architectural debt, especially in houses, to the Low Countries.

Many early buildings were in wood, but a few in stone, sometimes
with a roof of thatch. With little skill available, doorways and windows
must be small lest they weaken the walls. No bishopric survived the
sub-Roman period in Britain, and the early English were essentially
rural ; so Britain and France contrast strongly, as the latter has
towns which have had bishops since Roman times, however much
the cathedrals may have been rebuilt.

It is abundantly proved that the Norman Conquest was followed
by tremendous building activity, one aspect of the general process
of organisation of church and state which that conquest so greatly
encouraged amongst us, but which had been begun, in some ways,
under Dunstan in the tenth century (p. 160).

In Normandy the Norsemen married native girls, and their
children were soon overawed by the supernatural terrors in the
armoury of the church. Time after time a Norman lord on a sick-bed
would give or promise things to the church to atone for his misdeeds,
and sometimes the promise was redeemed. The Normans in fact
became great church builders, and claimed support from the church,
William of Normandy for example gaining the Pope's blessing for his
attack on England.

Monasteries of the Order of St. Benedict had spread into the west
from the seventh century, and a number had been established in
Britain before the tenth century. The revival of towns and commerce

on the continent, after that century, when the Norsemen had become co-operative instead of destructive, led to discussion of ecclesiastical doctrines and practices and to reform movements. The Benedictine Abbeys of Cluny and Citeaux in Burgundy started successive reforms of the Order and founded new establishments, the Cluniacs reaching Britain a few years after 1066, the Cistercians (founded in 1092) early in the twelfth century. In East Anglia the Cluniacs had seven houses, the Benedictines thirty-three, including most of the very important ones. The Norman conquerors, mostly still illiterate, needed the help of churchmen in organising the country under their control; churchmen and soldiers thus formed an uneasy partnership, which made the institution of bishoprics as well as of administrative units go ahead rapidly from 1070 onwards.

The Benedictine abbeys had been for the most part in or just outside what came to be towns in the tenth and eleventh centuries, or, in a few cases, even earlier. As there were in early English days no old-established cities with bishops, it came to be a peculiarity of Britain that monastic churches situated in closes in several cases became at the same time bishops' seats. Canterbury, Rochester, Winchester, Worcester and Lindisfarne are early pre-Conquest examples here, while Norwich and Ely abbeys acquired bishops soon after the conquest. The Benedictine Abbey of Canterbury became the metropolitan church of all England. Peterborough, Gloucester and Chester had Benedictine churches which became cathedrals after they had ceased to be abbeys under Henry VIII. St. Albans abbey church, surviving into modern times, became a cathedral in 1878. The churches of the Cluniac reformers were often in rural places, and so did not become bishop's churches; and the same is true in greater degree of the Cistercian churches, so well known in the valleys of Wales and of the north of England, where they gave a great impetus to sheep rearing and the wool trade.

During the reform movement after 1050 A.D. the popes urged the group of clergy belonging to a bishop's or other large church (other than an abbey) to adopt some rule. They were called Canons regular, but were not to be monks; they were rather to serve churches. They gradually adopted rules found in a letter written by St. Augustine of Hippo to a nunnery, and so were known as Augustinian Canons (Black Canons). The clergy of St. Paul's adopted the rule and so did those of Chichester, but the cathedrals affected were mainly those farther away from Canterbury—Exeter, Wells, Salisbury, Hereford, the Welsh cathedrals, Lichfield, Lincoln, York, Carlisle, Man and St. Andrews are the list for the early Middle Ages.

The Welsh dioceses are often ascribed to a very early period, 500-560 A.D., and the diocese entitled Sodor and Man has claimed a foundation in 447 A.D. These dates refer to a period before St. Augustine's mission to Canterbury, and it is a matter of some doubt whether terms such as bishop and diocese are really applicable to the organisation of the

FIG. 70

Saxon Church, Bradford-on-Avon, Wiltshire

Celtic Church. There is every reason to accept St. David's, Bangor, St. Asaph, Llandaff, and St. German's in the Isle of Man as quite early ecclesiastical centres, and they certainly came under the influence of the reform of the eleventh and twelfth centuries. Man diocese lost its relation to the Hebrides (Sudreys, Sodor) in the fifteenth century.

Among the eleventh century reforms was the moving of bishops' sees to towns from villages, which had been appropriate in Anglo-Saxon times when towns were so few and small. The see of Crediton (founded 909) was moved to Exeter in 1049. This tendency became a definite rule about 1075. The sees of Dunwich (631) and Elmham (673) were amalgamated at Elmham in 870 and moved to Thetford in 1078

PLATE XXVII

John Markham

JOHN WESLEY'S CHAPEL, City Road, London. A typical eighteenth century design

PLATE XXVIII

PART OF THE BAYEUX TAPESTRY representing a Motte and Bailey Castle at Dinan

then to Norwich in 1094. In 1075 Chichester replaced Selsey (709). In 1074 what had been the see of Dorchester-on-Thames was moved to Lincoln. The importance of Lincoln, Norwich and Exeter as ports at that time should be noticed. With the growth of intercourse in the eleventh century Britain was becoming a producer of wool for export to Flanders. The shift of the ancient see of Lindisfarne to Chester-le-Street in 883 and on to Durham in 995 was a result of the devastation of the sacred isle, and, in the last stage, of a desire for a defensible site, in which respect Durham is almost unique. The bishopric of Wells was for a time transferred to Bath but eventually became that of Bath and Wells.

Among early dioceses Winchester, Lichfield, and Dorchester-on-Thames are of interest in another way. Winchester in early days was almost metropolitan as a focus behind alternative landings in Southampton Water and the east side of the Solent. It took charge of south England between the Weald and Salisbury Plain. Its bishopric (662) gave birth to that of Selsey (709), later Chichester, on the east, and to that of Sherborne (705) on the west. Sherborne was moved to Old Sarum in connection with the general urbanisation of bishoprics in 1075, and, when Old Sarum was deserted in favour of Salisbury, the see was naturally moved too (1228). This redevelopment of the ceremonial importance of Salisbury Plain (p. 51) should be specially noted. Lichfield, near the gap by which the Watling Street goes into the Cheshire-Shropshire lowlands, was an early see (669) for the "land beyond", (see also p. 15), and Worcester (679) (plate 25, p. 286) and Hereford (678) were almost immediately made separate ; but Lichfield diocese long reached north to the Ribble and west at least to the Dee. Dorchester-on-Thames, another early see (634 and 679), is near the western end of the Goring Gap of the Thames between the Chiltern Hills and the Berkshire downs, so it is at an important entry from the south-east into the England of the Jurassic Rocks forming a belt from the Humber to beyond the Cotswolds. This belt was, more or less, the diocese. After various temporary sub-divisions the centre of the diocese was moved to Lincoln as above stated.

Under Henry VIII in 1541-42 some additional changes were made. The church which had been a Benedictine Abbey became the cathedral of the new bishopric of Peterborough. At Oxford the former house of St. Mary Osney was made the cathedral of a new diocese of Oxford but Osney was destroyed and the college chapel of the new College of Christchurch became the cathedral. It had been the chapel of the nunnery of St. Frideswide's in Saxon times and had later passed under the control of Austin Canons. The previously Benedictine Abbeys of Chester and Gloucester became seats of new Bishops and the church of the Austin canons at Bristol became a cathedral, but the see was suppressed and then revived in 1897. Westminster also had a bishop for a very short time, but soon regained its unique status.

Nineteenth-century changes in distribution of population and the growth of historic interest in church matters have led to the creation of a number of new sees, using sometimes an old abbey, such as St. Albans, sometimes what was in the Middle Ages a collegiate church of canons, such as Manchester, often a large parish church such as S. Nicholas, Newcastle, and sometimes building a new cathedral as has been done at Liverpool, Guildford and Truro. These modern changes are envisaged by some as a step towards a larger increase in numbers of sees, making a bishop less a peer of parliament and more a head of his clergy as he is in many countries of Europe.

The ancient Scottish bishoprics began with St. Andrews, which came under Austin Canons. It was supplemented by other dioceses created by the sons of Queen Margaret, who, under her influence, sought to make Scotland a feudal state on the lines adopted by the Normans in England. By about the middle of the twelfth century Scotland was covered with bishoprics and the archiepiscopal sees came to be at St. Andrews for the east coast and Glasgow for the west coast, an indication of the importance of coastwise communications in a mountainous land.

It has been characteristic in many cathedrals of Britain that their Austin Canons imitated the abbey-cathedrals in enclosing their grounds, so that the situation of a cathedral on the market place, as it is in many places on the continent, is rare in Britain. Amongst us the old cathedral was typically in a Close, which might have an impressive gateway, generally of late medieval date. The abbey-cathedrals once had the full equipment of monastic buildings but most of these latter were destroyed in the sixteenth and seventeenth centuries. At first, it seems, the clergy had no special chamber for the business of the church, but by the middle of the fourteenth century both the abbey-cathedrals and the canons' cathedrals had chapter houses, which usually were octagonal with a central pillar. Southwell's builder dared to omit the pillar, as did the architect at York, but the latter was dealing with a wooden roof. At Southwell the chapter house is uniquely decorated with beautifully delicate stone-carving and the architect ventured to build without a central pillar. The canons' cathedrals, and often their churches, usually had a college in which priests lived. That of the once collegiate church at Manchester became Chetham's hospital (charity school) and lending library in the seventeenth century, and thus has been preserved; it retains these functions now. The church is now the Cathedral. A collegiate church was under a college of priests who served a number of outlying churches; it was a scheme aiming at the maintenance of better standards than would have been probable had each remote rural church had a priest in full residence and consequently very isolated.

The ideas of church building brought by the Normans to England before, and especially after, 1066 were partly from Lombardy (Lanfranc was a Lombard), and partly from adaptations worked out in France. One basic idea was the semi-circular arch, but for a time the Norman builders could not trust themselves to make a large door or window lest a wall should be weakened. Large windows, moreover, were not appropriate in Italy, where they would be sun-traps making the church too hot in the warm months. Doors and sometimes windows were made to look larger by building an arch and pillars with several orders or lines of stones, each projecting beyond the one beneath. These recessed doorways are among the most beautiful remains we have of the Norman or Romanesque style. The great doorway in the castle at Durham is often mentioned as a special triumph. With longer experience, doorways and windows were made larger; and Tewkesbury Abbey is one of the gems of this style, which is also illustrated in most successful fashion by the chapter house of what has become Bristol Cathedral.

One of the earliest and best known Norman buildings in Britain is St. John's Chapel in the Tower of London, (about 1075); a later one is the church of St. Bartholomew the Great, Smithfield, London, the church that belonged to the historic hospital founded by Rahere, the minstrel of King Henry I of England. Whereas St. John's at its east end has the distinct and separate terminations of nave and aisles such as one finds in many old churches in Lombardy, St. Bartholomew's interior illustrates a different principle. This principle, first worked out in France, was the provision of aisles and of an ambulatory joining the aisles by going around behind the sanctuary ; it was valuable for supporting the higher main body, or nave and chancel, of the church. This increase of height, and the ambulatory, are wonderfully exemplified in the late twelfth century work of William of Sens, and his pupil and successor William the Englishman, at Canterbury Cathedral.

Sometimes unskilled workmen failed to make the two halves of an arch meet accurately or to ensure that the arch was strong enough to stand the weight above it. A part of St. Albans Abbey (now cathedral) collapsed in 1323. Another difficulty was the internal roofing, which was at first usually of oak carved and sometimes coloured for decoration. But wood was liable to burn or to become diseased, and experiments were made with stone arches crossing one another diagonally and having the interspaces filled. This stone vaulting added enormously to the weight the pillars had to support and tended to thrust them outwards. Some of this thrust could be countered by external buttresses on a level with the pillars. But the architects of northern France in the second half of the twelfth century realised that, if an arch were pointed instead of round, each half would, as it were, lean against the other half, and so thrusts would partly neutralise one another. This was one factor of the evolution of the style called in modern times Gothic (in French usually *ogival*) that prevailed increasingly after about 1175. The work of William of Sens at Canterbury, just mentioned, was an early example in Britain. The idea was applied in the reconstruction of many churches, especially as reconstruction was being carried out far and wide in the late twelfth century. The pointed arch had been used for several centuries in Muslim countries, but it had not been clearly related to the idea of utilising thrust and counterthrust in supporting a heavy stone vault.

In the eleventh century Lanfranc had tried to enforce celibacy of the secular clergy, with only moderate success ; but the reformed monastic orders and their enthusiasm made the idea spread. Henceforth, therefore, more than ever, the clergy, and especially the lower ranks, must be continuously recruited from the people. Popular traditions thus seeped into the church, which met the situation by increased emphasis on the cult of the Virgin Mary, to replace those of the immemorial Mother Goddess lingering among the populace. This cult aroused vast enthusiasm, and in France and Britain there was an outburst of dedications, sometimes replacing older ones, to " Notre Dame " or St. Mary the Virgin, while many cathedrals and

PLATE 25

John Markham

WORCESTER CATHEDRAL, mainly twelfth and thirteenth century, on the
River Severn. September

PLATE 26

The 6-6---- British Cistercian Abbey; ruin twelfth century with a fifteenth-century tower:

other large churches had a Lady Chapel added at the east end, save sometimes when the church as a whole is dedicated to the Virgin. The Lady Chapel could be used as a support for a higher choir and sanctuary ; and it was becoming understood that the main thrusts could be concentrated on the ribs of the arches and countered by buttresses outside. It was thus increasingly possible to have larger windows and so to reduce the heavy stonework. This was an advantage in our western climate for another reason. It was mentioned above that in Lombardy large glazed windows would make the church uncomfortably hot in the warm months. It is quite otherwise with us in the north-west. Warmth is welcome in a great stone building, and light is valuable, especially as the use of stained glass prized for beauty and for its value in telling a story to the illiterate, inevitably limited the intake of light. In some parts of Italy the light from small windows is reflected from mosaic covering the walls and, again, telling a story. It is characteristic that, in France, Chartres, with its cathedral which is the greatest of all churches dedicated to the Virgin, became one of the chief centres for making stained glass ; and a little of the work of Chartres glaziers came right to York.

In Britain the nave was rarely made as high as in France, and a long narrow window pointed at the top, the lancet, came to be widely used. The five great lancets side by side in the north transept of York Minster are among the finest of their kind. The east end of Durham Cathedral is of this period (thirteenth century) and offers a striking contrast to the nave, which is often considered to be one of the finest Norman (Romanesque) constructions surviving. Fountains Abbey in its ruined state still shows that it must have been a triumph of Romanesque architecture (plate 26, p. 287). The east end of the Abbey church was a long rectangle with nine early Gothic windows iike that at Durham. Each of these had an altar against the long east wall. The British churches with pointed arches and lancet windows and a number of other contemporary features are described as being in " Early English Style " ; this was a part of the revival of British life after the Norman-French dominion. Salisbury Cathedral (1220-58) is the great example here. It has pillars of Purbeck marble with alternate shafts polished and unpolished. Its spire's unique beauty has inspired our artists.

In the late twelfth century one also finds the idea of a Round Church, copying the Church of the Holy Sepulchre at Jerusalem. The

U

typical orientation of a Christian Church is towards the east, no doubt a heritage from long pre-Christian times as many a prehistoric monument suggests. The ecclesiastical explanation, for the purpose of superseding the old myth, was that the church, in the West, pointed towards the Holy Sepulchre, an orientation naturally replaced at the Sepulchre itself by the round form with the Sepulchre at the centre. The beautiful " Round " at the west end of the Temple Church in London, heavily damaged by bombs in the war of 1939-45, the castle-chapel at Ludlow and the west part of the Churches of the Holy Sepulchre at Cambridge and Northampton are important British examples. The Northampton church may be a late eleventh-century building. It is interesting that there are several round churches in Denmark, including the remote isle of Bornholm, then, like Britain, a country on the fringe of European civilisation. Whereas the Benedictines had for the most part fixed themselves in or just outside already existing towns, Cluniac reformers were mainly rural, and the Cistercians (1092 onwards) often went out into the wilds and their abbeys in the valleys of Wales and of the North of England are most notable. Developing the Benedictine tradition of useful economic activity, the Cistercians in Britain became sheep masters, and they appear to have greatly improved sheep rearing and wool production. Their early regulations enforced simplicity and no towers or spires were to be built ; but in later centuries a great tower was added at Fountains Abbey. As the twelfth century was the period of Cistercian spiritual enthusiasm, most of their buildings are in the Romanesque or quite early English styles. The tower at Fountains and some other late efforts in various abbeys are less the products of pure enthusiasm than the effects of a desire for display of power and wealth.

As builders learned to direct the stresses and counter-stresses of their vaults they were able to make larger and larger windows. Sometimes two small lancets would be placed side by side under a pointed arch common to both, and the space above the lancets and beneath the point was an additional light, the stonework being arranged as geometric tracery. From this early development they went on and the geometric tracery became more elaborate. This stage of evolution is called the Decorated or Geometric Gothic ; the classic British examples are the Angel Choir at Lincoln Cathedral built in the second half of the thirteenth century and the nave of York Minster (1291-1355). Designs made with a pair of compasses are apt to lack vitality, however orderly they may be, and this affected the development of the style. It is noteworthy that this development occurred at a time when organisation was being emphasised, when Edward I of England was ordering the holding of pleas to discover the warrants for local custom, the *placita de quo warranto*, and when assize rolls and records of taxation were being compiled; while at the same time the western church was claiming extended powers and organising persecution of heretics.

In France, builders emancipated themselves from the geometric style and began to make flowing tracery, often called *flamboyant* from the frequent use of the shape of a candle flame; but examples of this are rare in Britain, though the famous west window (1335-40) of York Minster is well known. It cannot quite be called flamboyant, but it has gone beyond typical geometric style. The flamboyant style lent itself to much elaboration, sometimes delicate enough, but often aberrant when worked out by tasteless seekers after originality.

Fig. 71

Romanesque (Norman) vaulting with semicircular arches (12th century)

In Britain development proceeded on other lines with large structural accompaniments. Here the emphasis was on increased, especially broadened, window space to get all the light and sun-warmth possible, and to give large opportunities for stained glass. In the west, probably at Gloucester Abbey (later becoming the cathedral) about 1336, there began experiments in broader windows with a more obtuse angle at the top, support being increased by making the tracery of the top of the window mainly vertical, with horizontal or oblique cross-bars. This Perpendicular Gothic, as it is called, maintained its vogue, as did the Flamboyant in France, until the sixteenth century.

In neither country did the new ideas develop very quickly; the Hundred Years' War with its devastation in France and exhaustion

FIG. 72

Early English (Early Gothic) vaulting
with pointed arches (late 12th and early
13th centuries)

in Britain was one hindrance. Another, perhaps greater, one was the Black Death with its immense reduction of population. And both factors led to social changes and discontents from which both countries began to emerge in the latter half of the fifteenth century. It is characteristic that builders then went on in the style begun in the fourteenth century. There was no great new religious enthusiasm such as the twelfth century had seen.

In Britain Edward IV began to redevelop organisation, and the effort was expanded under Henry VII. By this time the old feudal nobility had become largely submerged, partly through the Wars of the Roses, partly by economic change. They were attached to a system of exchange of goods and services; a money and wages economy had little place for them.

The Black Death had for a time given the labourer an enhanced value increasingly represented in money instead of in local rights or privileges. Towards the middle of the fourteenth century, also, Flemish weavers in East Anglia were building up the manufacture of woollen cloths and we find that such Norfolk names as Worstead (worsted) and Suffolk names such as Kersey and Lindsey (not Lindsey in Lincolnshire) became attached to types of woollen goods. The Cotswolds and Somerset also took up the woollen industry and it began in those Yorkshire valleys which have water from the Millstone Grit. As

PLATE XXIX

CAERNARVON CASTLE and its dependent "Bastide" Town planned under Edward I. Note the parallel streets within the wall

PLATE XXX

F. Frith and Co. Ltd.

STOKESAY CASTLE, Shropshire. A moated manor, partly thirteenth-century

Britain recovered from the French Wars, the Black Death and its long drawn-out consequences, as well as the Wars of the Roses, this new activity became dominant and was increasing the wealth of the country, and at the same time bringing forward a new aristocracy of industrial

FIG. 73

More elaborate Gothic vaulting with incipient perpendicular tracery in the window (early 14th century)

wealth, becoming landed property owners and appropriating the monastic land, to take the place of the feudal nobility. It was to lead to widespread enclosure of hitherto open fields in the sixteenth century so that More said the sheep were eating the men out of England. In the latter half of the fifteenth century, however, organisation and increase of wealth were the key-notes, and the medieval church was still in spiritual dominance, so the ideas that had been current before the Black Death still had power.

In many parts of Britain the feudal aristocracy had helped church building, often as a death-bed means of escaping punishment in an after-life. In East Anglia, where there was to some extent a different tradition (see p. 138), and village and manor did not correspond so closely, and manors tended to be small, more churches were built by the efforts and gifts of non-noble benefactors. This tendency found large-scale expression when wool trade profits grew, and the churches of East Anglia, the Cotswolds and Somerset, as well as those of other wool areas, bear abundant evidence of the activities carried on in the fifteenth century. Lavenham, Suffolk, had its chancel built in the fourteenth but its nave and the great flint tower in the later fifteenth and early sixteenth centuries (plate 28, p. 303). Walpole St. Peter and Terrington St. Clement are special Norfolk examples of the style on a large scale. Many a church had its roof raised and vaulted in stone and its windows remodelled. Chipping Campden and other

FIG. 74

Late Gothic vaulting (fan vaulting) (14th, 15th and early 16th centuries)

Cotswold centres show parallel changes, and so does many a village and town in Somerset, Berkshire and elsewhere. In Yorkshire, York itself was so under the influence of regulations by its medieval guilds that the new industry fixed itself in outside localities, and Leeds and Bradford and other towns began to grow ; they have town-churches of this time.

Often the wall between one window and the next was reduced to pillar-width and the ribs of the pillar, with sufficient skill, might be made to fan out into the vault and thus to collect the stresses. An early and splendid ribbed vault was made in the fourteenth century at Exeter Cathedral ; and the cloister of Gloucester is another famous instance from the end of the fourteenth century. But it was in the late fifteenth century that the idea of large windows and fan vaulting became really widespread. Its final development is illustrated in three famous chapels—St. George's Chapel at Windsor, King's College Chapel at Cambridge and Henry VII's chapel at Westminster Abbey. The masonry in these buildings is reduced to a frame for the glass, yet it supports the roof effectively. It is an interesting fact that at Christchurch, Oxford, in 1640, the ribs of a column were made to fan out in all directions on the vault roofing the staircase up to the Hall, a highly successful effort in a style that otherwise had been dead for years.

The spoliation of the monasteries brought an era of church destruction rather than building. St. Edmundsbury's great Benedictine Abbey in its pride had helped to build churches for the townsfolk, so that they might not claim a share in the ceremonies of the monastic church. The result was that the abbey was considered superfluous and was destroyed, whereas Gloucester and Chester abbeys were retained and converted into cathedrals. In the abbey-cathedrals of the Middle Ages the bishop had to some extent taken the position of the abbot, but he could not devote his time to the monastery so a prior, acted for him. Under Henry VIII's schemes the plan of a Dean and Canons (no longer Austin Canons) was applied to the old abbey-cathedrals and also to the cathedrals of the newly created dioceses, as well as to what had been the Canons' Cathedrals.

In secular buildings of Tudor times in Britain one finds suggestions apparently derived from the Renascence architecture of Italy and France ; but there was no thorough study and utilisation of Renascence style until the days of Inigo Jones (first half of the seventeenth century), a royalist full of sympathy for the Stuart kings' inclinations towards France. In that country, Renascence architecture, as a revival of classical tradition, had burst upon the country with immense power in the sixteenth century ; and churches and secular buildings alike illustrate what a return to the classics meant. Thus, again, France and Britain took divergent ways, and the late flowering of Renascence architecture in Britain gave opportunities of adaptation and originality, most notable in the work of Sir Christopher Wren and Hawkesmoor. And of course the destruction wrought by the Great Fire of London gave them a unique opportunity. There was a reaction agains medieval Gothic, an increased appreciation of classical styles and of the proportions involved, and an absence of strong religious enthusiasms among leaders of society, whatever might be going on among dissenting groups. The fact that John Bunyan and *The Pilgrim's Progress* belong to this time makes it necessary to mark the distinction between those in high places and the small groups of dissenters. Apart from the new building of London churches (see plate 27, p. 302), most of all St. Paul's and some work at Westminster Abbey, not a great deal of new construction was attempted in churches until the eighteenth century, when the reaction against the Middle Ages led to the replacement of Banbury's old parish church by a classical building, as well as to strange doings at Llandaff Cathedral. As towns grew after 1689, staid and moderate-sized parish churches were built, with no indications of the extravagances and fancies enthusiasm engenders. On the other hand, from the Restoration of Charles II onwards, the " elegant " world had bought products of fine craftmanship and adorned its mansions with landscape and other pictures. There was thus a great development of the arts and crafts—plaster moulding, pargetting and other devices for walls and ceilings, and all manner of woodwork. The craftsmen in wood gained a great impetus from experiments in various hard-woods brought into use or imported from the intertropical lands to relieve the demand on oak, the sparse resource for building the navy. Chancel screens sometimes date from pre-Reformation days, sometimes from the seventeenth or early eighteenth centuries. Church pews of elaborate character for the squire and his connections are often of the early eighteenth century. These craft luxuries were paid for with profits from land used for root crops and enclosures which made possible larger and better herds, and also with gains beginning to accumulate from trade with the Levant, India and China, West Africa and America.

From 1689 onwards dissenting chapels of simple but sometimes very dignified character began to be built, that at Cross Street, Manchester (then Presbyterian, later non-subscribing Presbyterian which is also called Unitarian) was a very early one with considerable character. These chapels continued to be built during the eighteenth century and John Wesley's chapel in City Road, London, is a famous example (plate XXVII, p. 282). At the end of the eighteenth century and the beginning of the nineteenth some revival of preaching in the Anglican church led to the building of churches which were primarily auditoria, St. Chad's, Shrewsbury, being a remarkable experiment in that direction.

Then came the spread of the historic sense, in which effort Sir Walter Scott played a great part, and not in Britain only. The Tractarian Movement in the Church of England was allied to this, or, in the opinion of some, an outgrowth from it. With the new religious movement came the desire to build once more in the Gothic style, a desire that was to find a measure of frustration because mechanical production by contract had so largely replaced handicraft, and, among the *nouveaux riches* of industry, standards of taste were often debased by love of display. The Gothic revival might produce a success here and there, but Sir Gilbert Scott's concessions to his wealthy patrons and committees of subscribers, and his almost lifeless copies of the medieval " Sainte Chapelle " of Paris are too well known and too distressing for longer comment. One need but add that others were worse than he, and that the Gothic revival style in chapels is apt to be the worst of all. Sir Patrick Geddes' comment on one of these buildings was a quotation from the Book of Genesis, using the old words with altered meaning : " Truly, this is a dreadful place ; it is none other than the House of God ". Restorations and stained glass windows of the Gothic revival have impoverished or disfigured many a building. Among non-ecclesiastical buildings of this period the Law Courts in London and the Town Hall and University in Manchester are notable and regrettable.

Experiments in church-building after the fading of the Gothic Revival have been rather lacking in confidence thus far, a natural accompaniment of a phase of intellectual perplexity in face of inevitable adjustments of thought resulting from scientific inferences concerning mankind in the universe.

One may venture the statement that castles have a more limited interest than churches as a form of social expression. They have their features determined by the evolution of methods of warfare which, as we so tragically know, have their more direct repercussions on social life.

For times before the Norman conquest we know of artificial mounds made at strategic spots under the later Anglo-Saxon kings and of those kings' efforts to provide local defence, as well as of the attempts of local lords to defend themselves, sometimes against the royal power.

A wooden building for a garrison at the top of the mound is suggested in the Bayeux Tapestry and was no doubt general in early Norman times (plate XXVIII, p. 283). The mound was surrounded by a ditch which probably had a palisade on its outer side and was crossed by a removable plank bridge. At a somewhat lower level than the top of the mound was a flat-topped mound, called the bailey.

William the Conqueror and his followers had constructed these " Motte (Mound) and Bailey " fortresses for rapid defence, but they were replaced in many cases by stone constructions, often on points of vantage which might be scarped to give a steep approach, or might be the original earth-mound raised or enlarged (plate XVa, p. 218).

The motte (or mound) and bailey is the fundamental idea. The bailey in some cases, notably in that of Windsor Castle, may be called a Ward (plate XXXI, p. 298). It is usually surrounded by a stone wall outside of which is a moat (with outer palisade) crossed by what has become a drawbridge pulled up or let down by machinery in the gatehouse above the entrance into the bailey. There would also be a portcullis. Intruders crossing the bridge or climbing from the ditch would therefore have to pass under the gatehouse garrisoned by a guard which could throw or pour down unpleasant material. The bailey must have stables for animals as well as habitations and work-shops for armourers and other necessary craftsmen. The mound was generally separated from the bailey by a second moat with drawbridge and portcullis, gatehouse and wall once more ; so that a thus-far successful intruder must get past these obstacles and climb the mound to the stone keep, several storeys high, at the top. The entrance to the keep was often raised well above the mound and had to be approached by stone steps flanking the keep wall so that defenders might shoot arrows at intruders' sides. The entry to the keep would have a port-cullis to be raised and let down as desired, and the floor on which this entrance opened had guard rooms and was primarily military. Below it were the stores and prisons. Above it was the great hall of the castle which might be 40-100 feet by 30-40 feet. To provide a wooden ceiling for such a hall would have been difficult and stone arches were thrown across on a series of pillars so as to make shorter timbers do the work. Above the hall were dormitories for those considered too important to sleep on the floor of the hall itself. The top of the keep has a walk for a sentry. The larger castles might have inner and outer baileys, a chapel and other additions.

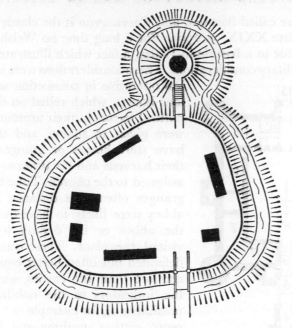

FIG. 75

Diagrammatic ground-plan of a motte and bailey of Norman times in Britain. The buildings shown in black on both motte and bailey are imaginary reconstructions. In many cases the building on the motte (mound) was made into the keep or donjon of the castle

The keeps were powerful defences so long as swords and spears, bows and arrows were the chief weapons. Their walls were very thick and had many little rooms in them. Later additions to the general plan were a barbican, outside the outer gatehouse, provided like the gatehouse with drawbridge and portcullis, and usually having a rampart-path leading to the gatehouse, for reinforcements or retreat. Many other devices were also added, so that the whole castle, rather than the keep, becomes the defence unit, and the prominence of the keep correspondingly declines. In many cases the castle, being at a strategic site such as the exit from a pass or a river crossing, gathered a town under its shadow, or it may have been built to overlook a town. The craftsmen and purveyors for the castle subsequently might often live in the town. Castle-towns deliberately founded by kings such as

Edward I, were called Bastides, and Caernarvon is the classic example for Britain (plate XXIX, p. 290). For a long time no Welshman was allowed to reside in a Bastide in Wales, a fact which illustrates the importance of military considerations. These considerations were somewhat

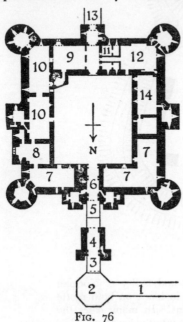

less operative in connection with religious houses, which relied on the supernatural terrors in their armoury. Lands were given to abbeys, and they must have store houses or granges to hold their harvests and the tithes so generally assigned to the church. Tithe barns and granges often at a distance from the abbey were likely to have quarters for the abbot or his deputy when they visited the place. These quarters, less defended but often better equipped for comfort than the castles, were one of the indicators to the nobility of the possibility of, for example, a "solar", a room getting sunshine and usable by the "inner circle", clergy or noble family as the case might be, overlooking but away from the hall with its thronging and noise. A solar might be a withdrawing room for the wife and daughters of the lord of the castle, but they seem to have been made specially in manor houses. These often had something like keep, bailey, gatehouse and moat, but fortification was a secondary consideration. Stokesay in south Salop is one of our best examples of a moated manor of the Middle Ages, its present gatehouse is Elizabethan (plate XXX, p. 291). Some others have lost

Fig. 76

Plan of late Medieval castle 1. Timbered causeway across the moat. 2. Fortified bridgehead. 3. Drawbridge. 4. Barbican. 5. Drawbridge. 6. Gatehouse. 7. Barracks for the garrison. 8. Chapel and priest's room. 9. Hall. 10. Lord's private rooms. 11. Butteries and pantries. 12. Kitchen. 13. Causeway and entrance for the Lord's use. 14. Possibly kitchen and dining hall for garrison

their more or less fortified portions but retain the moat.

It is a commonplace that artillery, in the sense of cannon, made the medieval castle of little use, and the growth of power of the central authority discouraged the giving of permission to local lords

PLATE XXXI

Aerofilms, Ltd.

WINDSOR CASTLE. An eighth-century mound and a thirteenth-century round tower altered in the fourteenth century and again by George IV. The Upper Ward has buildings remade under Charles II. The Lower Ward has St. George's Chapel (1473–1507)

PLATE XXXII

G. H. C. Matthews

MULES' STEPWAY, Exeter. Steps are broad for pack-mules taking loads from the old port up to the city

to fortify. More than this, however, the feudal lords had killed off or
ruined many of their kind in the Wars of the Roses, the ideas of comfort
and privacy spread from the abbey granges and moated manors, and
the rise to wealth and power of new families active in the woollen
industry or profiting by grants of monastic lands all combined to make
the castle obsolete. It was increasingly superseded by what may be
called the Mansion, some mention of which has been made in Chapters
11 and 12. Some castles continued to be used without great change into
the seventeenth century and, in certain cases, were blown up by the
Parliamentarians in the Civil War of Charles I's reign.

The addition of St. George's Chapel (p. 293) and other buildings
to the South Ward of Windsor Castle marks a great step in its transition
from being a fortress to becoming a palace ; and another much later
step is characteristically marked by the rebuilding of the quarters
in the North Ward under Charles II. Windsor Castle, however,
remains a castle, with a keep, in spite of its majestic development as a
palace (plate XXXI, p. 298). One notes the contrast between this
characteristically British feature and the French development of the
Louvre and Tuileries and Versailles as new expressions of the new
type of monarchy. It is paralleled by many other contrasts between
the two nations.

REFERENCES : see end of Chapter 15, p. 313.

COMMUNICATIONS AND TRANSPORT

EVIDENCE of transport for early times is culled especially from distributions of special products. Flints of toffee-like appearance known to come only from Pressigny (western France) are found some hundreds of miles north, east and south of their place of origin. Stone implements from Craig Lwyd, Penmaenmawr, North Wales, were taken to the Cotswolds, probably by a maritime route around the Welsh coasts. Callais[1] beads of unknown origin are found in megalithic monuments dated to the third millennium B.C. in South France, South Spain, Portugal (1100) and Morbihan, Brittany (about 800), and a few (27) have been collected from Prinkipo Island near the Bosporus. None has ever been found in Finistère, Brittany, nor in the British Isles, which have beads of Danish amber, no trace of which is known from the Morbihan. These callais and amber finds from great stone monuments illustrate maritime connections, the continuation of which into later times is indicated by segmented faience beads, of presumed Egyptian origin and dateable in their primary home about 1400-1350 B.C., which have been found in no fewer than 36 graves in Wiltshire. Sutton Veny, also in Wiltshire, has yielded a similar segmented bead, in tin. Odoorn (Netherlands) has yielded a necklace of similar segmented beads, 4 in faience and 25 in tin. Irish gold, water-sifted from Glendalough and perhaps other gravels, was made into crescent-shaped flat ornaments called lunulae at an early period in the Bronze Age. Outside Ireland they have been found at Llanllyfni in Caernarvonshire (1), Penzance (1), Lesnewth (1) and Harlyn Bay, Cornwall (2), in Morayshire (1), Lanarkshire (2) ; Manche (3), Vendée (2) and Côtes du Nord (1) in France, in north-west Spain (1),

---

[1] Callais is a material thought to be allied to turquoise ; its place of origin is unknown.

Luxembourg (1), Hanover (1), Fünen (1) and Zeeland (1) in Denmark. Irish gold torcs which were probably neck ornaments were also made and several have been found in Britain and France, and one has been collected just south of the Dardanelles at Hissarlik (the second city), dated about 2700-1900 B.C., the sixth city being Homer's Troy destroyed by the Greeks 1184 B.C. What has been claimed to be Irish gold has also been collected in Palestine. There is thus much evidence of long-distance transport during the second and even the third millennium B.C., vidence which corroborates that derived from the distribution of the prehistoric great stone monuments themselves (Chapter 3).

Coastwise boating seems to have been important, and to have been supplemented by transverse routes across peninsulas to avoid the dangers of tide-races and cross-currents of the vicinity of their terminal headlands. But the distribution of Pressigny flints and, in Britain, of Beaker pottery allow us to infer considerable movement over land, probably along zones of relatively open country, often above the clay lowlands which were largely covered with damp oakwood. The famous ridgeway or green road near the northern brow of the Berkshire Downs (plate Vb, p. 82) is, in a general sense, of immemorial antiquity, but its definite restriction to a track of fairly uniform breadth is a later adjustment. Here and there the clay lowland would have to be crossed, and a causey,[1] surfaced with brushwood and logs was some-times made, at any rate from the Bronze Age onwards.

Detailed mapping of finds of bronze tools and weapons has shown that river gravel-banks were zones of movement, and coracles (plate 4, p. 27) may have been made. Further, it is probable that river-flow was then more regular ; the vast woodlands would act as sponges holding the water which therefore trickled away gradually instead of, as so often now, racing down bare hillsides. But, on the other hand, river banks were not yet much controlled. We should therefore imagine people often wading along the shallower zones of a river's course.

In the later Bronze Age, when casting had become the chief metallurgical process, scrap bronze was collected by itinerant smiths for remelting; and communications thereby became more varied and more important. The woodland also became more useful for supplies of firewood for what were, in a broad sense, the predecessors of later travelling tinkers, who still, not very long ago, formed what was

---

[1] The name causey for a deliberately made trackway is an adaptation of an old form of the French word *chaussée*. Causey has curiously become modified into causeway.

almost a caste like that of the gipsies. One wonders whether there were already *Bacaudae* (p. 113) doing wicker-work, and shoe-men, using alder for shoe-soles, in the wetter woodlands; both occupations of small groups of wanderers have at any rate been quite important in later times.

But communications over long distances in the Bronze Age have further social importance. Copper and tin are rarely found together, save in Bohemia. Typically the bronze workers had to bring them together to make the famous alloy, standardised at about 90 per cent copper to 10 per cent tin. Tin was collected mainly by sorting special sands in water, some sands yielding black tin sand (cassiterite). Tin sands have occurred in various river-banks especially in regions of former mountains of the Permo-carboniferous (Variscan) folding, now usually reduced to plateaux. North-west Spain (Spanish Galicia) and the Vilaine river in south Brittany were sources of tin sand ; the Cornish vein-tin was not used until much later. Copper became known in the west from south Spain, from Alderley Edge and some Welsh sites, including Anglesey, and from Ireland. The transport of material, largely by boat, and the need of wood for the fires, made bronze-workers favour the vicinity of streams that had dry gravel banks and adjacent forest. Lest anyone should think that transport was available in prehistoric times only for small articles it is appropriate to remind the reader of what was said in an earlier chapter (p. 54) about the transport of large stones from Pembrokeshire to Stonehenge.

Unfortunately we as yet know nothing of the boats of the British region at any rate, in days before the Early Iron Age, but we can guess that some were of hide-covered wickerwork and may have had a mid-mast and a hide-sail like Irish curraghs of later times. One would wish to know whether some boats had wooden sides on a keel which was adapted from a dug-out, the boat made from a hollowed log ; the dug-out was a very early vehicle of water transport.

Unfortunately, again, we know nothing as yet concerning animal porterage or traction before the late Bronze Age in Britain ; and negative evidence is notoriously unsafe. For the moment we must think of human carriers[1] and of mules and the pulling of drags or slides, used in several rural areas until the eighteenth century A.D. Some places unsuited to wheeled traffic use them still.

[1] Dr. Huxley tells me of the stand erected at the west end of the south side of Piccadilly, London, in 1861, so that porters might rest their loads.

PLATE 27

John Markham

Bow Church, Cheapside, London. Though the church was ruined in the
war of 1939-45 the spire still stands as one of Wren's masterpieces which had
much influence in New England

PLATE 28

S. C. Porter

LAVENHAM CHURCH of St. Peter and St. Paul. A fine example of the churches of the fifteenth and sixteenth centuries built during the prosperity of the wool-weaving industry in East Anglia. March

In Chapter 4 some changes wrought side by side with the spread of iron were outlined. As already stated the development of both land and sea communications was very marked. A few points must be expanded here. Earthworks used in the early age of the use of metal such as the Trundle near Chichester, were adapted for use once more, and new earthworks were made in several places, usually on hill brows. Trackways, the Berkshire Ridgeway and others, were in use probably in the last two centuries B.C., when Iron Age B (see p. 93) had begun. The Berkshire Ridgeway near the brow of the Downs is obviously related to Uffington Camp (plate Vb, p. 82). Another ancient trackway goes along the steep slope below the brow ; some think it a later development, others believe it was used in dry weather, while the Ridgeway, being on the surface of the Chalk, would be useful and fairly dry at almost all times. From the Ridgeway one can go to the Icknield Way below the scarp face of the more wooded Chilterns and so by ancient tracks to Norfolk ; or one may follow the crest or the scarp slope of the North Downs (the track is called Harroway in North Hampshire) or those of the South Downs. The Pilgrims' Way along the south slope of the North Downs is another ancient trackway used later by the Canterbury pilgrims (plate 29, p. 306). One may also cross a fairly narrow lowland and get to the Cotswolds, Northampton Heights and Lincoln Edge (the track is called Pottergate just south of Lincoln and Middle Street just to the north). Across another lowland one gets to Mendip-side ; and still another crossing gives access to the Blackdown Hills on the way to the peninsula of south-west Britain. Salisbury Plain may therefore be considered a nodal, indeed a metropolitan, area for early Britain.

Reference has been made earlier to the story of the bringing of the " foreign stones " to Stonehenge, a story embedded in Geoffrey of Monmouth's romantic *Histories of the Kings of Britain*. The same author also has references to the making of trackways, and this part of his romance is approximately dated, so far as one can speak of dating when no figures are given and when one is dealing with Geoffrey, to some forty reigns before the entry of Julius Cæsar on the scene. It is further noteworthy that the trackways are said to have been laid down under Belinus, son of Dunwallo Molmutius, founder of a new dynasty of Cornish origin after a period of disorder. It is stated that there had been disputes about the limits of trackways, a point perhaps worth relating to what was said above about the early lack of definition of the

X

paths which were, in effect, broad zones. Whether the story is rightly interpreted by supposing that an effort at closer delimitation was made at this time must be left for future discoveries to settle.

The Geoffrey story may have a basis in folk tradition embodying the coming of the able and enterprising men of Iron Age B into Atlantic Britain, notably into the south-west, and spreading into the Midlands (Geoffrey's *Loegria*) ; the earthwork of Hunsbury in Northamptonshire is well known and the ridge of limestone (p. 1)— Cotswolds, Edgehill, Northampton Heights and Lincoln Edge—had already from earlier times served as a zone of movement. The men of Iron Age B came after a period of relative poverty and fragmentation varied by occasional links to Gaul (these also are mentioned by Geoffrey).

Probably the trackways, or improvements of older zones of transit, in Iron Age B, had as one purpose the movements of warrior groups, but one cannot think of the tracks as seriously comparable with the Roman roads built essentially for movement of organised armies between established centres of a deliberately created system of defence, offence, and rule. Roman roads in Britain have been discussed by specialists in so many ways and places that it would serve little purpose to give a non-specialist account here. A few points are of value for our general argument.

The trackways or transit-zones of pre-Roman times in southern England more or less radiated from Salisbury Plain mainly along, or near, hill brows. Entries from the sea in Cornwall, Devon, Dorset, and Hampshire played their part, as did Kentish entries, at times especially that of the Medway.

Under the Romans, Kent became predominantly important as an entry, and Portchester (West Sussex) was also very active ; Salisbury Plain on the other hand lost something of its older status. Once in Britain, having arrived by Kent and made it their primary base, the Roman armies were concerned to defend northern and western frontiers and to transport war material as well as to march soldiers towards what have become the Scottish and Welsh borders respectively. To do this from Kent the Thames must be crossed, and, for the northward journey especially, a Thames crossing should be as far east as possible. Whatever may be discovered in the future about a possible pre-Roman London there is no doubt whatever that Roman London became the chief city of the country, and it grew at the lowest crossing of the Thames which had an approach of fairly dry land on both banks. The road to the north (in due course to York and Hadrian's Wall) and that to the Welsh border (Uriconium and Chester, the Watling Street) were the two primary strategic creations, while the Fosse Way from Exeter via Bath and Cirencester to Lincoln cross-connected the two and offered a means of movement in defence of the more settled areas to the south-east of it, the region of villas, the larger-scale agricultural establishments discussed in Chapter 5. As has already been stated, it seems that the old, more or less metropolitan, area of Salisbury Plain was to a large extent left to the subjugated British people.

A Roman Road was distinguished from all previous trackways in western Europe and Britain firstly by being laid out in remarkably straight lines from point to point, and secondly by being built, and not merely adapted. The straightness has sometimes been a little exaggerated but is most noteworthy ; it may have originated from the method of sighting from point to point ; it often paid little attention to gradients. The construction methods naturally varied a good deal according to the importance of the road and the soil or rock over which it passed. A main road near Rome would have its margins first marked out by trenches going down to below the loose soil, which would then be removed from the belt between the trenches. Then flat stones, if available, would be set in two or three layers, and might be mortared or might have fine material stamped in between them; a layer of smaller stones with concrete or stamped material would then be laid, and in some cases covered with concrete, on which regular paving stones would be close-set. The whole scheme might make up a thickness of several feet. Naturally, in remote regions such as Britain, the full elaboration was rarely used, and the main filling material was stamped gravel, sometimes with cobbles at the surface ; the cross-section of the road curved down on either side of a crest, which was often more marked in the cases of roads of less elaborate construction; it was a device for drainage of the road. The road for wheeled traffic might be as wide as 14 feet with a pedestrian side-walk on each flank in the more elaborate cases. It seems that, on occasion, the practically-minded Romans used, and doubtless improved more or less, trackways already made ; it is thus not always easy to establish how far an old road is or is not Roman. Moreover the prestige of the Roman power has led to the giving of the Roman name to many things that had little or nothing to do with the imperial people. All this has made the " discovery " of Roman roads a happy hunting ground for the venturesome. Careful research on the subject has been greatly promoted in recent years by the work of Mr. Margary in Sussex.

The primarily military purpose of the Roman road was a main reason for the good surfacing and the curving (camber) of the surface to keep it drained. That purpose is also demonstrated indirectly by the fact that, while the road goes very directly from one station or town to another, villas (rural establishments), are not aligned to it and may in fact be some distance away.

When the Roman power was broken in Britain, and urban life declined to almost nothing, the Roman road was no longer a station-to-station affair ; there was little long-distance transport and there was no skill and little slave-labour for road-repair. But, even in our climate, rain and frost did not entirely destroy the work of the Roman civil engineers, and their roads are often identifiable to-day : indeed not a few have been rehabilitated in part since the motor car led to the road-revival of 1920 and onwards.

In sub-Roman days it is likely that the Roman roads were a haunt of marauders and that, later on, Danish armies found them very useful even in their poor condition after centuries of neglect. But it is nevertheless of interest that in sub-Roman times the Roman roads in Kent seem to have been used a good deal. Kent, we know, went on exchanging goods with the continent, and there certainly was movement to and fro across the Straits of Dover. In Kent, post-Roman villages are often on Roman roads, but this is rarely the case elsewhere ; the early English immigrants in general were not interested in these roads. London, at the Thames crossing of the Watling Street, may have continued, however reduced, following the Kent fashion, or may have been desolate for a time.

North of London the early English seem to have had little to do with the Roman roads ; they came to Britain by boat and rowed upstream to suitable sites for settlement. A system of roads from London to the Wall, to Uriconium, etc., meant little to them. The Fosse Way (Lincoln to Gloucester, etc.), was too far west for those who came up the Ouse to near Cambridge and apparently spread thence south-westwards.

From the fall of the Roman power in Britain until the eighteenth century of our era little was done for our roads. Bridges might be

PLATE 29

Robert Atkinson

PILGRIM'S WAY, an ancient trackway along the southern flank of the North Downs, used in the Middle Ages by pilgrims to the shrine of St. Thomas à Becket at Canterbury. November

PLATE 30

Eric Hosking

a. Cowsic Clapper-Bridge, Dartmoor. September

John Markham

b. Packhorse Bridge, Arenig, North Wales. September

Before the eighteenth century mules, asses and horses carried packed goods, and bridges were characteristically narrow. That at Cowsic is made of local large stone slabs, that at Arenig shows an arch

built over rivers, especially by monks interested in pilgrimages ; and monastic houses might keep a bridge more or less in repair. There are many legends, on a basis of fact, concerning a sacrifice of something to the evil spirits of the river before the bridge was brought into use, and this was sometimes transformed, under monastic guidance, into the building of a chapel on the bridge. At the " Devil's Bridge " in Cardiganshire we find the legend that the devil was to have the first living being that crossed the bridge, built by monks and called in Welsh Pont a'r fynach. An animal was driven across. This is a story of the same class as that of the offering up of Isaac by Abraham. Both indicate transition from human to animal sacrifice. Bridges drew trackways to themselves, and it is possible in some areas to get a rough notion of trackways before the eighteenth century by mapping the old bridges and then examining intervening country for what at least seem to be old trackways. Occasionally accessory evidence can be gleaned from a dedicated site or some local name.

While some groups in Iron Age B and the Romans in Britain had wheeled vehicles, it seems that there were only a few of these (p. 122) in the period 500-1500 A.D. People used asses, horses, mules and oxen, often pulling sleds or slypes (carts on two poles, the ends of which drag along the ground). This meant that no great width of track was needed, and that, failing effective surfacing, it was desirable to have gradients for drainage and to have the track along the hillside well above a valley bottom for the same reason. If a really steep climb had to be made, a stepway was sometimes built with steps broad enough for mules. Some paths by which people went to church, and especially those by which corpses were carried to the churchyard, had stone slabs. A stone-built step-way for mules leads from the old quay at Exeter up Stepcote hill (plate XXXII, p. 299). A long stone-slabbed path with many steps leads high up over the moors past Rhinog Fawr in Merionethshire and is characteristically called the Roman Steps, without any reasonable justification for any dating to Roman times at present (plate XVb, p. 218).

In our Middle Ages there were some wheeled vehicles of the nature of a long waggon with a cover of material such as canvas supported on hooks. The waggon had four wheels and was drawn by four or five horses in single file. It was probably used mainly for women and children ; men rode, and goods were carried by animals or pulled by them. The long waggon-like vehicle was called a char. In the fifteenth century a better, or at any rate lighter, vehicle was developed at Kotze in Hungary, from which place it appears that we get our word coach. It still had a covering of woven material and four rather clumsy wheels. It could often be pulled by two horses harnessed abreast. It must have been an adventure to go any long journey in a coach on the roads of that time.

The roads were supposed to be repaired under the direction of each local authority by the work of the inhabitants, who must each give or hire so many days' work, a system known in French as *corvée*. The *corvée* was still maintained for the roads in Sark in the Channel Islands quite recently ; and there it worked with reasonable efficiency. In the little island there were no boundaries between one authority and another.

The dissolution of the monasteries may have adversely affected the mending of bridges and such little work as might be done on the roads. At any rate there were many disputes about bridge-mending and so on in the seventeenth century, an indication that wheeled traffic had become more frequent. And, by the time of Charles II, there was a Company of Coach and Harness Makers. By this time glass had come into fairly widespread use for windows of houses, and it was adapted early in the seventeenth century for windows of coaches, or smaller vehicles called chariots, which could now be closed in by wood and glass, giving protection from weather and mud. Coaches for the public, called stage-coaches, were introduced before the Civil War of Charles I's reign, and large waggons had begun to carry goods about the country. Maps of counties were being printed in colour, another indication of more movement and wider interest among larger numbers of people. A picture by Hogarth in the early eighteenth century shows some passengers in a basket between the hind wheels of a stage-coach.

The use of glass made possible in the early eighteenth century the introduction of sedan-chairs, a small " chariot ", as it were, of wood and glass with shafts front and back. It seated one person, and was carried by two men, one in front and one behind.

Another experiment was the attempt to support the body of a smallish coach on leather bands, and, later, to insert springs as a substitute, both devices being aimed at reducing the jolting which must have been very trying on the rough roads of the time, even in the towns. One imagines that wheeled vehicles for passengers were largely an affair of the towns and perhaps a few of the better trackways in the country.

Mrs. A. L. Thomas in 1934 published a detailed study of the attempted improvements in communications in the eighteenth century, taking the Potteries District of Staffordshire as her field of work (published by the William Salt Archaeological Society). She drew attention to the importance of fords, gradually supplemented at the busier spots by bridges, built in some cases by public-spirited persons. Some of these were mere packhorse bridges (plate 30, p. 307) and were replaced here and there by others strong and wide enough to allow a loaded cart to go over. There were many disputes about bridge repairs after floods. From Ogilby's map of 1675, onwards, maps began to include roads, and carriers were becoming more important, while rates for carriage of goods by waggon or by packhorse were in some cases fixed by local Justices of the Peace.

The state of roads, and often of bridges, was so bad that, under Charles II, toll-gates for exaction of contributions towards repair were set up along the Great North Road under control of local Justices of the Peace. The system became more general from the early eighteenth century onwards and prominent men in a locality would be constituted into a board of trustees for what was called a Turnpike Road. Sometimes the trustees let out the right of taking tolls to the highest bidder, thus passing on the detailed administrative responsibility. It is not surprising, in view of the type of goods he wished to transport, that the famous potter Josiah Wedgwood was an enthusiast for turnpike roads from about the mid-eighteenth century. The proceeds of the turnpike tolls were intended to supplement the grants from the parishes, not to be a substitute for these ; the parish remained responsible, at least in theory. The parish was entirely responsible for roads which had no turnpike tolls. Roads and bridges increased markedly in number in the last quarter of the eighteenth century, but it seems that the quality of roads was still very poor, there being no scientific principles of construction or repair, and parish authorities being often very ignorant or indolent, while some mortgaged the tolls to get money for other purposes. In France enough was known about Roman roads to encourage efforts to use methods of the Roman engineers such as the stone foundation or the paved surfacing.

Bridge-building and design became an important activity from the end of the eighteenth century onwards. Numerous bridges across the

Thames were added to the historic London Bridge, which itself was replaced by a new structure, designed by Rennie and completed in 1831 by his son. His masterpiece, however, was Waterloo Bridge, which has had to give place to a massive twentieth-century one (plate 32a, p. 315). Other specially modern British bridges are the Clifton Suspension Bridge (plate 31, p. 314) and the Forth Bridge (plate 32b, p. 315).

For our British roads, still without hard surfaces in 1800, waggons with narrow wheels were deemed dangerous, as they made too deep a furrow ; great broad wheels, on the other hand, were thought to help to roll the surface flat and some might be 16 inches across the rim, a clumsy scheme.

The obvious difficulties of transport under these conditions were especially felt as the country was struggling to develop manufactures on a large scale ; one need but reflect on the risks involved in carrying cups and saucers on ponies or mules from Wedgwood's factories in the Potteries to Bridgnorth or Bewdley on the Severn to be put on barges, or from Leeds, where good pots were made, to Liverpool, where a sailor coming home might pay to have his name and that of his wife printed on a tea-pot or coffee-pot by transfer. Transport on barges was clearly safer than on mule-back. Thus men's attention was drawn to improvement of waterways.

Canals of small dimensions for irrigation had been dug in very ancient times, in Mesopotamia and Egypt at least, and the idea appears to have spread to prehistoric India and China. Some of these ancient canals were made navigable for small boats. As in so many other matters, the Romans copied, and their engineers developed, the schemes of older civilisations. In Britain they made the Foss Dyke (Lincoln to Trent) and Caer Dyke (Lincoln to Peterborough); but, like all ancient canals, these were restricted to the very slightest changes of level.

Here and there in Britain rivers had their banks strengthened to reduce flood damage, and, sometimes to confine the channel and so to deepen the stream ; but work of this kind progressed relatively little until the agrarian revolution of the eighteenth century liberated initiative, and industry began to look to water transport.

Britain lagged behind France in arrangements for water transport, as in most matters save the application of mechanical power in industry, the improvement of shipbuilding and the growth of at least a measure of respect for conscience.

Circumstances had driven the Dutch and the Venetians to take an interest in waterways, and it is not really known whether it was in Holland or in North Italy, in the fifteenth century, that the idea of a canal-lock was first thought out. It is known that Leonardo da Vinci built locks to join various canals at Milan, but the actual invention of the canal-lock is not claimed for his almost universal genius.

Whatever be the real story of canal development, there is no doubt that the French did much during their period of extraordinary activity in navigation, colonisation, organisation and so on, following the work of Henry IV and Sully in the early seventeenth century, and continuing until autocracy and ecclesiastical persecution dulled the vital spark. After one or two minor but important efforts they made the famous Canal du Midi from the Mediterranean to the Gironde. It rises to 620 feet above sea-level and has in all 119 locks. The depth of water was fixed at 6½ feet. This great effort was spread over many years and the canal was completed in 1681. At that time there was as yet little parallel effort in Britain, though river-bank work appears to have been increasing. In 1720 powers were obtained to make the river Weaver navigable up to Winsford in Cheshire. In 1759 the Duke of Bridgewater was given power to make his famous canal from the collieries at Worsley to Manchester, and the engineers Brindley and Smeaton were at this time pressing their proposition for a canal right across England from Liverpool to Hull. Brindley was the Duke of Bridgewater's engineer and a man of great energy, who is said to have remained illiterate and to have worked without calculations or measured drawings, even for the high aqueduct carrying the Bridgewater Canal over the Irwell at Barton. He built the canal from the Mersey to the Trent and planned many others, and from his time (d. 1772) onwards for half a century canal building was going forward enthusiastically. And, at the same time, rivers were banked, weirs were constructed to dam streams, and a lock was made at the side of the weir. This scheme of making rivers more navigable was applicable only on rather low gradients. When the river ran very steeply too many weirs and locks were needed, and dangers of flood damage were great.

It is of importance to notice that one of the engineers connected with these developments was William Smith, whose experience led him to appreciate successions of layers in the rocks and he thus became the father of stratigraphical geology.

While canal development was going on, engineers began to apply scientific principles to road construction in Britain, which in this matter, was far behind Napoleonic France. Telford, in Britain, became the apostle of the firm foundation, while Macadam pleaded for rolling in broken stone until a hard even surface was obtained. With these men, road construction began again to be scientific and the idea of turnpike roads seemed thenceforth for some years to promise well, in spite of stoppages to pay tolls and of many changes of control as one passed along a road from parish to parish.

The advent of the railway and later of the effective steamship gave a set-back to the development both of roads and of canals. Long-distance traffic almost disappeared off the roads, and many an old roadside inn went to sleep, as it were, pending the changes the twentieth century was to bring. The railways were a product of almost the bleakest age of individualist politics, and they paid little regard to the amenities of the towns they served : also there were built many superfluous competing lines, the cost of which, and of not a few un-necessary tunnels, weighted the capital accounts of some railway companies very heavily. The difficulties all this brought in the days of renewed competition after 1914-18 are too well known to need long description. But, for a time, the railways were triumphant and south London shows what they could do to disfigure a city.

The roads began to improve when steam-rollers came into use to roll broken stones into a continuous hard surface, and, once this was done, there was no desire to continue the heavy broad-wheeled type of waggon, especially as goods now went across country, for a time, mainly by rail. The light narrow wheel, steel-rimmed, allowed a horse to trot faster and the surface of the road was now hard enough to permit this, though heavy rain soon wrought havoc. " Sets ", rectangular blocks of granite or other specially hard rock, were used in many towns, and the blocks were laid in elaborate patterns to try to reduce slipping of the horses, but the surface of the block was only too apt to get smooth, almost polished, especially when the rainfall was heavy.

The canals, many bought by the railway companies, were allowed to go out of repair and many of them have long been disused and have become choked with weed. A canal needs to have its banks specially strengthened just above and below water level, so that the wash created by boats and barges in passing shall not injure them. Trouble from wash would naturally be greater if barges were propelled by steam engines than if they depended on the slow and patient horse. Now (1949) that railways and canals have become public property we may see a revival of use of some canals and an increased use of those which had not been entirely discarded.

Early in the twentieth century asphalt products came to be used for surfacing roads—asphalted wood-blocks and " tarmac ", from the name of Macadam, using crushed stone and tar poured hot on a prepared road surface. The advent of the rubber tyre for vehicles, in the later years of the last century, and of the internal combustion engine, has revived the roads and roadside hotels, and has told heavily against the railways, especially since large lorries with trailers have carried great loads about the country, and frequent motor-buses have revolutionised life in villages, even in remote rural areas. It is still rather too early to discuss profitably the changes that aviation will make in internal communications and transport in Britain. Air-travel is becoming increasingly common, for instance in the Scottish Highlands and Islands and on routes across the various channels around our island.

REFERENCES TO CHAPTERS 13, 14 and 15: British Association *Handbooks*, Darby (1936), Dickinson (1947), Geddes (1915), Gomme (1914), Grundy (1934, 1937, 1938), Hammond and Hammond (1919, 1925, 1930, 1934, 1937), Haverfield (1913), Jackman (1916), *Medieval Towns Series*, Pirenne (1925), Simpson (1939-44), Smith (1949), Stamp and Beaver (1941), Tait (1936), A. L. Thomas (1934), Thompson (1912), Tout (1920), Town and Country Planning *Reports*, Webb and Webb (1913), Wheeler (1927-35).

CHAPTER 16

POPULATION

CHAPTER 5 gave a brief outline of the growth of population in early Britain. Perhaps a few hundreds in the later part of the Old Stone Age had become a few thousands during the Mesolithic Age. The desire for sons to take part in defence and hunting no doubt played a great part in social life ; indeed one may say that the desire for large families continued until the late nineteenth century. When food-production and a more settled life were established in Britain somewhat more than 4,000 years ago (Chapter 3), the population evidently increased considerably, but there was still ample unoccupied space. We must think of immigrant seamen and warriors appropriating to themselves native girls. The exclusive duty of the men would be to fight, hunt, clear bush, fish, build huts, take part in ritual and help build the great stone monuments ; that of the women would be the bearing and rearing of children. Both would be occupied with cultivation, the women with handmade pottery, sewing, probably some leatherwork, spinning and weaving, the men with work in stone and wood and, increasingly, in metal, as well as with war. Infant mortality, probably somewhat less than in the Mesolithic Age, would still be high ; so probably women had to bear an average of six children each to keep the population from decreasing.

With the increase in the use of copper and bronze came more specialization. There seem to have been itinerant copper or bronze smiths, and, later on, some temporary centres of manufacture of metal implements, probably sited near supplies of wood suitable for fires. The utilisation of scrap bronze for remelting is a notable feature and implies the existence of itinerant collectors. All this is of some import-ance in a survey of population problems as it shows that early industry did not necessarily cause the creation of towns. As in parts of inter-

PLATE 31

Robert Atkinson

CLIFTON SUSPENSION BRIDGE over the Avon, below Bristol. Designed by
Sir Isambard K. Brunel and built 1832-64

PLATE 32

John Markham

a. WATERLOO BRIDGE, London. Designed by Sir Giles Gilbert Scott and built 1937-42 to replace Rennie's fine old bridge

John Markham

b. FORTH BRIDGE, near Edinburgh, over one mile long. Designed by Sir Benjamin Baker and built 1882-1889

tropical Africa recently, some craft groups seem to have been itinerants. As such they would be outside the little kinship-groups which lived in clusters for mutual aid in defence, but which no doubt co-operated with other groups on a larger scale for ceremonial purposes. Whether the early Bronze Age population exceeded 100,000 one cannot at present guess. That the total did increase later in the Bronze Age seems probable from the scattering of implements.

Whether bronze became scarce or not, the end of the Bronze Age seems to have been a period of poverty and disorder ; and as is discussed in Chapter 4, we have evidence of climatic change and growth of bog at the expense of forest. It is probable that the population declined for a while. But in the third and second centuries B.C. came new vigour (Chapter 4) especially with the warrior traders of Iron Age B. The old story of intermarriage with native girls was repeated, and both population and communications increased. Great fortresses, such as Maiden Castle near Dorchester (Dorset) (plate Va, p. 82), Maiden Castle at Eddisbury, Cheshire, Dinorben in North Wales, and Almondbury near Huddersfield, suggest possibilities of large settlements near them but we have practically no evidence. Sometimes a village or hamlet lies suspiciously near one of the old hill fortresses and may once have been the normal home of the warriors. And Professor Bowen and Mr. Emrys Jones think they also have in Wales traces of serf-settlements, i.e., settlements of the older, and conquered, inhabitants.

Nothing of the nature of a town can be traced before the Belgic (and perhaps some immediately pre-Belgic) peoples invaded the southeast in the last century B.C., probably before and after the incursion of Julius Cæsar. To these late pre-Roman invaders may be ascribed a first stage of the evolution of Colchester, as well as Wheathampstead which was to be replaced by Verulamium just before, and in, Roman times. Those who have sufficient faith in legend may feel that London was also begun. These late prehistoric invaders had ploughs with coulters and could no doubt grow more food (cereals) than their predecessors, and legend tells of the valour and skill of their rulers. A considerable increase in population at this time, in the south-east, may be postulated. But it was when Roman order and power opened up regular commercial relations with the continent on a larger scale that population must have increased rapidly, as it has done so markedly in China, Japan, Java, India, Egypt, etc., with the development of commerce and communications. In Chapter 5 an estimate of 600,000 has been given for Roman Britain, necessarily largely guesswork. Londinium seems to have had some 20,000 souls ; but we have seen that urbanisation did not succeed very well in Britain, and it is likely that, towards the end of Roman power, population decreased sharply, partly by emigration of some more Romanised elements to Gaul, as well as through disorder.

The early English, with their clearing of woodland and founding of new villages, seem to have inaugurated a fresh increase of population after a while ; and the Danish conquerors apparently had or developed ideas of organised communications and town life. London was already important again about 600 A.D., Canterbury, Rochester, Winchester, Selsey, and many other places were acquiring town rank in the seventh and eighth centuries, and Oxford and Cambridge also had their Anglo-Saxon phase. All indications go to show (Chapter 6) that there was development of the basis of social organisation from kinship to neighbourhood, a sure sign that groups were larger, though still very small in comparison with those of Elizabethan and later times. There is little doubt about the organising ability of the kings from Egbert to Edgar, but their work was hampered by trouble between English and Danes and Vikings. Growth of towns under shelter of fortresses may have occurred (Oxford is a likely instance) but commerce remained small, though wine-merchants from Rouen had an agency at the Dowgate (Dourgate=Watergate, from Celtic *Dwr* which means water) a little above London Bridge, near the future Steelyard. The last sentence must not be held to imply a belief in the existence of a London Bridge at any particular period before Norman times, save during the Roman rule. It is likely that a wooden bridge existed, at least from time to time. But we have the nursery rhyme " London Bridge is broken down " to remind us of what was wont to happen until, in the reign of John, the famous stone bridge with twenty arches was built ; it made London-river, the water below the bridge, the all-important port-area thenceforth. The twenty narrow arches made a difficulty for boats passing it and even for the flow of water and of the tides.

The Norman Conquest and the resulting increase of relations with Flanders (export of wool from English ports), Normandy and Aquitaine, together with the strong new organisation of government, and the development of Lincoln, Norwich, Chichester, Exeter and many another town, imply increase of population. Estimates of one million have been

made for early Norman times, probably with a rise to 1,500,000 and
more fairly soon, and a further increase, about 1150-1200, when
urbanisation was spreading. The increase seems to have continued
until the Black Death of the mid-fourteenth century (1348-9, 1361-2,
1368-9), which reduced rural population by probably 30-40 per cent
and apparently gave rise to the great agitations for higher standards
of living (see Chapter 8). But we cannot say that those agitations were
accompanied by a marked decline of the birth-rate as they were
between 1920 and 1940. In social life we always have a marked
hangover from the past, and no doubt the large family idea maintained itself, all the more because for a long time there was a sellers'
market in labour. Exports of wheat to north Europe suggest that
population was not expanding very rapidly ; but, in the second
half of the fifteenth century, England recovered from the drain of the
French Wars, and aristocratic conservatism diminished through the
killing off of old landed families in the Wars of the Roses.

New monied folk rose to influence as woollen manufacture increased,
and the woollen towns grew, often at the expense of villages once
dependent on wheatfields soon transformed into sheep lands. One
must mention the introduction of serious venereal disease, probably
early in the sixteenth century, and the increase of mortality from epidemics in the growing towns. On the other hand, improvements in
shipbuilding and seamanship opened up opportunities on the ocean as
well as in commerce. The firm organisation of the Tudors, the ending of
religious celibacy, the desire to be rid of such foreign control as that of
the Papacy or the Hanse all promoted enterprise. On the whole, then,
the population no doubt increased in Tudor times and rough estimates suggest about 5,000,000 including perhaps 100,000 in London,
still limited by water-supply problems.

Elizabeth and James I were much troubled by what was, for their
time, the overgrowth of London. How could it be fed and supplied
with water ? How could the danger of fire be diminished while burnt
brick remained a material only for mansions, and ordinary houses
were timber-framed, sometimes with shingle roofs, though tiles were
common ? The question of water-supply was solved for seventeenth-
century requirements by the New River scheme with its reservoirs
and pipes, at first of elm, then of lead. The growth of Smithfield
market, when root-crops in the eighteenth century began to give more
cattle-food, helped the nutrition problem. The plague of 1665, the

worst of a series, made the problem of crowding temporarily less urgent. The fire of 1666 was followed by rebuilding in brick or stone ; brick building spread over the country quite rapidly and gave an impetus to general growth of towns and their industries. The end of Stuart troubles, and the development of more settled administration and of partial toleration after 1689, led to further growth of towns with winter residences of the local landed gentry and more shops and amenities. In Wales sheep increased greatly and little wool-towns developed. In England root-crops increased stock-farming, and led to building of farmhouses, often in brick, away from the old village-clusters, as well as to mansions in parks, Blenheim Palace being one of the largest examples we have. Dutch engineers reclaimed fen-lands and Huguenots brought industrial skill and experience.

Political difficulties hampered Antwerp from the mid-seventeenth until well into the nineteenth century. Dutch commerce suffered a decline in the eighteenth century, and European continental interests turned the attention of France away from the sea after her colonisation efforts of the first half of the seventeenth century. Spain and Portugal had fallen back and the Hanse had lost its power. It was under these circumstances that British enterprise found a special opportunity : to commerce was added banking, with the foundation of the Bank of England at the end of the seventeenth century. London became the entrepot and banking centre for Atlantic Europe ; Liverpool began her great development ; Scottish towns and agriculture developed rapidly towards the end of the eighteenth century (pp. 252, 277).

All in all, population and commerce with India (London), with the West Indies (Bristol), and with North America (Liverpool and Glasgow) increased, and, at the beginning of the nineteenth century, London had approximately a million people and Great Britain some ten and a half millions. London's wealth led to the building of mansions on the Taplow gravel-terrace west of Piccadilly Circus, including the old May Fairground, and by 1830 Regent Street was set out between the closely built-up Soho foreign quarter and the residences of the wealthy supplied with water from wells sunk in the terrace gravel of their gardens. A beginning had previously been made towards the reclamation of land between the Taplow gravel terrace and the Thames. We note the Tudor St. James's Palace, the conversion of a swamp into St. James's Park and lake under Charles II, and the laying out of St. James's Square and of ground for the game known as Pall Mall, the latter ground a social centre to be built upon in the nineteenth century as club-land between Whitehall and the Piccadilly-Mayfair quarter, occupied more and more by a new aristocracy recruited from successful merchants and bankers.

Bath in the eighteenth century, Weymouth towards the end of that century and Brighton early in the nineteenth century became fashionable resorts. In the growing industrial towns of the north the laying out of residential quarters was less spectacular and on the whole came somewhat later, though Brook Street and St. John's Street in Manchester and Rodney Street in Liverpool are in the main creations of the early nineteenth century. They have largely lost their original residential character, and parts of west London are doing the same now, as is seen very clearly in Berkeley Square and St. James's Square. The northern towns already in the last quarter of the eighteenth century had been receiving immigrants, chiefly from within a thirty-mile radius, into their long rows of small houses, back to back, in dismal streets ; and the process went on during several decades of the nineteenth century.

It was the accompaniment of what is usually called the First Industrial Revolution, but might almost better be named the Applied Science Revolution, because, while steampower and machinery developed rapidly and inaugurated manufacturing processes, there were also myriad industrial applications of the science that was growing, thanks to the increasing liberation of minds from medievalism and its equally repressive aftermath. Road surfaces were improved, canals built, tram-roads laid down for horse-drawn trucks of coal, Jenner started inoculation against smallpox, Percival and probably others started the medical use of cod-liver oil ; and other developments presaged the later fight against infant mortality. Malthus worked out his famous ideas on population, and the revolt of the human conscience against slavery gained strength in those regions in which the hang-over from medievalism was less powerful.

The birth-rate, generally, remained high in Britain until the last quarter of the nineteenth century, but the death-rate, which, until 1800, or perhaps 1750, had been the dominating factor in population-numbers, began to diminish under more or less scientific and, to a very limited extent, humanitarian control, though the latter was all too little in evidence in the first half, even the first two-thirds, of the century. Both birth-rate and death-rate were high until 1870,

Y

indeed they rose during 1860-70; and both have fallen remarkably since. There was large-scale emigration from Britain to U.S.A., Canada, Australia, New Zealand, and South Africa during the whole of the nineteenth century and the first quarter of the twentieth century, but the restrictions on immigration into U.S.A. after 1923, the economic world storm of 1930, and the decline of the British birth-rate have made emigration almost insignificant for the period 1930-46. It remains to be seen whether projects now being attempted will durably renew the flow.

The population of Great Britain, from the censuses, may be summarised as follows :—

Year	England and Wales— Population in millions	Percentage annual increase	Scotland— Population in millions	Percentage annual increase
1801 (*first census*)	8.89	—	1.61	—
1811	10.16	1.43	1.81	1.23
1821	12.00	1.81	2.09	1.58
1831	13.90	1.58	2.34	1.30
1841	15.91	1.43	2.60	1.08
1851	17.93	1.27	2.89	1.02
1861	20.07	1.19	3.06	0.60
1871	22.71	1.32	3.36	0.97
1881	25.97	1.44	3.74	1.12
1891	29.00	1.17	4.03	0.78
1901	32.53	1.22	4.47	1.11
1911	36.07	1.09	4.76	0.65
1921	37.89	0.49	4.88	0.25
1931	39.95	0.55	4.84	0.08
1951	43.74	0.47	5.10	0.26

England and Wales have about 750 persons per square mile and Scotland about 173, but the latter figure means little because one third of the total Scottish population is in Lanark county and nearly three-quarters are in the Firth-Clyde lowlands. Urban population in 1951 was 80.7 per cent of the total for England and Wales and 70 per cent for Scotland. During 1931-51 emigration from Scotland exceeded immigration by 220,000, but England and Wales had an immigration surplus, with contributions from Scotland, Ireland, parts of Europe, the West Indies, etc. There was also a net movement from Wales into

England. Estimated population for 1956 was 44.67 million for England and Wales and nearly 5.15 million for Scotland, but estimates are usually on the high side.

The large increase in both regions for the period 1811-1821 accompanies a peak of immigration into the industrial towns from the country-side, and the increase remained high, with fluctuations, until 1881, in spite of emigration, which was very considerable, especially during 1881-91 and 1901-21 for England and Wales. For Scotland, though these decades stand out, they are surpassed by the large emigration of 1921-31. It should further be remembered that the net emigration figures would have been even higher save for the incoming of Irish labour, most notably to Liverpool and Glasgow but also over much of the country.

As, throughout the nineteenth century, the expectation of life at birth never reached forty-five years for males, and was probably below forty before 1861, and for females passed the forty-five mark only after 1880, the population until the end of the century was a younger one than it has since been. In England and Wales the average age at death in 1939 and in 1956 was 61.8 and 65.7 years for men and 65.8 and 70.4 years for women respectively. 64.8 per cent of the men but only 50.02 per cent of the women die before attaining 75 years of age. The figures for Scotland are 67.9 and 56.1. The proportion of females to males is about 108.1 per cent in England and Wales and 109.3 per cent in Scotland. The proportions of births is about 106 males to 100 females in England and Wales and about 105 in Scotland. The female excess in the total population is most marked in the higher ages.

In spite of delays in sanitary improvement of the more crowded quarters of towns, medical advance has made deaths from smallpox and diphtheria rare and reduced tuberculosis and enteric troubles. Consequent reduction of the death rate has been a main factor in the increase of population. The birth rate was naturally high (20.6 per thousand persons in England and Wales and 22.3 in Scotland) following the return home of men and women from war service. In 1956 the figures were 15.6 for England and Wales and 18.5 for Scotland. Births are more numerous in the first half of the year.

Death-rates, the number of deaths per 1,000 of the population, called by statisticians crude death-rates, are known for the years since 1861. By then they had been reduced to below 23. A temporary but marked rise connected with epidemics and trade depression occured between 1860 and 1870, after which the rate fell fairly continuously until 1930, especially after 1890. There is much probability that medical research, antiseptics, better food for the manual workers and better opportunities for open-air sports were main factors of this change and to some extent masked the number of deaths of old people, which must rise as a consequence of the longer average life, unless there is a further fall in childhood death-rates. Inevitably, during the period of muddle following the severe world crisis of 1930-31, the death-rate tended upwards again, but by this time it was only in the neighbourhood of 12 and, among civilians in Britain, it has fallen since 1940, and it stands at 11.7 for England and Wales and 12 for Scotland in 1956, thanks largely to reduction of infant deaths. The later stages of the fall in the crude death-rate have been due to the medical social work, which has led to the establishment of maternity and infant welfare clinics, as well as to boys' and girls' clubs, scouts and guides, and supplies of vitamins in various forms to mothers and children.

At the end of the nineteenth century about 150 infants out of every thousand born died before their first birthday anniversary. The proportion was reduced to 50 in 1939, 34 in 1948 and 23.7 in 1956 for England and Wales. The slower reduction in Scotland leaves the rate at 29.0 in 1956. Interesting figures for England and Wales are contained in the Registrars General's Quarterly Return for March 1957. They show that deaths of children between 5 and 14 were 19,878 in 1911 and 2,753 in 1955. Tuberculosis killed 4,373 (22 per cent of the total) in 1911 and 55 (2 per cent) in 1955, other infections killed 4,572 (23 per cent) and 165 (6 per cent), accidents killed 1,790 (9 per cent) and 880 (32 per cent), cancer 200 (1 per cent) and 412 (15 per cent). Milk and orange juice, playing fields, slum clearance, school meals, diagnostic progress and medical advance have all played their part and the country is especially indebted to the late Miss Eleanor Rathbone, M.P., for her work to this end. Congenital malformations, birth injuries, post-natal asphyxia, immaturity and other special causes still contribute to death rates of infants, especially among boys.

In the late nineteenth century less than a quarter of a million marriages and well over 900,000 births per annum were characteristic for England and Wales, with some 770,000 children surviving their first year. In 1939 the corresponding figures were 360,000 marriages, 610,000 live births with 580,000 children surviving for at least a year.

1956 saw about 353,000 marriages and 698,331 live births. Scotland in 1956 had 43,971 marriages and 95,313 live births. The birth rate, marriage rate (7.9 per thousand persons in England and Wales, 8.3 in Scotland), proportion of births to marriages, and death rate in childhood and in age are all rather higher in Scotland. The figures show the recent influence of the welfare-state and also the distinction developing between marriage and parenthood. The prosecution of Mrs. Annie Besant and Mr. Charles Bradlaugh for their advocacy of birth control gave wide publicity to that practice and greatly increased its employment.

Soon also followed the unforeseen influence of the Education Act of 1870. It was reducing illiteracy, and, as a consequence, spreading among wage-earners a consciousness of their poverty and precarious social position. It was to lead on to the Trade Union movement. The wage-earners were no longer unconsciously begetting machine-fodder. Coal miners were sacrificing ease and amenities so that their sons might not become miners in their turn.

During the last quarter of the nineteenth century, also, the growth of British industry was not keeping pace with the growth of population. In the last year of the century, the achievement of economic schemes for transmission of electric power over long distances, and of installations for generation of that power from falling water, presaged vast changes in the world distribution of industry. Soon there followed the idea of the internal combustion engine and the likelihood of the supersession of coal for a number of purposes. In brief, the second industrial revolution was on the march. At the same time, Germany and the U.S.A. were obviously becoming far stronger industrially and it was evident that the latter would soon cease to rank among the debtor nations; the common shares of American railroad companies almost disappeared from the London Stock Exchange, where they had once been favourite gambling counters.

All these changes had effects by the last decade of the nineteenth century not only on the directors of industrial concerns, but also on the minds of their workpeople, thanks to the widening of knowledge. That widening forced into the wage-earners the thought that directors and masters were not a superior breed, as had been a sort of unconscious belief under feudal conditions, but that these were now often the not very capable sons and grandsons of men who had made lucky fortunes in the early industrial revolution and had "founded families". The less capable of those sons and grandsons were selling their businesses, sometimes at inflated rates, to limited companies so that there remained little besides the cash nexus between employers and employed ; in fact, the employers were often mere shareholders without knowledge of the business.

Widespread critisim of a system that seemed to involve conscious poverty for all save a favoured few naturally led to questioning of the large family, especially as the landed gentry had almost given up the big family as a consequence of the decline in the effective value of agricultural land. What could be more natural than that the reduction of birth-rates should spread from the often impoverished landed gentry and rural clergy to the " middle class ", well aware of the insecurity of the economic future, and so to the wage-earners ? It hardly affected the casual labour group, whose minds were often not active enough to think things through. Amongst these last, the disastrous trinity of drink, gambling and sex, which were the relaxations left to the workpeople of the early nineteenth century by the factory owners continued, and in some measure still continue, to increase social problems such as mental deficiency and juvenile crime.

A recent demographic feature is the creation of New Towns, usually around old nuclei, on a larger scale than the garden-cities (Letchworth and Welwyn Garden City) which grew in the earlier part of this century. Welwyn Garden City has become the new town of Welwyn. A special aim has been to reduce congested travel into and out of London, often an hour or more each way, which has become a daily routine harmful to health and quality of work. Basildon (in Billericay urban district, Essex) and Hemel Hempstead (Hertfordshire) had well over 20,000 people each in 1951, and Welwyn nearly 20,000. Mostly having between 5,000 and about 10,000 in 1951 were Bracknell (Berkshire), Crawley (Surrey-Sussex border), Harlow (Essex-Hertfordtshire border), Hatfield and Stevenage (both Hertfordshire). Unfortunately, in some cases, men and women living in the new towns are travelling daily to work in London, so there is still danger that new towns may in effect extend *la cité tentaculaire*. Questions of amenities, shopping facilities and local government face the new towns, and a storm-disaster at Hatfield has revealed bad house-building. Planning schemes are only too apt to overlook some crucial factors of a situation. There is need to consider whether radical decentralisation, especially of government departments and London County Council administrations, would help without diminishing such efficiency of working as has been reached. The building of large blocks of flats in and quite near London is being tried as an experiment to reduce congested rush-hour travel. The other very large centres are for the most part trying to reduce inner congestion by a combination of suburban development and green-belt protection.

One may mention also Corby, the new town on the Northampton-shire iron-field and Cwm Bran (Monmouthshire) as new towns born of industrial change and, in 1951, attaining between ten and twenty thousand inhabitants each.

Another aspect of the population question of considerable social interest is the language census. Apart from the use of a few non-British languages in special areas in London, Liverpool, Manchester, Glasgow, Cardiff and a few other places, usually ports, the main feature of interest is the survival, and to a certain extent the revival, of old Celtic languages. These are divided by scholars into two main groups—Gaelic or Goidelic in the Scottish Highlands and Islands of the west and formerly in the Isle of Man, and Brythonic or Welsh and the now extinct Cornish and Westmorland languages. Welsh and Cornish are in a sense parents of Breton, the rural speech of West Brittany in France. The Gaelic of the Scottish west is akin to the Irish language.

Data collected from census-forms are inevitably of limited value as regards the language spoken. The form used in English counties did not ask about Welsh speech, so a considerable number who can and do speak Welsh are left out of count. In Wales, some who can speak Welsh, but only rarely do so, write themselves down as English-speaking, while a few who are more fluent in their national language call them-selves monoglot Welsh. It is indeed probable that there are practic-ally no fully monoglot Gaels or Welsh in Great Britain. Gaelic has lost ground in recent decades and is spoken, in Scotland, by less than 100,000 persons. Welsh has been retreating up the valleys from the border as a language of conversation, worship and current reading. It is still in widespread use in the more moorland areas of the counties of Anglesey, Carnavon, Denbigh, Merioneth, Cardigan and Carmarthen and on high rural areas in Flint, Montgomery, Brecon, West Glamorgan and North Pembroke. The language boundary in Pembroke between the Welsh north and the Little England of the south is fairly stable. Books and journals, dictionaries and gazetteers, standardisation of spelling, school and college-teaching, all help to maintain the language, at any rate for special purposes, particularly worship. The subject is well treated by J. G. Thomas in " Wales " (edited by Prof. Bowen, 1957) and " Geographical Distribution of the Welsh Language " (Geogr. Journal, C XXII 1956, pp. 71-9).

EPILOGUE

HAVING NOW come to the thin and ever-moving curtain, always impenetrable, that separates the past from the future and is called the present, it behoves us to have a care about suggestions of prognostication. In 1850 no one would have foreseen the changes in social life and equipment that were to follow the advent of transmissible electric power and the invention of the internal combustion engine, the crises of thought that would follow the penetration of the idea of evolution into the problems of society, the new methods of spreading information that wires and wireless would bring, the claims of the workers to well-being that were to follow the spread of education for all. The quickening of the pace of change, over all the world, is perhaps the most salient fact of our time ; we " plan " and want to see results ourselves. Rarely do we realise that this haste, however inevitable we may have made it, is a new and dangerous portent in the realm of the natural history of man.

Some of the difficulty is due to the old time acceptance of the idea of creation of the universe by *Fiat* in six days about 6,000 years ago. That idea of creation is dead, but a subconscious residue remains and leads men, unwittingly, to think of change on a great scale in short periods. If the universe were 6,000 years old, the last 2,000 years would represent one third of its duration. The geologists have estimated the age of the earth, as a body with a solid crust, at far more than 1,000,000,000 years. Human time has become some 600,000 years. This makes the period since men emerged from mere collecting and hunting into the more organised life of food production little more than the last one per cent of the human age. During the previous 99 per cent of men's life on earth they lived in small in-bred groups often much isolated from other groups. And life of small groups went on, for a great part of our British population, until barely two centuries

327

ago, when agglomeration metamorphosed so many members of small
social groups into isolated units in a crowd.

It has become clear that men drifted into Britain from the south
in the long intervals between the ice-phases of the Pleistocene period,
and, so far as stone implements allow us to judge, made only quite
moderate advances over a period of 250,000 years. Later on, hunters
with means of action at a distance show an appreciable amount
of evolution of their tools in, perhaps, 25,000 years. The final
passing of the ice-phases brought little opportunity to Britain,
but did promote· a certain amount of change in perhaps 5,000
years.

Then comes the great change in Britain to organised food production by cultivation and herding, introduced by immigrants from
the continent and the Mediterranean. Ritual, trade and various arts
developed in a society under the leadership of immigrant males and
their descendants through unions with indigenous girls. The situation
probably had its analogies with that which is picturesquely described
for us in the beginning of the sixth chapter of the book of *Genesis*. If
we may judge from the monuments left from that time there must have
been a considerable labour force implying an increase in population,
and in the agglomeration of population, both no doubt made more
feasible by food production. Probably the indigenous elements were
largely bondmen unless they gained personal power as magicians or
priests.

The coasts, both east and west, brought in new elements from time
to time through immigration, and trade and ideas spread inland on
the east side as far as, and sometimes beyond, the Jurassic scarp. On
the west immigrant ideas found only small lowlands such as parts of
Cornwall, Glamorgan, Pembrokeshire, Anglesey, Galloway and the
Scottish Isles. The moorlands, largely belonging to the west, received
immigrant ideas mainly by slow infiltration and preserved down to
our century a good deal of the intimacy of the traditional small groups
with members nearly all related to one another or at least linked in
chains of relationship.

Towards medieval times the fact of relationship-grouping seems
to have given place on the lowlands to proximity-grouping. A little
mobility of population had become possible and agglomeration had
certainly increased, so that relationships between individuals became
hard to trace. The humbler folk still mainly chose wives from within

a radius of a few miles ; the wealthier people often married farther afield.

Tradition in a hierarchical society obtained until the eve of modern times. Then diversities of belief and ritual engendered new ways of thought, commerce brought wider contacts, and refugees from religious persecution gave Britain an intellectual and spiritual élite and a fount of initiative.

So we find a growing population seeking to maintain its sociality of small groups by gathering around chapels, small collections of like-minded people on a voluntary basis and full of initiative in various directions. They prepared the way not only for the industrial revolution but also for increasing freedom of conscience.

At the same time, the spread of root-crops loosened out the old village and led to enclosure of former open-fields, with compact farms as a result. There was much technical agricultural improvement, but the enclosures were carried through with heartless disregard of the welfare of the humbler folk. Goldsmith's *Deserted Village* remains a classic on this subject. Humble families were metamorphosed into a sort of social flotsam and jetsam, and the industrial revolution changed man from his former status as a member of a small group into an often lonely unit in a crowd. A great deal in his mental make-up that had been accumulating and consolidating during hundreds of thousands of years of small-group-membership was left to atrophy, and an attempt was made to start what was almost a new mentality. We cannot wonder, therefore, that there have been conspicuous maladjustments and that the old deep-rooted tendencies have shown their vigour once more in the efforts to create the Social-Service State.

Our thinkers are face to face with a triple problem. Production and distribution of many goods and services have to be thought out on a world basis. Social life has to be reshaped on the basis of groups that are not too large. Personality and initiative have to be cherished as the fountain of originality and the only means of keeping social life and thought from mechanised direction by authoritarian doctrine.

BIBLIOGRAPHY

ANGUS, W. G. (1949). *in* Scientific Survey of North-east England. *Brit. Assoc. Adv. Sci.* : 69-74.

ANTIQUARIES JOURNAL, published by the Society of Antiquaries, London.

ANTIQUITY, quarterly, published at 24, Parkend Road, Gloucester.

ARCHAEOLOGIA, published by the Society of Antiquaries, London.

ARCHAEOLOGICAL JOURNAL, published by the Royal Archaeological Institute, London.

ARMSTRONG, A. LESLIE (1939). Palaeolithic Man in the North Midlands. *Mem. Manchr. Lit. Phil. Soc. 83* : 87-116.

ARMSTRONG, A. LESLIE (1940). Note on discovery of figurine of Mother Goddess. *Antiq. J. 20* : 541.

Note on female skull found near Cresswell, delivered verbally at the Royal Anthropological Institute 1948, not yet published.

ATKINSON, R. (1949). Island Going. London, Collins.

BEDDOE, J. (1885). The Races of Britain. London, Trubner.

BEDDOE, J. and ROWE, J. H. (1907). Ethnology of West Yorkshire. *Yorks. Archaeol. J. 19* : 31-60.

BERSU, G., material as yet unpublished, but see Kinvig, R. H.

BLOCH, M. (1931). Les Caractères originaux de l'Histoire rurale française. Oslo. Aschehoug.

BOAS, F. (1911). Changes in the Bodily Form of Descendants of Immigrants (to U.S.A.). *61st Congress, 2nd Session, Senate Document 208.* Washington, D.C., U.S.A.

BOAS, F. (1940). Race, Language and Culture. New York, Macmillan.

BOWEN, E. G. (1933). Incidence of Phthisis in relation to Race Type and Social Environment in Wales. *J. Roy. Anthrop. Inst. 63* : 49-63.

BOWEN, E. G. (1941). Wales. Cardiff, Univ. Wales Press.

BRADBROOKE, W. and PARSONS, F. G. (1922). Anthropology, Chiltern Hills. *J. Roy. Anthrop. Inst. 52* : 113-26.

BREUIL, H. (1939). Pleistocene Succession, Somme Valley (France). *Proc. Prehist. Soc. 5* : 33-38.

BRITISH ASSOCIATION FOR THE ADVANCEMENT OF SCIENCE. Handbooks written concerning cities, and their districts, at which the annual meetings have been held.

BRITISH MUSEUM HANDBOOKS. Stone Age, Bronze Age, Early Iron Age, Britain in Roman times, Anglo-Saxon Antiquities.

BRØGGER, A. W. (1929). Ancient Emigrants. Oxford, Clarendon Press.

BROOM, R. (1923). Craniology, Yellow-skinned Races, South Africa. *J. Roy. Anthrop. Inst., 53* : 132-49.

BULLEID, A. and GRAY, H. St. George (1911-1917). Glastonbury. Glastonbury Antiq. Soc., 2 vols.

CARR-SAUNDERS, Sir A. M. (1922). The Population Problem. Oxford, Clarendon Press.

CARR-SAUNDERS, Sir A. M. (1936). World Population. Oxford, Clarendon Press.

CHADWICK, H. M. (1907). Origin of the English Nation. Cambridge, University Press.

CHARLES, B. G. (1934). Old Norse Relations with Wales. Cardiff, University of Wales Press.

CHARLESWORTH, M. P. (1949). The Lost Province or the Worth of Britain. Cardiff, Univ. Wales Press.

CHILDE, V. G. (1931). Skara Brae. London, Kegan Paul.

CHILDE, V. G. (1935). Prehistory of Scotland. London, Kegan Paul.

CHILDE, V. G. (1947). Prehistoric Communities of the British Isles. London, Chambers.

CLAPHAM, Sir J. H. and POWER, Eileen (1941). Cambridge Economic History. Cambridge University Press, vol. *1.*

CLARK, J. G. D. (1932). The Mesolithic Age in Britain. Cambridge, University Press.

CLARK, J. G. D. (1936). The Mesolithic Settlement of Northern Europe. Cambridge, University Press.

CLARK, J. G. D. (1940). Prehistoric England. London, Batsford.

COLLIGNON, R. (1894). Anthropologie de la France ; Dordogne, etc. *Mem. Soc. Anthrop. Paris,* ser. 3, *1,* fasc. 3 : 3-79.

COLLINGWOOD, R. G. (1930). Archaeology of Roman Britain. London, Methuen.

COLLINGWOOD, R. G. and MYRES, J. N. L. (1936). Roman Britain and the English Settlements. Oxford, Clarendon Press.

CONWAY, M. (later Lord Conway) (1901). The Domain of Art. London, John Murray.

CONZEN, M. R. G. (1949). *in* Scientific Survey of North-east England. *Brit. Assoc. Adv. Sci.* : 75-83 and map.

COON, C. S. (1939). The Races of Europe. New York and London, Macmillan.

COULTON, G. G. (1925). The Mediaeval Village. Cambridge, University Press.

COUNTY ARCHAEOLOGIES. A Series of Books. London, Methuen.

CRAWFORD, O. G. S. (1928). Air Survey and Archaeology. *Ordnance Survey Professional Papers*, n. ser., no. 7 : 2nd ed.

CRAWFORD, O. G. S. (1940). Report on Sutton Hoo. *Antiquity, 14* : 64-68 (part of the summary report on the Sutton Hoo Ship-Burial, by various writers, ibid. 6-87).

CRAWFORD, O. G. S. and KEILLER, A. (1928). Wessex from the Air. Oxford, Clarendon Press.

CUNNINGTON, M. E. (1923). The Early Iron Age inhabited site at All Cannings Cross. Devizes, Simpson & Co.

CURLE, A. O. (1932-35). Jarlshof, Shetland. *Proc. Soc. Antiq. Scot., 67* : 82-136 ; *68* : 224-319 ; *69* : 85-107, 265-321 ; *70* : 237-70.

DA COSTA FERREIRA (1913). A Galiza . . . Minha e Tras es Montes. *Rev. Univ. Coimbra, 11*, no. 1.

DARBY, H. C., ed. (1936). Historical Geography of England and Wales before 1800. Cambridge, University Press.

DARLINGTON, C. D. (1947). The Genetic Component of Language. *Heredity, 1* : 269-86.

DAVIES, E., and FLEURE, H. J. (1936). Anthropometric Survey, Isle of Man. *J. Roy. Anthrop. Inst. 66* : 129-88.

DAVIES, (née Dunlop) Margaret (1945-46). Megalithic Monuments, Irish Sea and North Channel Coastlands. *Antiq. J. 25* : 125-44 ; *26* : 38-60.

DICKINSON, R. E. (1947). City, Region and Regionalism. London, Kegan Paul.

DUCKWORTH, W. H. L. (1911). Craniology, Sardinia. *Z. Morph. Anthrop.* Stuttgart, *13* : 439-504.

ELLIS, Havelock (1904). A Study of British Genius. London, Hurst and Blackett.

EKWALL, E. (1936). Concise Oxford Dictionary of English Place-names. Oxford, Clarendon Press.

ENGLISH PLACE NAMES SOCIETY. Series of County Volumes. Cambridge, University Press.

EVANS, E. Estyn (1942). Irish Heritage. Dundalk (Ireland), Tempest.

EVANS, E. Estyn, MOGEY, J. M., McCOURT, See Mogey, J. M.

FLEURE, H. J. (1920). Early Neanthropic Types. *J. Roy. Anthrop. Inst. 50* : 12-40.

FLEURE, H. J. (1947). Aspects of British Civilisation. Sir James Frazer Memorial Lecture. Oxford, Clarendon Press.

FLEURE, H. J. and NEELY, G. H. J. (1936). Cashtal yn Ard, Isle of Man *Antiq. J. 16* : 373-95.

FLEURE, H. J. and DUNLOP, Margaret (1942). Glendarragh Circle, Braaid, Isle of Man. *Antiq. J.* 22 : 39-53.

FLEURE, H. J. and JAMES, T. C. (1916). Geographical Distribution of Anthropological Types in Wales. *J. Roy. Anthrop. Inst.* 46 : 35-153.

Fox, Sir Cyril (1923). Archaeology of the Cambridge Region. Cambridge University Press.

Fox, Sir Cyril (1926-31, 1934). Offa's Dyke. *Archaeologia Cambrensis, 81* : 133-79 ; *82* : 232-68 ; *83* : 33-110 ; *84* : 1-60 ; *85* : 1-73 ; *86* : 1-74 ; *89* : 205-78.

Fox, Sir Cyril (1946). A Find of the Early Iron Age from Llyn Cerrig Bach, Anglesey. Cardiff, National Museum of Wales.

Fox, Sir Cyril (1947). The Personality of Britain. Cardiff, National Museum of Wales, 4th ed.

FULLARD, H. (1938). Anthropometric Survey, Rochdale District. *Trans. Rochdale Lit. Sci. Soc. 20* : 29-55.

FUSSELL, G. E. (1949). The English Rural Labourer. London, Batchworth.

GARDNER, Willoughby (1926). The Native forts in North Wales. *Archaeologia Cambrensis*, ser. 7, *7* : 221-82 (includes references to Dr. Gardner's earlier papers).

GARROD, Dorothy (1938). The upper Palaeolithic in the Light of Recent Discovery. *Proc. Prehist. Soc. 4* : 1-26.

GEDDES, Sir P. (1915). Cities in Evolution. London, Williams and Norgate.

DE GEER, Gerard (1940). Geochronologica Suecica, Principles. *K. Svenska VetenskAkad. Handl. 18* : 1-360.

GEOLOGICAL SURVEY, Regional Monographs. London, H.M. Stationery Office.

GLASS, D. V. (1940). Population Policies and Movements. London, Oxford University Press.

GLASS, D. V. and BLACKER, C. P. (1935). Population and Fertility. London, Population Investigation Commission.

GODWIN, H. (1940). Pollen Analysis and Quaternary Geology. *Proc. Geol. Assoc. 52* : 328-61.

GODWIN, H. (1940). Pollen Analysis and Forest History, England and Wales. *New Phytol. 39* : 370-400.

GOMME, Sir G. Laurence (1914). London. London, Williams and Norgate.

GRAHAM, H. G. (1950). Social Life in Scotland in the Eighteenth Century. London, Black, 4th ed.

GRAY, H. L. (1915). English Field Systems (*Harvard Hist. Stud.*). London, Oxford University Press.

GRIERSON, Sir G. A. (1933). Linguistic Survey of India. Delhi ; Department of Publications ; and see J. H. Hutton (1933).

GRUNDY, G. B. (1934-38). Articles on Old Roads *in Archaeol. J. 91* : 66-96, 241-68 ; *92* : 98-141 (Worcs. and Mid-Severn, 1934-35) ; *94* : 257-90 ; *95* : 174-223 (Dorset, Somerset and S.W. England, 1937-38).

HAMMOND, J. L. and Barbara (1919). The Skilled Labourer. London, Longmans.

HAMMOND, J. L. and Barbara (1925). The Town Labourer. London, Longmans.

HAMMOND, J. L. and Barbara (1930). The Age of the Chartists. London, Longmans.

HAMMOND, J. L. and Barbara (1934). The Bleak Age. London, Longmans (revised and re-issued as a Penguin Book, 1947).

HAMMOND, J. L. and Barbara (1937). The Rise of Modern Industry. London, Methuen.

HAMMOND, J. L. and Barbara (1948). The Village Labourer. London, Longmans, revised ed.

HAVERFIELD, F. J. (1913). Ancient Town Planning. Oxford, Clarendon Press.

HAVERFIELD, F. J. (1923). The Romanisation of Roman Britain. Oxford, Clarendon Press, 4th ed., ed. Sir G. Macdonald.

HAVERFIELD, F. J. (1924). The Roman Occupation of Britain. Oxford, Clarendon Press, ed. Sir G. Macdonald.

HAWKES, C. F. C. (1940). The Prehistoric Foundations of Europe to the Mycenean Age. London, Methuen.

HEALTH, MINISTRY OF. Reports.

HENCKEN, H. O'N. (1932). County Archaeologies ; Cornwall and Scilly. London, Methuen.

HILER, H. S. (1929). Introduction to the Study of Costume. New York, Weyhe.

HODGKIN, R. H. (1935). A History of the Anglo-Saxons. Oxford, Clarendon Press.

HRDLIČKA, A. (1928). Catalogue of Human Crania, U.S. National Museum Collections. *Proc. U.S. Nat. Mus. 71* : no. 24.

HUGHES, Harold (1907). Excavations at Tre'r Ceiri. *Archaeologia Cambrensis,* ser. 6. 7: 38-62.

HUTTON, J. H. (1933). Report, Census of India, 1931. Delhi, vol. *1*, part 1, sections 154-57, on pp. 357-69.

HUXLEY, J. S. and HADDON, A. C. (1935). We Europeans. London, Cape.

JACKMAN, W. T. (1916). The Development of Transportation in Modern England. Cambridge, University Press.

JONES, Emrys (1945). Settlement Patterns in the Middle Teifi Valley. *Geography, 30* : 103-11.

z

JONES, Sir John Morris (1899). Appendix B *to* J. Rhys & D. Brynmor-Jones (1900). The Welsh People, pp. 617-41.

JONES, S. J. (1938). Gorsey Bigbury. *Univ. Bristol Spelaeol. Soc. 5* : 3-56.

KEITH, Sir Arthur (1948). A New Theory of Human Evolution. London, Watts.

KELLY, F. M. and SCHWABE, R. (1925). Historic Costume. London, Batsford.

KENDRICK, T. D. (1930). A History of the Vikings. London, Methuen.

KENDRICK, T. D. (1938). Anglo-Saxon Art. London, Methuen.

KENDRICK, T. D. (1949). Late Saxon and Viking Art. London, Methuen.

KENDRICK T. D. and HAWKES, C. F. C. (1932). Archaeology in England and Wales, 1914-1931. London, Methuen.

KINVIG, R. H. (1944). History of the Isle of Man. Douglas, Manx Society.

KIRK, D. (1946). Europe's Population in the Inter-war Years. Princeton, U.S.A. *League of Nations Publns.*, 1946 II A.8. 312 pp.

KISSLING, W. (1943). The Hebridean Black House. *J. Roy. Anthrop. Inst. 73* : 75-100.

" KLEIDUNG " (1926). *in* Reallexikon der Vorgeschichte Berlin, vol. *6* : 380-94.

KUCZYNSKI, R. (1935). The Measurement of Population Growth. London, Sidgwick & Jackson.

KUCZYNSKI, R. (1942). The New Population Statistics. Cambridge, University Press.

LAND UTILISATION SURVEY. County Monographs. London, Land Utilisn. Survey.

LEEDS, E. T. (1913). Archaeology of the Anglo-Saxon Settlements. Oxford, Clarendon Press.

LETHBRIDGE, T. C. (1948). Merlin's Island. London, Methuen.

LOCKYER, Sir N. (1901-05). Notes on Stonehenge. *Nature, 65, 66, 71, 72, 73* : 57 ; *71* : 297-300, 345-348, 367-368, 391-393, 535-538.
(A criticism is given by A. R. Hinks in the *Nineteenth Century, 1903* : 1009.

MACKINDER, Sir H. J. (1906). Britain and the British Seas. London, Frowde.

MARGARY, I. D. (1948). Roman Ways in the Weald. London, Phoenix House.

MARSTON, A. T. (1937). The Swanscombe Skull. *J. Roy. Anthrop. Inst. 67* : 339-406.

MAWER, Sir Allen (1924). Chief Elements in English Place Names. Cambridge, University Press.

MEDIAEVAL TOWNS SERIES. Volumes on British Towns include London, Edinburgh, Canterbury, Oxford, Cambridge and Coventry. London, Dent.

MEITZEN, A. (1895). Siedelung und Agrarwesen. Berlin.

MILANKOVITCH, M. (1938). Astronomische Mittel zur Erforschung der Erdgeschichtlichen Klimate. *Handb. Geophvs. Berlin, 9* : 593-698.

MOGEY, J. M. (1947). The Rural Community in Northern Ireland. London. Oxford University Press.

MORANT, G. M. (1926). Craniology, England and Wales. *Biometrika, 18* : 56-98.

MORANT, G. M. (1930-31). Upper Palaeolithic Skulls of Europe. *Ann. Eugen. 4* : 109-214.

MORANT, G. M. (assisted by F. M. HOADLEY) (1931) : Crania, Spitalfields, London. *Biometrika, 23* : 191-248.

MORANT, G. M. and SAMSON, O. (1936). Examination of investigations by Fishberg and Boas on Jews in New York. *Biometrika, 28* : 1-31.

NØRLUND, P. (1948). Trelleborg. Copenhagen, Nordiske Vorlag.

NORTH, F. J., CAMPBELL, B., SCOTT, R. (1949). Snowdonia. London, Collins.

OAKLEY, K. P. and ASHLEY-MONTAGU, M. F. (1949). A reconsideration of the Galley Hill skeleton. *Bull. Brit. Mus. Nat. Hist., Geol., I. No. 2*.

OLIVER, B. (1929). The Cottages of England. London, Batsford.

O'NEIL, Helen (1945). Roman Villa at Park Street near St. Albans. *Archaeol. J. 102* : 21-110.

ORDNANCE SURVEY (1928-38). *Maps of* Roman Britain (1928), Neolithic Wessex (1932), Trent Basin (1933), South Wales (1936), Britain in the Dark Ages (South Sheet 1935, North Sheet 1938).

ORWIN, C. S. and ORWIN C. S. (1938). The Open Field. Oxford, Clarendon Press.

PARSONS, F. G. (1920). The Colour Index of the British Isles. *J. Roy. Anthrop. Inst. 50* : 159-82.

PAYNE, F. G. (1947). The Plough in Ancient Britain. *Archaeol. J. 104* : 82-111.

PEAKE, H. J. E. (1922). The English Village. London, Benn.

PEAKE, H. J. E. (1927). Beginnings of Civilisation. *J. Roy. Anthrop. Inst. 57* : 19-38.

PEAKE, H. J. E. (1940). The Study of Prehistoric Times. *J. Roy. Anthrop. Inst. 70* : 103-46.

PEAKE, H. J. E. and FLEURE, H. J. (1927 onwards). Corridors of Time. Oxford, Clarendon Press, 9 vols.

PEARSALL, W. H. (1950). Mountains and Moorlands. London, Collins.

PEATE, I. C. (1940). The Welsh House. London, Cymmrodorion Society.

PELHAM, R. A. (1931). The Distribution of Caen Stone in Sussex. *Sussex Archaeol. Coll. Lewes, 72* : 175-78.

PERCIVAL, J. (1921). The Wheat Plant. London, Duckworth.

PIGGOTT, H. Stuart (1939). Timber Circles. *Archaeol. J., 96* : 193-222.
PIGGOTT, H. Stuart (1947). Note on Stonehenge. *Archaeol. J., 104* : 4-6.
PIRENNE, H. (1925). Mediaeval Cities. Princeton, University Press.
POLITICAL AND ECONOMIC PLANNING (1948). Population Policy in Great Britain. London, P.E.P.
PRAEGER, R. Ll. (1947). The Way that I Went. Dublin, Hodges Figgis.
PREHISTORIC SOCIETY, PROCEEDINGS OF THE. London.
PULBROOK, E. C. (1925). The English Countryside. London, Batsford
PULBROOK, E. C. (1923). English Country Life and Work. London, Batsford.
QUENNELL, Marjorie, and QUENNELL, C. H. B. (1918-19). History of Everyday Things in England. London, Batsford, 2 vols.
QUENNELL, Marjorie, and QUENNELL, C. H. B. (1926). Everyday Life in Saxon, Viking and Norman times. London, Batsford.
REGISTRAR GENERAL'S REPORTS.
REID, R. W. and MORANT, G. M. (1928). A Study of Scottish Short Cist Crania. *Biometrika, 20* : 379-88.
RHYS, J. and BRYNMOR-JONES, D. (1900). The Welsh People. London, Fisher Unwin.
RICHMOND, I. A. (1949). *in* Scientific Survey of North-east England. *Brit. Assoc. Adv. Sci.* : 61-68.
RIPLEY, W. Z. (1900). The Races of Europe. London, Kegan Paul.
ROYAL COMMISSIONS on ancient and historical monuments, for England, Scotland, Wales, County Reports.
SALAMAN, R. N. (1949). History and Social Influence of the Potato. Cambridge University Press.
SHARP, T. (1946). The Anatomy of the Village. London, Penguin Books.
SHRUBSALL, F. C. (1924). Health and Physique through the Centuries. Presidential address, section H., *Brit. Assoc. Adv. Sci.*
SIMPSON, W. Douglas (1939-44). Articles on Castles. *Archaeol. J. 96*: 142-58 ; *98* : 87-98 ; *99* : 110-22 ; *101* : 119-28.
SMITH, Wilfred (1949). An Economic Geography of Great Britain. London, Methuen.
SOLLAS, W. J. (1913). Paviland Cave. *J. Roy. Anthrop. Inst. 43* : 325-74.
STAMP, L. Dudley (1936). The Geographical Evolution of the North Sea Basin. *J. Conseil, Copenhagen, II*, No. 2 : 137-63.
STAMP, L. Dudley and BEAVER, S. H. (1941). The British Isles. London, Longmans, 3rd ed.
STENTON, Sir F. M. (1927). The Danes in England. London, British Academy.
STENTON, Sir F. M. (1943). Anglo-Saxon England. Oxford, Clarendon Press.

STEVENS, F. (1924). Stonehenge, To-day and Yesterday. London, H.M. Stationery Office.

STOESSIGER, Brenda, and MORANT, G. M. (1932). Crania, St. Leonard's, Hythe. *Biometrika, 24* : 135-202.

SWANSCOMBE COMMITTEE OF THE ROY. ANTHROP. INST. (1938). Report on the Swanscombe Skull. *J. Roy, Anthrop. Inst. 68* : 17-98.

SYLVESTER, Dorothy (1948). The Hill Villages of England and Wales. *Geogr. J. 110* : 76-93.

TAIT, J. (1936). The Mediaeval English Borough. Manchester, University Press.

TAYLOR, Isaac (1882). Words and Places. London, Macmillan.

THOMAS, Annie L. (1934). Transport and Communications, North Staffordshire. *Mem. William Salt Archaeol. Soc.*

THOMAS, H. H. (1923-4). See Stevens, F. above.

THOMPSON, A. Hamilton (1912). Military Architecture in England during the Middle Ages. London, Frowde.

TOCHER, J. F. (1924). Anthropometric Characteristics, North-east Scotland. Henderson Trust, Edinburgh, Oliver & Boyd.

TOUT, T. F. (1934). Mediaeval Town Planning. Manchester, University Press, 2nd ed.

TOWN AND COUNTRY PLANNING. Many Reports on, and by Ministry of.

TREVELYAN, G. M. (1946). English Social History. London, Longmans.

TURNER, Sir W. (1915). Craniology of the people of Scotland II. Prehistoric, Descriptive and Ethnographical. *Trans. Roy. Soc. Edin. 51* : 171-255.

VARLEY, W. J. and JACKSON, J. W. (1940). Prehistoric Cheshire. Chester, Cheshire Rural Community Council.

VAVILOV, N. I. (1926). Studies on Origin of Cultivated Plants. Leningrad.

VICTORIA AND ALBERT MUSEUM (1924). Guide to Collection of Old English Costumes. London, Victoria and Albert Museum.

VICTORIA HISTORY OF THE COUNTIES OF ENGLAND. Many volumes. London, ed. H. A. Doubleday and W. Page, 1912 onwards.

WEBB, Sidney and Beatrice (1913). English Local Government, The Story of the Highway. London, Longmans.

WHEELER, R. E. M. (1925). Prehistoric and Roman Wales. Oxford, Clarendon Press.

WHEELER, R. E. M. (1927-35). London Museum Catalogues :—London and the Vikings (1927), London in Roman Times (1930), London and the Saxons (1935).

WHEELER, R. E. M. (1943). Maiden Castle, Dorset. London, Society of Antiquaries.

WHEELER, R. E. M. and WHEELER, Tessa V. (1936). Verulamium, London, Society of Antiquaries.

WICKHAM, A. K. (1933). The Villages of England. London, Batsford.
WOOLDRIDGE, S. W. (1936). A Study of Anglo-Saxon Settlement. *See* Darby, H. C. above.
WRIGHT, W. B. (1939). Tools and the Man. London, Bell.
ZEUNER, F. E. (1946). Dating the Past. London, Methuen.

A Small Selective List of Recent Works
mostly published since the issue
of the first edition

STUART PIGGOTT. The Neolithic Cultures of the British Isles. 1954.

CLARK, J. G. D. Prehistoric Europe. The Economic Basis. 1952.
Excavations at Star Carr. 1954.

ATKINSON, R. J. C. Stonehenge. 1956.

BULLEID, A. and ST. GEORGE GRAY, H. The Meare Lake Village. Vol. I. 1945. Vol. II. 1953.

HAMILTON, J. R. C. Excavations at Jarlshof, Shetland. 1956.

ed. WAINWRIGHT, F. T. The Problem of the Picts. 1955.

RICHMOND, I. A. 10th Edition of the Handbook to the Roman Wall. 1947.

MARGARY, I. D. Roman Roads in Britain. Vol. I. 1955. Vol. II. 1957.

NASH WILLIAMS, V. E. Early Christian Monuments of Wales. 1950.

BOWEN, E. G. The Settlements of the Celtic Saints in Wales. 1954.

ed. BOWEN, E. G. Wales. 1957.

ed. HARDEN, D. B. Studies in Dark Age Britain. 1956.

FOX, SIR CYRIL. Offa's Dyke. 1955.

SMITH, A. H. English Place Names. 2 vols. 1956.

DARBY, H. C. The Domesday Geography of England. 1952 *et seq.*

HARVEY, J. Gothic England. 1947.

ATKINSON, T. D. Local Styles in English Architecture. 1947.

FOX, SIR CYRIL and LORD RAGLAN. Monmouthshire Houses. Vol. I. 1951; Vol. II. 1953; Vol. III. 1954.

TWISTON DAVIES, SIR L. and Lloyd Johnes, H. J. Welsh Furniture. 1950.

TOY, S. The Castles of Great Britain. 1953.

HUSSEY, C. English Country Houses. Vol. I. 1955; Vol. II. 1956.

SCHUBERT, H. R. History of the British Iron and Steel Industry, B.C. 400 to A.D. 1775. 1957.

There are also several valuable works in this field published by the Penguin Press, including a number in their Pelican History of Art. Messrs. Batsford's Lists also give a number of relevant books, usually richly illustrated.

INDEX

Figures in heavy type refer to pages opposite which
illustrations will be found